"*The Lonely Nest* is a compe
Codding documenting a tragi
ultimately led to the deaths oi .... and Janice Falcone. *The Lonely Nest* is a true, painfully honest and courageous account of the horror that was allowed to exist behind closed doors, attributed by the silence of its victims and the indifference of others choosing to turn a blind eye. Falcone-Codding is the voice of victims unable to speak for themselves. *The Lonely Nest* is a reminder to all of us of how the unspeakable horror of domestic violence and incest will continue to victimize the innocent if we choose to be silent."

Ray Hackett retired Editorial Editor of The Norwich (CT) Bulletin

"Concetta Falcone-Codding is a first time author but has written a bestseller right out of the ballpark! Her memoir is about the lives of her mother and sister who perished from domestic violence. Abuse of any kind is dark and ugly yet a fact of life for many. Falcone-Codding has managed to weave the truth telling how the abuse of her mother and sister began and how it continued until their deaths. *The Lonely Nest* is a story of lies and deceit told by the one person Rose and Janice Falcone trusted the most. Anyone who has been touched by abuse will certainly identify with this well-written novel. *The Lonely Nest* is a must-read for anyone that likes to get pulled into a story with intriguing characters that provoke an emotional bond and more chilling is the fact this story actually happened. I could not put this book down!"

Kathy Bosworth, Author of "Your Mother Has Suffered a Slight Stroke"

"I have just finished reading *The Lonely Nest* by Concetta Falcone-Codding; it is one of the best books I have read in years. In many ways this book is comparable to Jeannette Walls's *The Glass Castle*. It is the story of a young girl growing up in the rural town of Bozrah Connecticut. It tells of her hardships concerning abuse, mistreatment and neglect spanning five decades beginning in the 1950s. The mistreatment Connie Mary witnessed was not only in her home, it also occurred in school, which should have been a safe haven. Many of the unspeakable acts she endured went unnoticed, by people who should have been protecting her.

Readers will be able to identify with the events of the times, which the author so keenly describes with her spot on memory. Falcone-Codding's raw honesty and sense of humor take us through many heart wrenching, as well as heart-warming situations. This book is an emotional roller coaster. You find yourself loving some characters and despising others. You will be crying one moment and laughing the next. I am surprised and disappointed that this wonderful book has not been duly recognized. I feel it should be required reading in every high school across the nation.

Thank you, Concetta Falcone-Codding."

Joan Park-Ryan
Hanover, Connecticut
Norwich Free Academy
Class of 1971

The Lonely Nest

*The Story of Two Women Whose Short Lives
Will One Day Make A Difference In The World.*

Concetta Falcone-Codding

Author's Note

This novel is based on true events surrounding the lives of Rose and Janice Lynn Falcone. Nearly all the names of those who appear in this book have remained intact. However, I have changed the names of a few people so as to protect their privacy. I have tried to recreate memories of past events, locales and conversations to the best of my ability to bring justice to those whom it was denied.

During the nine years it took to complete this novel, I have relied on first-hand witnesses, relatives and friends who provided me with knowledgeable facts about the lives of my mother and sister. Since then, time has passed and certain characteristics and details concerning towns, places and buildings may have been changed, renamed, or completely removed.

ISBN- 978-1-7369089-0-7 (paperback)
ISBN- 978-1-7369089-1-4 (eBook/Kindle format)
ISBN- 978-1-7369089-2-1 (eBook/EPUB format)

Library of Congress Control Number: 2021905784
BISAC: Biography & Memoir / Domestic Violence/Incest/ Mental Illness

Shetucket River Press
United States of America

For my mother and sister...

Rose Falcone, September 27, 1926 – January 20, 1999
Janice Lynn Falcone, July 3, 1948 – March 26, 1989

Contents

Part I Welcome to the 1950's 1

  1. Where It All Began… 3

  2. The Alpha 25

  3. Duck and Cover 52

  4. The Sign Of The Cross 64

  5. The Omega 86

  6. Staying Silent 102

  7. Snitches End Up In Ditches 131

  8. Nonno's Justice 146

  9. Goodbye Gregory 162

  10. The Lost Souls Of Kettle 175

  11. Farewell Good Soldier 204

Part II The Demise of Rose and Janice Falcone 221

  12. Life Is Worth The Trip 223

  13. Nonno's New Life 238

  14. A Child Of God 253

  15. Chains Are Made To Be broken 266

  16. The Greatest Teacher Of All 282

  17. The Escape 296

  18. Goodbye My Beautiful Sister 308

  19. The Murder of Rose Falcone 320

Part III My Father's New Life 341

  20. Be Careful What You Wish 345

There's Not a Bird With Lonely Nest
By Baptist W. Noel (1799-1873).

There's not a bird with lonely nest,
In pathless wood or mountain crest,
Nor meaner thing, which does not share,
O God, in Thy paternal care.

Each barren crag, each desert rude,
Holds Thee within its solitude:
And Thou dost bless the wand'rer there,
Who makes his solitary prayer.

In busy mart and crowded street,
No less than in the still retreat,
Thou, Lord, art near, our souls to bless
With all a parent's tenderness.

And we, where'er our lot is cast,
While life, and thought, and feeling last,
Through all the years, in every place,
Will bless Thee for Thy boundless grace.

The Lonely Nest

"The line between watching an abuser and becoming an abuser is translucently thin, weaved as intricately as a spider's web."

My Mother in the Mirror

One weekend, my husband cleaned the garage
And there it was triumphantly hanging, almost grinning
My mother's mirror, the one that saw everything, but never told
That damn mirror
"Take it down," I said
"Why? It is a fine mirror," argued my husband
Needless to say, the mirror stayed
At first, I looked the other way
Until I saw my mother staring back at me
Her unfinished life had become my life
Her voice; my voice
Oh, my beautiful silent mother, why didn't you leave?
We were unable to express our love, our relationship, volatile and stifled
I watched her face change over time
As Graves' disease ravaged the eyes and grotesquely expanded the jowls
I was angry at her loyalty to an abuser, and, in a fit of rage, called her ugly!
Life is strange, beware…everything we say and do comes back
An autoimmune disease turned my mother's face into Frankenstein
As Sjogren's Syndrome has done to mine
When I looked in the mirror I discovered my mother was me and I her
For a long time, I stared at the face of my worried mother until I declared
Do not worry Mom—evil will not win twice,
For I found not only your voice, but mine as well
And when a lost female finds her voice
Every generation of women
From the beginning of time
Applauds.

Part I

Welcome to the 1950's

1

Where It All Began...

It is 1957 and I am four years old. My memory of my father begins here. I am riding in my stroller through the bright morning light with Manfred the Wonder Dog sleeping in my arms. Smiling and laughing, my big sister Janice skips by my side as a soft breeze lifts her hair. My mother pushes my stroller while my father walks ahead. Today, we are visiting a wonderful place called *The Philadelphia Zoo,* where black gorillas with glowing red eyes look back at us from dark cages. Next to the gorillas are magnificent tigers that growl as we approach. My mother likes the tigers best, but my sister is too scared to go near. When we stop, I look back and see my father pushing my mother away from my stroller. My mother's gentle hands are replaced by my father's rough, dirty fingers.

"I want my mother, not my father to push me!" I scream.

Even as I scratch, bite and squeeze his fingers, my father continues to push my stroller. He does his best to ignore my tantrum, but after a few minutes, he has enough and throws his hands into the air.

"*She wants you!*" He shouts to my mother before giving in to my way.

I recall this memory vividly. It is the exact moment I knew I was stronger than my father.

Two years later...

At first I thought it was normal, how my sister falls down and hurts herself. As time passes I begin to wonder why my sister is different from other children. Why she hurls herself against hard objects in a constant frenzied motion—running, rampaging, thrashing back and forth in a desperate attempt to maneuver a body that is out of control. Why does my sister flounder so helplessly like a fish flopping upon the shore?

My mother does not know what happens when she is gone. My father's anger often leads to a push, a slap, or a pounding on the bottom. The pain is horrific. It reminds me of how salt has the power to pull and squeeze blood out of raw meat. My father may slap once, but the pain throbs all day and night.

I am five years old and want to do everything my big sister does, even when my father forbids me. When my sister and cousin Joyce ride bicycles around Gus's Pond, I want to go with them. Even though my father said *no* three times, I insisted on going and run for the door. When I realize I am not tall enough to reach the door handle, I become hysterical, throwing myself on the floor crying, "I want Jan-ness, I want Jan-ness!"

When I see the look on my father's face, I realize what a terrible choice I have made. When he lunges and yanks me in the air by my elbow, I feel something in my shoulder *snap*. The snap is followed by turbulent waves of pain and I cry even harder, begging for my mother. My father pays no attention and slaps me hard across the backside. My eyes sting and tears burst, but I stay silent. When he finally puts me down I cannot walk without falling. Feeling foolish, I wobble away like a little old lady, broken and frail. I try to lift my arms and discover one arm will not move. My father stands above with his arms crisscrossed and smiles menacingly. "You needed a Goshdamn slap didn't you? You're getting to be a spoiled brat, you know that Connie Mary?"

I do not remember when my arm came back to life or when my mother came home, *but I never told—we never told*—what always happens when she is gone.

My earliest memory of Janice and my father still torments me.

I remember missing my mother and watching *Walt Disney Presents* on television. Tonight, Walt Disney is introducing a special cat named Cheshire. Cheshire likes to grin, exposing long rows of glistening teeth and then magically disappears leaving nothing behind but his smile. At first I refuse to acknowledge what I hear, but then I listen closer and realize it resembles the whimper of a puppy. As the crying grows stronger and louder, I realize it is Janice, crying from a place I cannot easily reach: the upstairs bedrooms. I run to the staircase and look up, only to feel that I am standing at the bottom of the highest mountain in the world. I decided this is the perfect time to have a temper tantrum.

"Ma!" I scream.

I hear nothing but silence screaming back at me. As I walk back to the couch, my slipper bumps into my sister's Little Lulu doll lying face down on the floor. This scares me more than anything because Janice would never leave her baby alone! The doll's legs are twisted and perfect banana curls tousled. *Oh Mommy, where are you? I know where my Daddy is—I can smell his daddy-drink in the dark—he's up at the top of the stairs with Janice!*

Holding Manfred tight, I am determined to make the treacherous journey to save my sister. Holding the banister, I walk up the first step. Feeling confident, I made it to the second step. When a bright light appears, I see my father standing above like a giant at the top of the stairs.

"Where's my sister?" I boldly demand—"What have you done with her?"

My father looks down at me with eyes that have no light. He reaches and flips a switch, leaving me to fumble through the darkness. Feeling hopeless, I crawl down the steps, and sit on the floor and cry. Suddenly I hear footsteps.

"Stop your fussing," growls my father from above. "And get away from those steps before you *get really hurt.*"

The footsteps fade. For a moment, I imagine I am brave enough to run into the night and ask the neighbors, Anna and Gus, for help. Then as if he had been watching me the whole time, my father calls from above. "*You* better be a good girl and go watch TV."

My *Lonely Nest* existed long before I was born. Inside the heart of my mother and father it grew, living and breathing through them and eventually me. Everyone is born with a lonely nest and a Mama Robin roosting within to tell them the difference between right and wrong. A lonely nest is a sacred space inside of us that holds our secrets, joys and sorrows. Unfortunately, as we grow, and experience more of life, some lonely nests become broken. It is a mystery as to why some lonely nests shatter into pieces while others remain unscathed even in the worst of times. I believe the worst thing that can happen to a person is when the Mama Robin refuses to keep secrets and flies away. Once she is gone and the lonely nest is broken, a person can no longer differentiate between right and wrong and will go on to commit the most hideous of crimes.

The lonely nest of my father, Albert Joseph Falcone, begins the day he is born, to parents Michael (Nunzio) Falcone and Rose Rizzuto in Norwich, Connecticut. The first thing Nonna Falcone notices when the baby boy is placed inside her arms is the blue knitted boots on his feet. With no understanding of how destiny comes from a place higher than the stars, my Nonna nicknamed my father "Bootsie" simply because she thought the boots were cute.

Michael and Rose Falcone were born in a quaint bucolic town in San Giocomo di Acri, Italy. Michael, my Nonno, is the son of Joseph and Philomena Sposato Falcone. Italians were treated poorly in the early 1900s, and many, like my grandfather, lived in poverty. This is why as a young boy Nonno worked hard, dreaming of the day he would come to America. There was no time for childish games or hugs and kisses. If Nonno did not obey his parents the punishment was severe. He had been a digger of wells, a fisherman, a bodyguard, a bouncer, a chauffeur, a tomato picker and runner for the Mafioso. There were other jobs Nonno does not mention. He said he would rather die first before telling me what they were.

Matched by their parents, Nonno and Nonna were strangers when they married. Eventually, survival overcame embarrassment and Mr. and Mrs. Michael Falcone settled in Norwich, Connecticut to raise a family with my father being the youngest of seven siblings.

My grandparent's first glimpse of America is seen from a ship docked alongside the foggy harbor in Ellis Island, New York. When Nonno first arrived in America, he could not speak a word of English. This did not discourage him from working as an operator and eventually co-owner of the Hallville Bus Line between 1906 and 1922. The Hallville Bus Line was an interurban trolley system that operated a 21-mile line through Norwich, Preston, Ledyard, North Stonington, Pawcatuck, and Westerly, Rhode Island. For most of its length, the route paralleled what is better known as Old Route 2. Included in its stops were Railroad Depot on Main Street in Norwich and the infamous Norwich State Hospital. The powerhouse and four-track car house were located at Hallville; a trolley park called Lincoln Park. The Hallville Bus line evolved during an era called "Once upon a time," and disappeared after faster (but never better) modes of transportation were deployed.

After the Hallville Bus Line, Nonno spent 23 years employed at

King-Seeley Thermos Division in Norwich, eventually working his way up to foreman. At the same time, he worked in the Disco Building as an elevator operator and for Norwich Public Schools as a crossing guard, often seen eating a long stick of salami while waving children safely across the road. Even after he retired, Nonno continued to work. Work provided a refuge where he did not have to think about the problems at home or what happened after he drank.

As long as Nonna was alive, he maintained his gorgeous Victorian home on Talman Street with the help of my father, a well-known refrigeration and appliance man in Norwich. Michael and Rose Falcone were known as generous people who shared their good fortune with every neighbor. However, would their children receive the same good fortune?

There will be times in my life when I am grateful for Nonno, and other times, I must look away. When my father speaks of Nonno, it is as if his painful childhood did not happen. *"In the end it doesn't matter whether Nonno has good or bad blood running through his veins. Nonno's blood is your blood. If you took a knife and cut your hand, you'd see your blood and Nonno's blood run one and the same. Don't ever forget what I'm telling you Connie Mary—no matter what, blood is thicker than water."*

My mother, Rose Calanna was born and raised in Philadelphia, Pennsylvania. Her lonely nest begins the moment parents Giuseppe (Joseph) and Concetta Mazzurra Calanna hold their beautiful baby girl and listen to the rhythm of her beating heart. Joseph and Concetta were born in Sicily, in Palermo and Messina, respectively. My mother's parents arrived at Ellis Island around the same time as my father's parents and settled on Millick Street in Philadelphia. Concetta died of pancreatic cancer in 1944, and Joseph died in 1955 from lung cancer, and so I have no memory of my mother's parents.

When Nonna Concetta first came to America, her work in a tailor shop was cut short by six pregnancies and the subsequent raising of six daughters. Her seventh child was a son named Archie who died of pneumonia at the age of five. Like many Italians, Nonno Calanna quickly learned the skills necessary to acquire money in America. In a very short time he became owner and landlord of a three-story apartment building on 60th Street in West Philly. On the ground floor Nonno Calanna ran a poolroom, which was his main source of income. Even though Nonno was a "pure" Italian and himself a member of the Mafioso, he still had to pay the Mafioso protection money. He also ran a side business as a number runner collecting bets from gamblers and delivering the payoff when they won. Nonno Calanna's granddaughter, Barbara Joan Bevilacqua remembers sitting on his lap waiting to perform an important job. Little Barbara Joan had the privilege of holding slips of white paper between her lips that contained numbers for individual bets. This was done in playfulness of course, but in a more serious tone Nonno Calanna would give Barbara Joan strict orders. "Iffa man come-a in dark blue monkey suit, with a badge, you chew—and-a swallow!" Barbara Joan was the closest grandchild to Nonno Calanna, and he treated her with kindness and love.

On the right hand side of the store was a hoagie shop where Nonno Calanna made delicious steak sandwiches and hoagies. Joe's Steaks were famous with the African American community who enjoyed the pool room. About three or four years before Nonna Calanna died, Nonno Calanna became intimate with a young girl named Susie. He met Susie on one of his many weekend trips to Atlantic City while staying at Caroline's Blue Bird Inn. Even as Nonna Calanna lay dying with her daughters by her side, Nonno Calanna and Susie were happily living in one of his West Philly apartments. Nonno Calanna's relationship with Susie lasted long after Nonna Calanna died and until his death in 1955. Susie feared Nonno's daughters and stayed hidden under his protection due to an incident when my mother's sisters once tried to beat her up. Due to his habit of smoking too many stogies, Nonno Calanna developed lung cancer and eventually died. Susie mysteriously disappeared knowing the girls would be coming. By this time the sisters were all married, holding true to the fantasy of Cinderella marrying her prince. Of course, this did not turn out as planned. Out of all the sisters, my mother and sister Josephine fared the worst. Both had leaped from the frying pan and into the fire.

$\mathbf{M}$y precious sister, Janice Lynn has the most beautiful lonely nest of anyone I ever met. Being the oldest, my sister grew closest to my mother and immediately became a human bulwark between my mother and father. Janice was a beautiful child with big brown eyes, olive skin and hair as black as night. Though my sister and I will spend an existence traveling blindly on two divergent paths, we will never forget the beauty of Fitchville Road, where rows of white houses line the street like beautiful presents waiting to be opened. Beebe's Fields is the pulse of Fitchville Road and the perfect home for dairy cows to graze on 24 acres. The heart of Fitchville Road emanates from a pond owned by Gustave O. Lorentz. Gus welcomes every neighbor to his pond as naturally as a mother embracing her child.

It was summer when my sister first introduced me to Beebe's Fields. We are going to pick wildflowers for her scrapbooks. My sister began life as an environmentalist long before anyone discussed the importance of protecting nature. My sister does not allow me to pick any flower. Intuitively, she knows picking a lady's slipper is never justified. On the other hand, picking a Queen Anne's lace or buttercup is perfectly acceptable. My sister knows where to find the most unusual wildflowers, like the green and purple Jack-in-the-pulpits that hide between the shadows. Before making the long journey home, we sit in solace intuitively understanding how fleeting the safety of this moment. When the chill of darkness falls upon the land, my sister stares with dread at the warm glow of houses in the distance and faces the inevitable.

"It's time to go home Con."

The era in which my sister and I live is both a blessing and a curse. It is darkness and light, freedom and confinement, hope and despair. It is an era where secrets hide in houses sealed tight with aluminum siding. One blessing is a good neighbor that watches over every neighboring child, creating a safety net unique to the mid-1900s. The type of neighbor I'm referring to will be difficult for present and future generations to understand. In today's world most neighbors exist from a distance.

For my family, one such neighbor was Gustave O. Lorentz. Born on January 3, 1901, Gus lived with his wife Anna who was three years younger. He often joked that this gave him the authority to be the boss. Gus was far from anyone's boss. He lived a humble existence by selflessly helping everyone who crossed his path. Gus was an Army Veteran of World War I. The medals he earned were stashed in his desk rather than brought to attention. As a young girl, Anna Lorentz met the man of her dreams. After a few years of marriage she had a terrible automobile accident leaving her unable to walk without crutches. This did not matter to Gus, who loved her even more. For decades, Anna and Gus were childless. It seemed like a miracle when Anna's sister had a baby boy and (for reasons unknown) asked Anna and Gus to adopt the baby. Anna and Gus named their new son, Gustave Lorentz Jr. Despite all good intentions, as Gustave Jr. grew, so did his attraction to delinquency. Somehow, he lost the good name

Gustave, and was demoted to "Pinky" due to having red hair and pink freckles. Many say Pinky's demise began the day Gus told him the truth.

"Pinky, we're not your real parents. You're adopted." For the rest of his life, Pinky lived a miserable existence. Between disturbing the peace with naughty pranks and spending nights in jail, Pinky married Shirley Smallridge and gave Anna and Gus three beautiful grandchildren. Because the children were connected to a father living in pain, Gustave (Cookie) Lorentz III, Debby Lorentz and Christopher J. Lorentz grew to lead tumultuous lives.

Anna worried about their future.

"Those poor grandchildren ain't got a wooden nickel to share between them. After we're gone, Gus and I want them to have everything we got, so they can have a good start in life." It is too bad Anna did not know the future was conspiring to steal what rightfully belonged to her grandchildren. If Anna had known what the future would bring, she would have prepared a will at that very moment.

On the other side of our house lived the Banell family. I thought the Banells were the perfect family until the oldest son, a sensitive young man, confided to my mother that his father beat him. Weeks later, he ran away and was never seen or heard from again. After the Banell family comes the Reverend Elsensohn, wife and three children. My father was fond of the Banell family because of a sick obsession with one particular person. From the beginning, he held no fondness for the Elsensohn family and devoted a great deal of time plotting to make them suffer.

Another neighbor worth mentioning is an elderly couple named Nolan. The Nolans look older than most people making the quiet Polish couple an easy target in my father's quest for prey. The Nolans live long enough to witness my mother's last days and the mental decline of my father. Of course, there are other neighbors worthy of mention, but the most significant is Kathy Grabowy Bosworth. Kathy lives across the street and will become a life-long friend and safe harbor for me in times of trouble. Last but not least, who can forget the Meyer sisters? After Anna and Gus pass, the Meyer sisters move in and for the next ten years celebrate each new day by drinking cocktails —no earlier than noon and no later than two o' clock. It is unfortunate as time progresses and old age beckons, the bold sister dies first leaving the meek one in a position to fend against the devilish pranks of my father. It is important to understand that as my father ages he behaves like a disturbed adolescent on Halloween night by committing random acts of violence against the elderly neighbors. In time, every neighbor will come to know the identity of the night demon that comes to destroy. But due to fear, they will never tell.

Fear is an interesting phenomenon. It comes uninvited, incapacitating the soul when you least expect. This is exactly what happened to the neighbors on Fitchville Road once they became elderly and discovered living next door to a real bogeyman is far scarier than the one hiding underneath your bed. Go ahead... try and picture a neighborhood utopia where neighbors may visit at a moment's notice and be welcomed with a big cup of instant Sanka coffee. Where houses are never clean nor dirty and neighbors work together to maintain the community motto, *"Love thy neighbor as thyself."*

Like most women in the neighborhood my mother does not work outside the home. This means the first five years of my life consists of lazy mornings watching my mother cook. When my mother cooks I know I am partaking in an event that is sacred. Today, my mother is preparing her famous tomato sauce that is both an escape and an Act of Contrition. My mother teaches me how to make the sauce long before I am tall enough to reach the stove.

"The process is not complicated Connie Mary, but there are steps one must take. First, you must place love in your heart," she says, tapping her chest with her hand. "That is *numero uno.* Next, you must always—no exceptions—use Italian brand tomatoes because the Pope in Italy blesses such tomatoes! And fresh garlic! Ah yes! You must always use fresh garlic to crush and fry in Filippo Berio's Extra Virgin olive oil. And use a black cast iron pot, no metal phony-baloney. We Italians know aluminum pots give women babies that are slow."

My mother lights a cigarette and inhales long drags between lessons. Sometimes she will turn and stare out the back door, looking up at the blue horizon where fluffy white clouds hang so low we might reach and touch. Exhaling, she bluntly crushes her cigarette into an ashtray and goes back to work.

"Okay, time to get down to business. Take the plum tomatoes and crush them with the strong hands God has given you for tools. Add two cans of tomato paste, crushed garlic, basil leaves and a little sugar to cut the bitter taste. Fry the tomatoes until they turn a flaming orange-red, more vivid and vibrant than any fall harvest you will ever see," My mother chuckles before reaching the last step. "Oh, and don't forget to add a good portion of Nonno's homemade wine. A little Nonno adds excitement and variety to any dish."

Now, *figlia,* when you make a sauce such as this, you will have created a tiny vision of Heaven—*Fatto!*"

We leave the sauce to simmer and step into the parlor to watch Ernest Borgnine play an awkward butcher named *Marty.* After the movie, my mother turns the television knob to search through the three available channels to find her favorite game show: *What's My Line.* The parlor is warm and familiar with old and faded furniture. The lamps and tables are dusty, yet no one complains. My sister arrives home from school at 3 o' clock and is delighted to find my mother and I watching *I Love Lucy*. She hugs my mother and hurries into the kitchen returning with three packages of Hostess Cupcakes and for the rest of the quiet afternoon, the three of us lounge in the parlor, watch television, and enjoy each other's company.

In many ways, the 1950's were a wonderful time for children. There are no after-school-activities we had to frantically run to. We had no pressing future ambitions and happily lived in the now, never once discussing scholarships, or how someday we would have to pay for some imaginary place called college. We had no doctor's appointments, no daycare and no indifferent babysitters who might ignore us while talking on the phone. It was just the three of us happily residing in a world the male culture has stamped and approved. It's no argument that the greatest blessing bestowed upon this era was how children played. After school, rain or shine, we played outside in the fresh air until the onset of dusk. We returned home with peaceful minds, our thoughts moving freely through a vast open space free from clutter and ready to create tomorrow. In contrast, the technological children of the future will never know such peace. They will end each day with overstimulated minds and nonsense information that will make it difficult to differentiate between the truth and a lie.

Some people are foolish enough to insinuate that mothers that stay home do not have enough to do, but my mother has responsibilities every day of the week.

Monday begins with shopping at the First National. I know we are on our way when my mother places me in the small metal basket inside the shopping cart and there is no other place in the world I would rather be. Our first stop is the Betty Crocker aisle displaying colorful tubes of frosting. My mother removes a small tube of blue frosting from the shelf and opens the cap before placing the tube in my hand. Knowing the routine, I bring the tube to my lips and pleasurably suck on the sugar as the carriage wheels move off-kilter. With blue fingers I am content to watch my mother do the two things she enjoys most: shop for food and spend my father's money. Hours seem to pass but eventually my mother pays the man behind the cash register for the groceries. She always forgets to pay for the tube of frosting I ate, though, as well as other items she had placed inside her purse. Once we reach our car, my mother gently lifts me, and the rest of her groceries out of the carriage leaving the empty tube of frosting behind.

As I grew older, I began to notice the little problem my mother had with placing items inside her purse. Husbands of this era would never believe such gentle creatures would be capable of stealing, but I knew for a fact that my mother was not the only mommy stealing in the stores we went to. All throughout childhood I saw all sorts of glamorous, pristine women stealing. This may have been a way for mothers to vent their anger or ease the pain of not having a voice. Besides, who in their right mind would suspect a lovely young mother of being a thief wearing a silk shirt, pearls and seamed nylons? Having heard my mother and aunts speak in hushed tones of loneliness and power imbalances, I was not surprised to realize that stealing was a genuine pastime for taciturn wives and frustrated women whose husbands ruled the roost. And when the roosters ruled, the hens raided the henhouse.

During the week, my mother buys American food at the local store. Every Sunday Nonno drives us to Westerly, Rhode Island to buy Italian food in his black Cadillac with dark windows. Nonna sits next to Nonno while my mother, sister and I sit in the back trying hard to be still and not move our feet too much. Everyone knows Nonno does not like his floor mats moved around by people's dirty feet. Today, Nonno is impeccably dressed in a black suit, thin white tie and a red carnation pinned to his lapel. Nonno's white hair is never amiss, always delicately slicked back with Italian grease. My mother says women turn their heads when Nonno passes, as he reeks of "*Italiana classe.*" My mother respects and fears Nonno, knowing he is monitoring the status of his floor mats as he drives. He has not driven more than a half-mile when he suspiciously glares at my mother with cool lime-green eyes in the rearview mirror.

"Rosie? You make-a sure you kids no move my floor mats 'round, *capisci?*" He continues to glare and my mother looks at us with her bottom lip quivering.

"Oh, no Pa! Girls, you won't move Nonno's floor mats around... will you?"

We return home by evening with a large ball of Parmigiano Reggiano cheese, a fat prosciutto ham, fresh basil, Genoa salami and imported olive oil from Italy. After we relax from shopping, sometimes in the late afternoon, my mother will spend the rest of the day talking on a large black telephone that sits on my father's desk. When my father is at work, my mother uses this telephone all she wants. When he is home, she cannot, because she needs to wait on my father. However, not even my father can pick up the telephone and dial it anytime he feels the urge. Before I attended school, we had a telephone system called a party line, which we shared with strangers. My mother did not mind sharing a party line, but my father hated it. Needless to say the party line did not last long. Every time my father picked up the telephone to dial he became enraged when he heard strangers talking and would yell—"GET THE HELL OFF THIS PHONE—NOW!" The party line ended after a vicious argument between my father and another man which my father "won" by ripping the telephone off the wall. Personally, I did not mind the party line and thought it fun. My mother missed the party line the most because she would talk to strangers when she was lonely. My father says my mother will talk on the telephone for hours with anyone who also has the luxury of wasting time. Of course, my mother does not think she is wasting time because she is sharing recipes, memories and most importantly the family secrets. How do I know? Eavesdropping to our mothers' conversation is how children of the 1950s acquired important information that affected our lives.

My mother did not always feel lonely and alone. Throughout her small circle of friends and family she was famously respected as The Maker of the Sauce. The smell of my mother's cooking attracted many lost and wandering souls to our dinner table. Like many women from this generation my mother has talents that would never be developed—talents that generations of women after her will take for granted. My mother had one particular talent that someday would prove to be of great importance. Throughout her life, my mother took hundreds of pictures with an Eastman Kodak Brownie Holiday Camera. When we asked her why, she would look at us and say, "Girls, you can try and tell someone the truth and they may not believe you. Words are easily dismissed. Show them a photograph and there is no denying the truth. A photograph never lies."

Another talent my mother has is being a gardener. Anything my mother touches grows and flourishes, and so it makes sense that she had her own garden. Her flowers would bloom in the spring and live through the long hot summer, but when they started to wither in September, my mother always looked lost. Her words still echo in my mind. "I feel sad when the roses die. For I know it is time for children to go back to school. I wish you did not have to go to school. School is where you will learn to suffer." My mother repeated this mantra often, not realizing the majority of our suffering comes from the one place she never thought possible: home.

It is the summer of 1958 and my carefree days with my mother are coming to an end. In August, I will be six-years old and able to join my sister in public school. With school approaching, Janice tries to teach me how to write my name, but after several attempts looks fearful. "For some reason Con, you write your name backwards," she whispers.

I look at my sister with hatred and throw my big fat red pencil across the room. "Liar!" I scream. "I did not!" Never speaking back in retaliation my sister walks away. The problem I have is similar to all children on the first day of school: they think they will never fail. Until the time comes, I will continue to watch my mother master the art of turning tomatoes into gold because there is nothing more important than making the sauce.

In addition to watching my mother cook, every week, my mother puts aside money by dropping coins into a glass piggy bank from Woolworth's Five and Dime. Since there is no opening at the bottom of the piggy bank, one cannot remove the coins without dire consequences to the pig. We would stand from a distance as she raised the hammer high. We held our breath, all the while listening to the high-pitched excitement in our mother's voice. "Stand back kids!"

The glass pig shattered upon impact. Small pieces of glass were strewn all over the plastic tarp she had laid across the parlor floor. My mother gathered the coins into a pillowcase and quickly rolled the tarp away. In the same swift motion, she reached underneath the couch to pull out an old metal box full of money. During the day, when my father was gone, my mother liked to open the box and count the money inside. Somehow, it gave her comfort knowing she had a secret stash. The box did not always hold money. It once contained a pistol belonging to my mother's Sicilian father. Before my mother married she brought my father home to meet her family. From the beginning Nonno Calanna did not like my father seeing nothing more than a two-faced, lying Calabrese. My mother's sister Grayce did not like him either, calling him a thug and gangster. No matter what anyone said to discourage my mother, she married him anyway. When it was time to leave Philadelphia and go with her husband to Norwich, Connecticut, Nonno Calanna pulled his daughter aside and slipped a small pistol into her hands.

"Rosie, you no trust-a Calabrese. When you no look, Calabrese stab-a knife in you back and smile. Calabrese, no good!"

My mother took the pistol home and placed it in the metal box. Years later, my mother looked inside the box and saw the gun had disappeared. Now and then my mother will stare at the metal box and say, "I no longer have a gun for protection. But I have money. And money will help me if we ever need to escape."

"No matter how good or how bad, bambino always yearns for the blood of papa and mama." I would come to understand these words my Nonno spoke, when I revisited the freezing afternoons I spent waiting outside for my father to come home from work.

One hour before my father is expected home, I hide behind my mother's rhododendron bush in order to surprise him. Every so often, my mother opens our kitchen window to yell hoping the tantalizing aroma of sauce simmering on the stove will make me come inside.

"Connie Mary! Get inside this house right now or you'll catch pneumonia!"

I pay no heed to my mother, preferring to risk pneumonia just to be the first to greet my father after a long day at work. I would have waited an eternity to hear my father say he loves me. The good news is I am not alone because Sam is by my side. Sam has been with our family for some time now. It was not so long ago when Pinky Lorentz stumbled into our yard drunk, dragging an orange and white mongrel by a frayed rope. At first, my mother did not notice the dog. She was hanging clothes and I was helping by holding the bag of clothespins. As Pinky approached, I remember thinking how terrible it was to tie such a beautiful dog to a rope, when the dog looked at me and seemed to smile inside his warm brown eyes. Struggling to hold the dog and stand at the same time, Pinky leaned forward, unstable on his feet. I was able to see an empty pint of whisky in his back pocket.

"Rose, I got just the dog fer' youse. This dog iss specshall! By Christ, Rose—this dog will grow to bees just like ones of you owns kids." He hiccupped through his explanation and inhaled loudly before continuing. "Christ Almighty Rose, thissa dog will bees in youse family for a long, longs time." Pinky swayed back and forth as if fighting against a strong wind. My mother did not know what to say. Finally, after losing patience, Pinky pushed the rope into my mother's hand and despite not wanting or needing a dog—my mother took the rope. Pinky walked away leaving my mother helplessly watching our new dog jump all over my clothes and I could not be happier.

"Ma, what are we going to name him?"

Without missing a beat my mother said, "Sam. His name is Sam." This created such a stir in the Universe that every sacred being whispered to my mother... *Rose, this dog is for you.* As Pinky predicted, Sam became a trusted family member and every so often my mother prayed for Pinky. "God help Pinky. Pinky has the broken heart of a drunk who knows the ugly truth in life which is why they drink in the first place."

There, I see my father now, rounding the corner! With chattering teeth and frozen hands I watch the truck rattle up the road with bald tires flopping to the tune of *Wop, Wop, Wop.* As he pulls into the driveway, I rush toward the truck with Sam following behind. When my father opens the door, I feel incredible joy as the grimy scent of oil and gasoline drift up my nose. Wearing his familiar oily clothes, he opens the door with a beautiful smile, holding his Thermos lunchbox and I smile because I know I will love him forever.

"Why, Sam and Connie... you scared me!" he says laughing. He lifts me up on his broad shoulders and sighs. "You're getting way too big for this Connie Mary. Still, I wish it could be like this forever."

Another childhood memory is a sacred and honored tradition called *the family vacation*. Our mother is able to save money for family vacations by collecting S&H Green Stamps. S&H Green Stamps were given out to faithful customers to reward them for purchasing groceries and gasoline. My sister and I would sit at the kitchen table with our mother and paste the stamps into booklets to redeem for merchandise. Once the pile of booklets was secured with a rubber band, we took a short drive to the local S&H store, where our mother chose items while my sister and I wandered through the furnished showrooms. Our house was filled with lamps, egg beaters, can openers, screwdrivers, flashlights, blankets, rakes, jackknives, games, pillows, shovels, perfume, Eastman Kodak Brownie Holiday Cameras, fishing poles, napkin holders, coffee percolators and more. With the money saved, my father could afford to take a vacation two weeks a year and drive his family sightseeing or visiting relatives. The last vacation I take before entering public school is a trip to Maine.

"This time we're going to have a good time no matter what happens," says my mother, forcing a smile. "Every night we'll have a warm fire inside our cozy cabin. Yes, tomorrow we leave for Maine." and stops smiling.

We ride away in my father's station wagon as the stars fade and dawn approaches, thinking we are leaving our troubles behind. Maine proves to be as bitter as it is cold and we spend our nights shivering underneath layers of scratchy wool blankets. My father does his best to start a morning fire but has no luck. Apparently, he left the kindling wood outside in the rain along with the box of matches. Our cabin is never quiet, especially at night when we inherit a family of squirrels that gallop across the roof smashing acorns, arguing, and act all lovey-dovey making up. This makes my father angry and he threatens to go into the nearest town to buy a gun and shoot them all! When I cry my father fakes a smile. *"Oh Connie Mary, I was just kidding."*

Before we left Connecticut my mother told my father he would be happier bringing his gigantic toolbox along, just in case he needs it. Well, right now, as my father jacks up the car and prepares to fix a flat tire in the rain… he looks ecstatic.

On August 5, 1959, my sixth birthday, we were still in Maine. To honor the event, my mother brings out six blue cupcakes and candles to celebrate. I try my hardest not to cry when I cannot blow out the candles because of the water leaking from the ceiling. The only one happy in Maine is Janice. She had been looking forward to this vacation more than anyone else. With acres and acres of woods filled with sharp sticks and jagged rocks, Maine proved to be a very dangerous place for my sister.

It finally stops raining on the third day we are in Maine. I am sitting on a pile of wet sticks in the bright morning light, listening to my father grumble and mumble about having to pour black oil into the car, when suddenly, in the distance, I see Janice running down the hillside with feet pounding the rocky path. Closer and closer she comes rounding the corner and then trips on a branch! She manages to prevent herself from falling and continues running on the path. I do not like the sound of my sister's black and white saddle shoes pounding the ground. It sounds like a herd of frightened elephants running away from death. In a haphazard fashion my sister jerks her body to the left in an effort to avoid several low hanging branches. She flies past my father—zooms past me—and almost makes it. *Oh no!* She does not see my father's long heavy toolbox lying across the path! And that's when it happens. My sister's screams slash the air like a razor cutting the sky in half.

My father stares in horror at my sister's body thrashing over the sharp stones and dirt. He looks as though he will cry and screams at the sky.

"Oh, Christ, it's my daughter! She fell over my toolbox—and I think she broke her arm! Help me Jesus, help me, help me, please, please, oh God Almighty help me!"

In agony my sister writhes and moans fitfully trying to grab hold of her crooked arm. When she rolls in the dirt her face turns black like Little Lulu lying at the bottom of the stairs. It is strange how I do not remember anything else that day except holding Manfred and leaving fast. My last memory about the toolbox is standing next to my mother in a strange hospital as doctors drill long silver pins into my sister's elbow. My sister is writhing and thrashing so much that the man in the white jacket has to call two nurses to hold her down. I do not like this place. When my sister is not screaming or crying she stares hopelessly into space. I do not know where my father is, but my mother never leaves my sister's side. I cannot hear the words my mother whispers to my sister because it is a secret language only they can understand. I do not want to see my sister's pain so I make myself feel better by imagining my sister is not real. Together Manfred and I search underneath the hospital bed to see if we can find my real sister because the one in bed, well, that's not my sister at all…she's only pretending.

The minute we arrive home my exhausted mother gives me a bath and immediately puts me to bed. After she kisses me good night and is halfway out the door, she stops abruptly and stares at the tiny crucifix on the wall.

"Connie Mary, I think we better start saying our prayers on a steady basis. Next week you start first grade."

2

The Alpha

AΩ   *"To find the way to Gus's Pond one must circle the pond like a loving mother reaching for her child. The best time to visit the pond is at the break of dawn when every flower reaches for the rising sun. Its light, like that which first appears in the womb, will guide you through a tunnel of darkness. From this sacred moment and every moment after—we yearn for the light never realizing, in the end, we leave in the same light from whence we came."*

My first day of school stands before me as a shadow shades the light. I am about to venture into unknown territory called first grade, not understanding how every event in our lives is the Alpha and Omega. My first day of school is my Alpha, my genesis, my first dawn. As a six-year-old, I do not know my bright and strong optimism is as fragile as glass and by the end of the day will be broken into a thousand minuscule pieces.

I wake and dress in clothes my mother bought at Mr. Big's department store in Taftville. I look in the mirror and admire my reflection, pleased with the green plaid dress, white knee socks and the red sweater Nonna Falcone knitted with love especially for me. The best part of all is the ponytail my mother made in my hair. I know my mother loves me very much because even when she is too sick to get out of bed she still finds the strength to make my ponytail.

I hop down the stairs admiring the sound of my black and white saddle shoes "clip-clopping" down each step and shoelaces dragging behind. In the kitchen my mother is a comforting sight cooking over the stove until I notice the empty chair. My father was here earlier leaving behind a plate of smeared yellow egg and an ashtray full of crushed cigarettes. I forgot my father left for work hours ago and will not be here to wish me good luck on my first day of school. I feel a terrible sadness inside my heart and remember how my sister calls this pain *the lonely nest.* I found out what a lonely nest was when I asked Janice why she spent so much time alone in her room reading books.

"I don't feel *the loneliness* when I am reading books," said my sister, looking up at me with a kind of sadness I will never know.

"Con, you're too young to understand, but someday, you, too, will feel *the loneliness* and remember what I said."

I was angry with my sister for thinking I was too young to understand what a lonely nest was—because I understood it quite well. As I walked away, I thought to myself,

The lonely nest is when a Mama Robin works and toils for days on end searching for anything that will make the nest safe and strong. The loneliness comes after the babies fly away and all that's left is an empty nest. Everyone has a lonely nest and a Mama Robin. It is not hard to understand. The nest is our heart and it becomes lonely when it is empty. The Mama Robin protects the lonely nest from becoming broken and tells us the difference between right and wrong.

My mind forgets about my lonely nest when I smell espresso and anisette pancakes simmering on the stove. Sam is lying by my mother's feet and I sit down on the floor so I can pull on his floppy ears. I do not notice that I'm sitting in spilled flour until my mother gives me a look I have never seen before.

"Connie Mary, please get off that floor. You'll get your clothes dirty and then your teacher won't like you. Hurry, it's time to eat!"

My mother moves about frantically watching the clock as if it were her judge, jury and executioner and I do my best to cheer her up. I sit at the kitchen table and comically pull my lips sideways mumbling incoherently.

"Ma, you likes my face?" Then I point to my shoes. "Ma, you likes my saddle shoes?" Encouraged by my mother's smile, I stretch my legs high, holding each shoe up by my fingertips. "Ma, why they call them saddle shoes? Is it because funny little horses wear 'em? Huh Ma? Is that true Ma?"

My mother says she does not want my sister and I riding the bus alone on the first day of school, so today she's going to drive us to school herself. After a particularly turbulent morning, my sister and I are finally packed and ready to go. We make it outside where my mother does her best to gather us inside the car without forgetting something. I keep tripping over my shoelaces and Janice keeps running back inside the house in search of another book. I slip on the wet grass, and look up at my mother, hoping she will notice that I fell, but she is frantically searching inside her pocketbook.

"Oh, no!" she cries, carelessly throwing a lit cigarette on top of my father's lawn forgetting what my father has said, not once, but a million times. "*Rose! How many times do I got to tell you before you learn? Never—ever—throw your damn, dirty cigarettes on top of my lawn. Don't you know Rose? It could kill the grass!*"

My mother finally dumps everything inside her pocketbook on the grass and stares across the vast blue sky. "I can't believe I lost my keys! —Oh sweet Mary, Jesus and Joseph! How could I be so stupid? Oh Jesus, Jesus, Jesus—help me!" My mother continues to look up at the sky and so do we, expecting the keys to drop through a hole in a cloud from heaven above. When the keys do not fall, my mother runs inside the house, knocking the pink plastic door wreath on the ground. I am still sitting on the grass when Janice meanders over and offers a gentle hand. I do not want my sister's help and slap her hand away.

"No! I want Mommy to help me—not you! Ma! Aren't you going to help me tie my shoelaces? Ma! Ma?"

My sister doesn't say a word. She only smiles and wanders away, following an orange and black butterfly fluttering above her head. She shouts toward the house with new excitement as if my mother cares about seeing a butterfly right now.

"Look Mommy—Look! A Monarch butterfly! Oh, Mommy, I absolutely love the black and orange colors… don't you Mommy? Don't you just love the black and orange colors?"

My mother rushes out of the house with her keys in hand, ignoring what my sister had said and ushers us into the car. My sister, knowing the front seat belongs to me, automatically climbs into the back. As we pull out of the driveway, the three of us look back and see Sam, barking and ferociously throwing himself against the dining room window. This amuses me and I point at the house, laughing.

"Look Ma, Sam's waving goodbye," I say, expecting my mother to smile.

"He's not saying goodbye, Connie Mary. He's warning us."

My mother says school is a mile or so down the road which gives me time to study my sister to see if she has anything I do not. When I see her shoelaces tied, I scream at the top of my lungs— "Ma! Why aren't my shoelaces tied?" My mother's foot slams on the brake and the car behind screeches to a stop in an effort to avoid hitting us.

My mother has smoked so many cigarettes this morning I have lost count. When we pull into the school's driveway my mother takes one long look at the lonely blue building and exhales a tired sigh.

"Well, there's your school Connie Mary. This is what you have been waiting all your life for." If my father had heard my mother's remark he would have said she was being a smart-ass. Somehow, I still have the nerve to ask her a question.

"Ma, what's my school called?"

My mother is rubbing a pair of scratched sunglasses along the hem of her dress. Showing no emotion, she spits out her words as if they taste bad.

"Fields Memorial. The name is Fields Memorial."

Janice recognizes it is time to go and is the first to leave. As usual, my sister has a goofy smile stretched across her face with eyes that look like squares of Hershey's chocolate melting in the morning sun. She reaches out and carefully touches my shoulder.

"Good luck little ConBon, see you later." My sweet sister dashes inside the building and is quietly swallowed behind cold grey doors and is seen no more. This is when I feel pain inside my lonely nest and wish I could tell my mother. But I cannot, because the pain inside my mother's lonely nest is far worse than mine.

"Ma—why is Janice walking into school without us?"

My mother solemnly stares across the beautiful playground not caring about the colorful swings or beautiful leaves turning orange, red and yellow.

"Janice is a big girl—she's in sixth grade now," says my mother, gritting her teeth. "She must walk into school by herself. Her mother is not allowed to walk with her anymore." Despite the horrific pain of watching two baby robins fly away on the same day, my mother finds the courage to lead me to my alpha.

Holding hands, we follow the arrows pointing us through a dark hallway that goes on like the black tunnel that leads babies into the light. We come to a sunny space with long high windows and I am amazed at the colorful pictures taped across each wall. To my delight, I saw two yellow and black bumblebees (Mr. Do-Bee and Mr. Don't-Bee) from a television show called *Romper Room*. When I ask my mother to read the words hanging underneath Mr. Do-Bee, her voice is sullen and sad.

"Girls and Boys: Do Bee a good student for teachers and not a bad Mr. Don't Bee." I choose to ignore my mother's tone and instead focus on how my heart is almost bursting with joy—I want to be a Good Do-Bee!

The classroom door is only inches away when my mother stops and holds my hand with a powerful grip. I peek inside my classroom and see children hard at work. I try my best to pull my body closer and notice one empty desk and chair in the middle of the room. *This is my desk and chair! If I do not go inside right now—I will lose my desk and chair and they will send me home where I will have to wait another year to go to school!* I desperately try to wiggle my hand free and my mother squeezes tighter! My new saddle shoes hurt from standing so long but I cannot tell my mother because she is crying too hard. I stare at little girls wearing the same plaid dress and ponytail as mine, and wondered if their mothers were sad like mine. The Mama Robin in my lonely nest knows if my mother could have found the courage that day, she would have scooped me up and taken me home. My mother is Sicilian and knows when bad things are going to happen. I wish someone could help my mother and tell her she looks beautiful wearing a white veiled hat, pearls and short white gloves. I notice a sign above the door and point directing my mother's eyes.

"What's that say Ma?"

My mother reads the sign in the most miserable and monotone voice you will ever hear:

"Welcome to First Grade. Best of luck Mrs. Hellerman." She seems unaware that my shoes are edging closer to the door and looks down at me with so much pain I must look away.

"Ti amo, figlia…" she whispers, as if these were the last words she will ever speak. Although I yearn to return to my mother, I do not, for this classroom is my alpha. And as suddenly as the colored paper chains my sister brings home every Christmas that inevitably fall apart, I tear myself away from my mother as easily as if we were both connected by a string of thin paper chains folded by Janice. Now separated by two different worlds, I stand inside the classroom and blow my mother a kiss goodbye.

"It'll be okay Mommy. I will be a Good Do-Bee for my teacher and you and Daddy too! *Ti amo, Madre!*" I turn away from my beautiful sad mother and say goodbye, my smile fixed, my head held high. I leave her standing against the wall in the lonely hallway because I know…my mother is not strong enough to leave me. Guided by the courage of Tom Terrific and his faithful dog Manfred, I rushed to sit in the last desk and chair. And even though the lonely nest inside of me can feel my mother softly weeping, I close my eyes and see my mother no more. For this is my alpha, my beginning, my first dawn.

I fold my hands observing the beautiful pictures taped to the walls.

I especially like the one of a smiling farmer on top of a red tractor with a barefoot boy chewing on a piece of grass in an enormous field of grazing cows. Across the classroom the walls have tall sunny windows with shelves displaying rows of books that my sister would love. In every corner, wooden apple boxes contain Lincoln Logs, dominoes, Candy Land, Chutes and Ladders, checkers, jacks and my all-time favorite: paper dolls. Upon the linoleum floor is a long green rug revealing a happy town painted with trees, mountains, rivers and a train track with a red caboose. Comic books sit on the shelves patiently waiting for children to learn how to read. I recognize *Casper the Friendly Ghost, Hot Stuff the Little Devil, Little Lulu and Little Lotta*. Out of everything that is bright and beautiful, the best part is the enormous clock hanging high above the teacher's desk with the smiling face of everyone's favorite...Captain Kangaroo. The Good Captain wears a red coat and loving smile below a grey mustache. The Captain's eyes are as beautiful as two blue marbles a child holds dear on a summer day. From high above us, the Good Captain waves to all his good children promising to guide and protect in the days ahead.

My teacher approaches and I am startled by the warning cry of the Mama Robin inside of me. She walks up and down the rows of obedient children, all who bow in reverence. Holding a yellow pad in one hand and a red pen in the other, my teacher bends whispering words to certain children the rest of us cannot hear. Growing bored, I find myself looking out the window at the enormous playground. At home my sister and I play on two rusty swings and a lopsided seesaw. This playground is a child's paradise with colorful swings, jungle gyms, and two double slides that almost touch the sky. As I stare at the playground, I'm reminded of the day Gus Lorentz revealed his secret to me. It was just a few weeks ago, on a hot summer day, when Anna Lorentz spotted me through her kitchen window.

"Connie Mary, come and see me! I made you some good Kool-Aid ice cube pops you love so well!" she yelled.

Once inside, it did not take Anna and me long to get as snug as two bugs in a rug. Anna drank muddy Sanka and smoked cigarettes while I sucked on a Kool-Aid pop and dripped water all over Anna's floor. I did not have to worry though. I knew I was more important to Anna than the floor. The Grandfather Clock chimed five times as Gus returned home from work. Gus looked as brown as a chestnut and as tired as an old horse. The first thing he did was look at me and giggle mischievously.

"Hey there, little 'talian girl. I heard you be startin' school pertty soon. Boy, do I got a secret for you!" Then he went over to Anna and kissed her smack dab on the lips! I was surprised because my father never kisses my mother like that! Without saying a word, he took a chipped cup out of Anna's cluttered sink and poured himself a cup of coffee from a blue and white speckled coffee pot. He noticed a Swanson Salisbury steak dinner in tin foil and thanked Anna for making his favorite supper. He sat down across from Anna and using his teeth, pulled a cigarette out of a wrinkled pack of Camels. I was surprised when he dragged a wooden matchstick across the kitchen table and it caught fire. With a sense of urgency, he lit his cigarette and inhaled deeply.

Anna worried about Gus and stared at him. "Papa, you got to blow them worries away like smoke and watch them disappear like the dreams of yesterday."

Gus placed his green work hat on the table and bowed his head as though he was about to speak to Jesus. With a stained handkerchief he wiped the sweat off his thin brown face and released an exhausted sigh.

"Whew, Mother! Long, hot day." He took a sip of coffee and grinned.

"Connie Mary, I got a little secret that you're gonna like. When you go to school and have recess, I want you to take a good long look at the nice black tar spread across the playground. It holds a magical secret for you and Jan."

I looked at Gus with awe, daring to pull on the frayed sleeve of his shirt.

"Come Gus, please tell me—now!"

No longer able to contain his composure, Gus bellowed loudly and laughed so hard tears rolled down his face. Anna frowned disapprovingly.

"Now Papa, don't tease little Connie Mary." She smiled at me with loving eyes. "It's not nice to tease good little 'talian girls, is it Connie Mary?"

"Okay, little Connie Mary, Mother says I gotta tell." No longer able to continue the game, Gus took a swig of coffee and relented. "Connie Mary, it wasn't but a few months back when me and my men laid that nice tar foundation. And—you know somein' else Connie Mary? When we was doing it I kept sayin' to myself, "Gus, maybe someday, when both your girls go to school here, they will remember their old friend Gus and how he laid this nice tar for them to play," and giggles. "See, I found a way to make you both remember me."

Gus dragged another match across the kitchen table, this time with eyes as sorrowful as Jesus looking down from the cross.

"Connie Mary, you're just a young-un. But I want you to know something. Old Anna and Gus here, well, we're lots older than you— even lots older than your Mama and Papa. The truth is Connie Mary—I'm just an old, broken down, beat-up World War I soldier who ain't going to live forever (looking forlornly at Anna) and neither is Mother here. Someday, the good Lord's going to call us both home to live with Him—and that day ain't so far away. When that happens, we won't be here like we are now talkin' at this kitchen table. We'll be with you in spirit."

I do not understand what Gus means by spirit but if Gus says it's true—it's true. My father and mother don't agree on much, but they both agree on one thing: "*Gus Lorentz ain't never learned how to tell a lie.*"

Anna knows Gus' tricks and plays along. "What'd you do next Papa?"

"I'm getting there, Mother, please, don't rush. See little one, I wanted to leave you something that you and Janice would see when you was playing your Jacks or Hopscotch in them wonderful childhood years. So you knows what silly thing I went and done? When you go to school and set your feet upon that nice tar playground—go and look next to the grand old oak standing straight as an arrow. And then you'll see that I wrote: 'To Connie and Janice, By Gustave O. Lorentz, XOX 1959' in the freshly laid tar."

My memory of Anna and Gus passed quickly like a bird soaring high above the pond. I look away from the playground and try to pay attention as I recount my mother's warning: "*Connie Mary, never forget what I say—it is important that your teacher likes you. If your teacher doesn't like you… then nothing can save you.*"

On every desk my teacher placed yellow-lined paper and a fat red pencil. I see other children writing and take my own pencil and write my name. I hold the paper high for everyone to see and proudly announce my accomplishment. "See? It says Connie!"

Some children look and giggle while others roll their eyes. Suddenly I feel very bad, not realizing I have written "EINNOC" as my name. I drop my pencil on the floor and wish I could run home. It is too late, for my teacher looms above me like a giant rain cloud blocking the sun. She does not smile, nor look anything like I imagined. She has two bony shoulders that carry the burden of an

35

enormous man-sweater that swallows the neck as a long black skirt touches the floor. Ugly wire-rimmed bifocals magnify a black hole in the center of each eye, igniting fear in the heart of every child. She is the hawk circling the robin's nest causing the babies to hide their heads. Then it happens. I barely see my teacher's shadow slide across my desk before she raises her hand and slaps me across the face. The brutality and strength of the slap causes my ears to implode like thunder snapping a tree in half.

My first awareness is silence. No longer can I hear. I begin to imagine I am underwater in my pool with ears filled with gurgling water. I am enjoying the soothing water when a horrible, crippling pain spills into my mouth and jaw. I am familiar with the burning sting from my father's hand. This is my first awakening to the violence of a stranger. Even when long tears slide down my face and disappear underneath my collar, I continue to be silent. My jaw hangs loose like the door of an old cupboard on a broken hinge. But my teacher is not fooling me. She may look like a teacher, but underneath that disguise is the evil wife of Crabby Appleton, Tom Terrific's worst enemy. I know because every word she says is dipped in snake venom.

"I have been watching *you* from the moment you entered this room. You—have—been—sitting—here—all—morning—doing—nothing—but daydreaming—when you should have been writing your name! Tell me young lady—*why?*"

I want to explain that I have been writing my name. Before I get the chance my teacher whips the paper off my desk holding it high between her thumb and forefinger as if it had a deadly disease.

"Is this some type of joke Connie Falcone? Do you think this is a game? Oh, you will learn that when Mrs. Hellerman tells you to do something—by *Jiminy Cricket*—you'll do it!"

I see children pointing and laughing at me when I look around the room. I never thought it bad when my father laughed at Janice, but now it feels different. The Mama Robin has given birth to a new egg. This one is called *Shame*.

"Mrs. Teacher, I did-dent mean to be a smarty pants. Honest. I did write my name. But I don't write frontways, only backways." Suddenly I recall with gratitude the times my sister tried to help me write my name. Janice knew.

With thin red lips my teacher displays a truculent smile that sends chills down my spine.

"So you write backways, do you? Tell me child, how is it that you were home for six long years with your mother and you cannot even write your name?" She chuckles. "I've already heard about your mother."

I lift my hand to my burning cheek, having no idea how to fix a jaw that is broken. I begin to smell something that is a combination of my father's Old Spice and week-old garbage. I turn in the direction of the sour aroma and see a strange-looking boy sitting in the desk next to mine. He is a large boy, taller and older-looking than others judging by the way his knees lift the desk. I stifle the urge to laugh at his shaved head and bulbous nose running with yellow snot that he continuously wipes across his sleeve. If Nonna ever saw him she would immediately make him change his pants as they are horribly stained from yesterday. A hilarious crooked tie hangs about his neck that convinces me—this is the funniest boy I have ever seen! Except for his eyes. His eyes are as beautiful as a Crayola crayon called Wild Blue Yonder. Every child knows the Wild Blue Yonder is that sacred place the rain goes after the sky clears.

The funny boy smiles nervously and looks both ways before whispering

"P-s-s-t, what's your name? I'm Gregory McGillis. I just wanted to say… uh… um… I just wanted to say—welcome to first grade!"

The pain inside my jaw jingles and tingles as if someone sewed sharp bells inside each cheek. I like this funny boy and hold my hand underneath my chin so it will not drop to the floor when I speak.

"Hello, Gregory McGillis, I'm Connie Mary. Welcome to first grade!"

After many torturous hours— I am home.

It is dark outside by the time I am on the parlor floor eating a bowl of *pasta e piselli* for supper and watching the peas float on top of the rich red sauce. My six-year old mind is already familiar with adapting to horrific situations and dismisses my first day of school as nothing more than a bad dream. This leaves me content enough to enjoy *Ranger Andy* playing his banjo on television. The moment my young father bursts through the door with tousled black hair and tender green eyes glistening with hope and love... *I know I must lie.* He stands before me smiling, but when he leans his body and touches my hand, he trembles with fear. The wishful hopefulness my father held all day releases when he kneels by my feet and winks at me with long dark eyelashes.

"Well? How was my beautiful daughter's first day of school? I worried about you all day. I couldn't even eat your mother's meatball grinder she made me for lunch. Well, how'd you do kid? Did you write your ABC's? Did you learn your numbers? How was your first day of school?" Without taking my eyes off Ranger Andy I shuffle my blue bunny slippers together and tell my first big lie.

"Great dad. It was great. I love my new teacher." My words extinguish his fear and he rises to tend to other pressing issues in life. If only my father had trusted the instincts of his Mama Robin. If he had he would have recognized a lie. To think bad things are happening to your child is one thing. But to *know* bad things are happening to your child is far too painful to acknowledge. So, that night my father chooses to ignore the warning signs of his Mama Robin and believe the lies of his favorite daughter.

"Pretend you're an airplane Connie Mary—and try flying as fast as you can, 'cause I'm a fast plane and I can catch you!" During recess, Gregory and I hold our arms out straight like an airplane rising off the ground and fly away as fast as we can. I love this game because my father's hobby is flying airplanes and sometimes he flies above our house. My mother will be in the kitchen cooking, when all of a sudden she will hear a low and familiar buzz. Out of the house she will run, pointing at the sky and calling to my father as if he can actually hear her.

"Janice, Connie, look! — There's your father! Hurry girls, Hurry! Oh I bet he's going to tilt his wings! Tilt your wings Albert Joseph. Tilt your wings when you catch a glimpse of Heaven!" Then sure enough, several times, my father tilts his wings back and forth causing the silver plane to sparkle like a diamond in the sky. We watch in awe as the plane glides through a translucent cloud and disappears into the Wild Blue Yonder. The three of us keep looking at the sky even though we no longer see our father. We stay until nothing is left but a thin trail of smoke. My sister and I return to the house, but our mother lingers by the barbed wire fence looking up at the clouds long after our father is gone as if saying a prayer.

"Vr-r-o-o-mmmm," I buzz as I fly around Gregory. "I'm going to catch a glimpse of Heaven like my father, come follow me!" It happens to be one of those days Gregory is wearing his Davy Crockett coonskin cap. The cap is the envy of every boy in school and earns Gregory the only respect he will ever know. This is why he holds one hand on top of his cap at all times.

When recess is over our teacher blows the whistle for line up and every child moans in protest. Gregory is far away from the line, sitting on the ground and drawing circles in the dirt. But it is too late now. My teacher's voice seems to scare away every bird in the sky.

"GREGORY MCGILLIS! Why, you lazy little boy! You would

rather play in the dirt like a little pig than follow my instructions."

She drags him to the classroom door and pushes him down on the ground.

"You stay by this door until I can think of an appropriate punishment for you." The rest of us miserably shuffle inside while Gregory is left sitting on the dirt talking to a patch of dying marigolds made brown by the sun.

When my teacher is not looking I try to silently communicate with Gregory.

Get up Gregory! Run to Johnson's General Store and tell Mr. and Mrs. Johnson your teacher is trying to kill you! It is hopeless. Gregory is already forgotten when Mrs. Hellerman gives the next assignment.

"Children take out your math books and crayons and turn to page two. Here you will see a picture of an empty glass." She goes to the board and writes the fraction ½. "Today, we are learning about the fraction one-half. I want you to take out a blue crayon and color the empty glass half-full imagining blue Kool-Aid. No one should have a problem with this task."

All of our mouths hang open as our minds register the same thought: *What'd she say?*

Upon seeing the puzzled faces Mrs. Hellerman mumbles with frustration.

"*Oh for Goodness sake, how dumb can these children be?* Here, I will draw an empty glass on the blackboard. Now watch as I color the glass one-half or half-full with blue chalk." When my teacher is finished she picks up a long thin stick with numbers and whacks it hard against the blackboard causing my teeth to vibrate. "Now, you do it."

I usually have Gregory to help me with math because Mrs. Hellerman says I am as dumb as a doorknob when it comes to math. My mother understands this because she says she is as dumb as a doorknob with math, too. But my father will never understand. My father is good at math and went to some fancy-dancy school in a place called Philly Cheese and repeats constantly, *'I'm tellin' you Connie Mary—MATH is the most important subject in school! If you know your times tables, you can do any math in the world!'*

I open my book, pausing to see how my teacher colored her glass. It looks easy enough, so I hum along to the Captain Kangaroo's theme song and color my glass half-full. When my teacher approaches I place my crayon next to the workbook and proudly fold my hands. Instead of placing a gold star on my paper like everyone else, my teacher slams the stick on my desk.

"You deserve a great big F!" and slashes an F across my entire paper. "What were you thinking young lady? You colored the top half of your glass full—not the bottom! Oh, Lord, have mercy, these children are going to be the death of me yet!"

Then, as if suddenly remembering something she lost, she shouts —"*Shit!*" and runs for the door. I peek through the window and see her yanking Gregory inside by his sleeve. Everyone gasps when his coat rips. Gregory tumbles inside and falls into the seat next to mine looking no worse than if given a long recess. Exhausted, my teacher slumps in her chair and yawns deeply. I look up at the Good Captain on the wall, confident that he is smiling down on everyone *except* the bad teacher. Soon I shall be home with Janice and my mother watching *I Love Lucy* and eating sauce on bread.

It is the end of the day when it is time for our teacher to read us a story. This is the only time of day her voice takes flight like a colony of beautiful butterflies rising to the ceiling.

"Today, I will read a fictional tale called: *The Little Engine That Could* written by Watty Piper. This tale is a lesson about never giving up, no matter what the odds. I hope all of you take this story to heart." My eyes soon become drowsy and I imagine I am running through Beebe's Fields with Sam following behind.

I wake up from my daydream and discover the horrible day is over. Soon everyone is shuffling outside to find their way home. With all the weariness of Mr. Beebe's Holsteins trudging up the hill at the end of the day, I waited in the crowded bus line. My sister stands protectively behind me, humming softly in an effort to disguise the unpredictability of our surroundings. I briefly close my eyes and feel Gregory pulling on my blue windbreaker.

"Connie Mary! Isn't it grand? Last night your mommy called my mommy and guess what? I swear on Davy Crockett—I'm going home with you today! I'm gonna see the bees in the fields, the fish in Gus's Pond and eat Chef Boy-R-D!"

The children exit the bus one by one and the next stop is my house. Mr. Lashinski swings the door open allowing Gregory and I to pass with Janice following behind us. Without warning, my sister runs across the road ignoring the speeding cars. Mr. Lashinski throws his cigarette out the window and yells— "Slow down, you good for nothing, crazy bastards!" and blasts the horn in a futile attempt to stop them. The two cars go even faster and disappear into a cloud of smoke. My sister continues skipping across the road, unaware of the near catastrophe witnessed. Gregory is pale and shaking after seeing Janice narrowly escape death.

"What's wrong with your sister anyways Connie Mary? Is she one of those retards?"

It surprises me that even a dunce like Gregory knows something is wrong with Janice. He studies the hurt look on my face. "No, no, Connie... I don't mean like me. I mean a *real* retard."

"She's not a retard!" I adamantly retort, hiking my nose into the air. "She just didn't hear the horn, that's all. Come on, let's put our boots on and wade through Gus's Pond."

My home was once a happy place until everything changed. Every night my father and I wrestled on the parlor floor trying to pin the other one down while laughing and pinching each other in the guts. One night, after I am pinned with my father sitting on my legs, I happen to look and see my mother watching in scrutiny as the two of us writhe across the floor. I feel the blazing scorch from her eyes and so does my father, who is pretending to huff and puff his way out of our match. Rising wobbly on one knee, he diverts his eyes and sighs.

"I ain't as young as I used to be Connie Mary."

Lying on my back I look into my father's luminous green eyes and laugh.

"Hey Dad, you know what comes on television tonight? — *Gunsmoke!*" My father's eyes race to look at the lopsided clock above the television.

"Oh Christ, I gotta mow the lawn. I don't wanna miss *Gunsmoke!*" He pushes past my mother, accidentally kicking her in the leg before flying out the back door.

I sit up as inconspicuous as possible in an effort to avoid the wrath on my mother's face. Then come the words that alter my future in an effort to protect me.

"Connie Mary, you're getting too big to wrestle with your father. It needs to stop now. It gives your father a feeling."

A terrible sadness sinks deep inside my lonely nest. Even though I do not understand what my mother means by 'a feeling', I know by her tone and expression this is not good.

"I'm telling you Connie Mary, you must stop wrestling with your father. It gets him too excited and then…"

I do not understand what just happened and blame myself for getting my father into trouble. I walk angrily to the kitchen and kick Sam's dirty rug across the room. *Why couldn't I have stayed little? Why did I have to become a big girl and spoil everything? Now I made my mother unhappy and my father and I can no longer wrestle! I wish I were a boy!*

Just as I am lamenting my girlhood, down the stairs Janice comes screaming and hollering.

"Ma! I'm bleeding to death—help me Ma! I'm bleeding in my underwear!"

Together we study my sister's backside. My sister is not making this up. She really is bleeding to death! Yucky red spots are splattered across the back of her skirt! My sister sobs hysterically and covers her face with both hands. When she decides to plop down on the couch, that's when I start praying: *Dear God, please don't let her sit on my side of the couch!*

"Mommy, everyone in school laughed at me today. No one would tell me what was wrong. All the girls kept passing notes giggling and when the teacher wasn't looking, the boys told me to get a rag because I was dirty." To hear this makes my mother very upset, as it confirms her Sicilian prophecies are coming true at last. Then for the zillionth time, my sister and I have to listen to the same speech my mother gives in every crisis.

"Oh Jesus, this is just the beginning! It's just the beginning for my girls!" She wails, crying far worse than Janice or I ever did. "Oh Janice, I wish those children weren't so mean to you. The kids were mean to me, too, in school. I should have told you Jan. I should have warned you about the blood and what a horrible place school really is."

My sister looks confused speaking in a voice mixed with sweet honey and bunny tails.

"What about the blood mommy? What should you have told me?"

My mother looks ashamed.

"I should have told you about menstruation and how girls bleed every month and have to wear Kotex pads inside their underwear to keep the blood from spreading. See Jan, every month you must be prepared. We don't know the exact day or time the blood will arrive or how long it will last." Janice looks more terrified than ever. I start to giggle because I think the words 'Kotex pads' sound funny until my mother just about knocks my socks off.

"Oh, Connie Mary. One day, you too, are going to menstruate as well."

My mother stands and shakes a fist at the ceiling. "Oh Lord why—why? Why must we Italian women suffer so much?"

I am not afraid like my sister because I am too mad to be afraid.

"Ma, don't dumb boys have to bleed and men-u-hate too?"

My mother walks over to the dining room mirror to dry her eyes with a Kleenex while attempting to center a messy bun. Tucking a few strands of gray hair behind one ear, she peers closer at the new wrinkles appearing around each eye. The room grows silent as we listen to the sound of my father's lawn mower fading in the distance and the garage door slamming shut. My mother begins to fidget with the safety pins that prevent her skirt from falling down.

"Oh, no Con, boys don't menstruate, only girls. Now quick Jan— go run upstairs and change your skirt and I'll give you some Kotex pads to put inside your underwear!" This leaves me unable to understand the whole bleeding thing involving girls and why boys do not have to bleed, which only confirms my experience in life so far. *It's not good to be a girl…*

School does teach me one thing: how to lie extremely well. I learn to lie so well that my father thinks I am smart in school. I effectively convince my parents until the mail lady, Mrs. Nye, delivers my report card into my mother's hands.

"Oh my god! Connie Mary! This report card is… awful! You're going to be punished, little girl! Just wait until your father gets home!"

I run downstairs and beg.

"No mommy! No! Please don't tell daddy about my grades! — Please!" I beg and beg my mother not to tell my father but she will not look at me. When children are bad, mothers threaten, but fathers hit. I know the second my father walks through the door, tired and grouchy, my mother will show him my report card.

Later that evening, my father comes home but misses the driveway and slams his truck into my little pool in the yard! It isn't as bad as it looks and he falls into the pool laughing with a big smile. My mother, however, is not laughing. She thinks my father will drown even though the water is only a few feet deep. Along with the neighbors, we watch my father swim around like a drunken monkey and listen to my mother yell.

"Albert, get out of that pool now! You want to leave your little daughters orphans?" My father's blue work shirt looks beautiful floating above the water as he swims circles around the pool doing the dog paddle.

"I love you Rose, the water's beautiful! Come in, we can skinny dip together; the water's warm as piss!"

Anna watches from the kitchen window and, sure enough, Gus meanders over to talk to my father in a way that only Gus is able.

"How's the water, Al?" says Gus looking at my father with sorrowful eyes. Gus is aware that every neighbor is watching my father and not laughing with him—but at him. When Gus looks at the neighbors laughing and pointing the men immediately lower their eyes. My father is floating on his back when he sees Gus and flip-flops on his belly like a baby orca playing in the ocean.

"Gus, my *buon amico* come on in, the water's beautiful!"

Gus gives my father a heartbreaking smile.

"Al, I'd love to join ya, but I think we're going to need a bigger pool. Why don't you come out and I'll show you where we can put a bigger pool with the help of my backhoe and son Pinky." My father comes out of the pool with blue lips and shivering. My mother pulls a scratchy blanket off the clothesline to wrap around his shoulders. My father is no longer happy and laughing but sad and melancholy as he reluctantly follows Gus into the house. My father goes in the refrigerator to grab a beer and offers one to Gus. Gus laughs and says he prefers my mother's muddy Sanka because Anna makes it the same way at home. At the kitchen table my father sits across from Gus looking miserable. Wet, black hair drips down his face becoming thinner with each passing day. He watches Gus draw a plan for a bigger pool on a napkin.

"See Al, you got this little pool here," he says, pointing with a mechanical pencil he pulls out of his pocket like magic. "I bet between the two of us—and my son Pinky of course, we can make the kids a bigger, better pool and put it in a more convenient place."

Thanks to Gus it isn't long before we have a bigger, better pool! The best part about Gus's plan is my pool is set behind three tall maple trees that will protect it from my father's truck.

Later that night, I overhear my mother talking to my father as he tries to sleep on the couch. "Albert—wake up… did you see Connie Mary's report card? It's terrible! Why, your daughter got an "F" in every subject including recess and gym!" I feel the mood in the house shift as my father forgets how happy he was in the pool. I stiffen in bed as he charges up the stairs and barges into my bedroom without knocking. I do not like it when my father does not knock before entering my room. I might be in my Tom Terrific underwear—or worse—wearing no clothes at all! My father is no longer a funny chimpanzee but a treacherous King Kong when he pushes me down so my backside is exposed and slaps me several times. It is unbelievable how one or two slaps from my father is so painful. Afterward the house is silent with no one left to hear me cry in the darkness. I am worried about the broken bones in my backside and if I will ever be able to sit in my chair at school. All night long I toss and turn because the pain hurts too much to sleep. Eventually I fall into a fitful sleep, recognizing with every passing day, with every minute and hour, the father I loved is disappearing before my very eyes.

Mrs. Hellerman says Gregory and I need a special reading group because our brains are not capable of learning like normal children. It is 1959 and children who learn slower are contemptuously viewed as a horrible deviation from the norm and labeled outcasts, dunces and imbeciles. My teacher is not the only one frustrated with her students. Why, it was only yesterday our teacher was out in the hallway talking to another first grade teacher named Miss Olive Oyl. The children call her Miss Olive Oyl because she is tall and bony with jet-black hair and looks exactly like Popeye's girlfriend. Miss Oyl and Mrs. Hellerman are good friends and not a day goes by when they do not talk about students, parents and every teacher they dislike in school.

Mrs. Hellerman moaned in exasperation. "My goodness Bernice, I'm at my wits' end with this class! I never had a first grade class with so many problems."

"Oh, Irma Ida, I know exactly what you mean," snorted Miss Oyl, vainly flipping her hair back with one hand. "Lord knows my class is the most talkative ever! Children behave far worse today then in previous years. This of course is the fault of ignorant mothers who leave their babies behind in order to compete with the ranks of men at work. What is this world coming to?"

Miss Oyl studied my teacher's oversized sweater and spoke to her like a child.

"Maybe I can be of some assistance to you, dear. We both know I have far more experience than you. Exactly which children are your biggest concerns?"

Mrs. Hellerman looked back at the children in her classroom with disgust.

"It's Gregory McGillis and Connie Falcone! Lord knows I have tried everything to get those two to read. Never have I seen such an ignorant pair of children! I am beginning to think they are from a different planet or maybe it's just me," and lowers her eyes in shame.

"Maybe, I'm not a good teacher."

Miss Oyl wrapped a long thin arm around my teacher's shoulders.

"Oh no dear! You are not a bad teacher! Why, I have my own ignorant children that I have placed far away from the intelligent ones and into a special group. I must say they are responding much better to a slower, individualized-paced program. You know Irma, I love the Scott Foresman Reading Series, but this is 1959, and we are seeing more social deviants coming out of the woodwork. I feel strongly that our present reading program is not adequate enough to meet the needs of everyone. Of course, it is our duty to feel compassion for those children who are unable to read. Oh hell, let's just call it what it is," and rolled her eyes in jest. "Some children are just plain stupid."

The two giggled like a couple of schoolgirls.

"By the way Bernice, I'll see you this Sunday at St. John's bake sale. I'm baking my prized pound cake that won first prize in The Betty Crocker Cook-Off last year—it should be a real hit!" As they walked away, I heard Miss Olive Oyl mumbling, *"Humph, I'd win a prize too, if I stole the recipe off the back of a box."*

The next day, our teacher's dark shadow approached us.

"*No* more recess for either one of you until you learn how to read! During recess the two of you shall report to the detention room each day. And if the need arises, both of you shall write every single word in the dictionary starting today." I look desperately out the window at the blue sky and fluffy white clouds that I will not be seeing for a very long time. I have not heard anything my teacher said except for two words—"*No recess.*"

By the end of March I have in my possession handfuls of papers, all filled with useless information and nonsense words. My fingers on my right hand are black and blue from writing so much. Eventually, my mother takes notice while hanging clothes on the line.

"My God Connie Mary! How did your fingers get so bruised?" Fear races through my mother's mind as she waits to hear the truth. Nervously, she takes my hand to examine closer.

Meanwhile, my father is on the roof throwing leaves down for me to pile in a wheelbarrow. When he hears the concern in my mother's voice he stops and listens. My sister is also outside, strolling through the yard alone. By some whim of fate, she overhears my mother's question and stares at my black and blue fingers. I do not want anyone to find out what a bad girl I have been and give an explanation that will keep my secret safe.

"We write lots in first grade to get smarter. My fingers got all worn out—that's all."

Satisfied with my answer, my father goes back to cleaning the gutters and my mother turns away knowing it would be far too painful to pursue the truth. For some reason my sister continues to stare at me with a condescending look.

"Con, when I was in first grade we never had bruises from writing—and we wrote intensely."

I make sure neither one of my parents is looking before rudely sticking out my tongue at my sister.

"Well, we do! We got lots more writing than you ever did! So there! See, you don't know everything, Miss Smarty Pants!" My sister slowly backs away and walks in the opposite direction. Out of curiosity, I watch her run down the dirt path circling Gus's Pond. When she reaches the middle, she stops and looks back, before releasing a bloodcurdling scream that no one hears except for me.

3

Duck and Cover

"Tonight I saw hundreds of fireflies flickering in the night, tiny sacred creatures from ancient times guiding travelers to the safe path. I have often wondered if fireflies were the spirits of long lost children leaving behind an effervescent light of endless love. "Goodnight Francis and Lilian Broullard! Goodnight Jodi Rajotte, Goodnight Gregory McGillis and Waynie Ormston. Goodnight to all the children I have loved and those I have never met."

As the months pass, my mother becomes more and more disturbed at the depth and length of my sister's suffering. She is horrified at the hurtful words Janice must endure spoken from the mouths of mere children. In addition to my sister's problems, something bad is about to happen to my mother. One day, after my father had left for work, we woke to the sound of hysterical crying.

"I'm going to die from cancer girls and your father doesn't even care! You just watch—he's going to bring another woman into this house! A younger one I know—because he's a *Miserabile Bastardo!*"

My sister and I carry on the best we can. My mother smokes in bed while staring listlessly at the ceiling. This means we must be cautious if we enter her room. When picture day arrives, I quietly tiptoe into my mother's bedroom with a bundle of wrinkled clothes in my hands. I smile and show all my teeth holding up a green and tan dress and the red sweater Nonna knitted for my birthday.

"Look Ma! Look what I picked out for picture day! Aren't you proud Ma? I'm getting dressed all by myself! Doesn't that make you happy Ma? Does it Ma? Are you happy now Ma?"

My mother gives me a strained smile before hiding underneath tangled blankets. This does not worry me because no matter how sick my mother feels, she still does something good for me every morning…she makes my ponytail! But even with my ponytail, picture day is not good. On the bus ride home, my lonely nest burns with shame as I recall how Mrs. Hellerman had to button the back of my dress before the pictures shouting at me, '*Goodness sakes! Can't your mother EVEN button a dress?*'

Saturday morning comes and I am aware that my mother is getting sicker. I am not happy knowing she will soon be leaving for Yale New Haven Hospital. I witness my mother's pain when she hands me a bowl of Sugar Pops and I spill it, causing her to burst into tears.

"Oh—Connie Mary, no! Can't you see I don't feel well? I'm going away tomorrow and I may never see you kids again."

My first thought spills out as carelessly as the milk dripping over the edge of the table.

"Ma, if you don't come back, who's going to fix my ponytail?"

My mother winces in pain dragging long fingers over flawless olive-colored skin and stares hopelessly into a cup of muddy Sanka as if she could see all the way to the other side of the world. I know my mother is holding back something I do not want to hear. She is taking longer than usual to respond.

"Connie Mary, I'm just going to say it. When I go to the hospital your Aunt Angie is going to come and take care of you and your sister every morning." She paused before continuing. "And she might stay overnight as well."

I roll my eyes.

"Now, Connie Mary, I want you to be nice to your father's sister. Your poor aunt has a lot of responsibility. She lost your Uncle Rodney, when he dropped dead from a heart attack right on the front lawn. Your aunt has a hard time being a beautician and owning Angie's Beauty Salon all by herself. The Lord knows she doesn't have a man to take care of her and do everything for her like we do, oh no—Aunt Angie has to work long, hard hours but somehow still finds time to help us out. Connie Mary, the people who help when you're down are your real friends."

My mother attempts to use *Romper Room* against me.

"Now, Connie Mary, I want you to be a good Do Bee and not a bad Mr. Don't Bee for your aunt, okay?"

I have my own Mr. Don't Be attitude. I hate the thought of Aunt Angie staying with us. I know Aunt Angie cares, but she is a bossy old woman who smokes too many cigarettes and then we have to listen to her moan about Uncle Rodney. Why, in just one day my aunt smokes more cigarettes than my mother, father, Pinky, Anna and Gus Lorentz put together. The worst thing about Aunt Angie is she will never admit that I'm right and she's wrong!

When I peek inside my mother's bedroom the next morning and see an empty bed, the loneliness wraps around me like a thick fog. My sister is frantically banging and slamming things because we both overslept and missed the bus. I dress quickly and find my way into the kitchen and immediately feel angry. Aunt Angie is sitting in the sunniest spot at the kitchen table smoking and drinking my mother's Diet Rite soda! I put my nose into the air and pretend not to see her. My aunt smiles and waves a cigarette through the air.

"Hel-looo, hel-looo, Connie Mary! Sit down and take a load off your feet. Look, I made you and Jan some eggs and bacon, because don't we know? Us girls gotta have plenty of protein to make our hair shiny and beautiful."

In my heart I really do want to be a good Do Bee. But then I look down at the runny eggs and black bacon thrown upon my plate and my doubts return. Beneath the table Sam's tail brushes against my legs and I thank the angels above for helping conjure a plan that will get me off the hook with my aunt and mother. My sister comes stumbling into the kitchen and when she sees the plate of runny eggs and black bacon, she tells the biggest lie ever.

"Yum, good, Aunt Angie! You're such a good cook—you cook as good as my mother."

Upon hearing my sister's comment, my aunt chokes on smoke and coughs white stuff into a napkin. She tries to regain composure while hacking away.

"It's okay Jan. I appreciate the compliment but I'll be the first one to admit, though your old aunt can fix hair all right, as far as cookin' goes…we gotta give the credit to the real cook around here—*your beautiful mother.*"

I do not like Aunt Angie sitting in my mother's chair and try to remember what Gus Lorentz tried to teach me. *Connie Mary, the first step in getting along with someone you don't like is finding something you both can agree on.* Gus may be smart, but I don't think he's ever met anyone like Aunt Angie because if he did—he'd change his tune.

The plan of attack is ready. I grab my plate in anticipation, waiting for the right moment. And then it comes. Aunt Angie turns to get another pack of cigarettes and I swiftly dump the entire contents of my plate right under Sam's nose. Feeling accomplished, I bring my empty plate up to my aunt who is none the wiser. My sister looks at me as if she's Miss Goody-Two-Shoes, and I stick out my tongue, knowing she would never dare tell on me. Aunt Angie never even notices the empty plate because she is too busy lighting up another cigarette.

"Gosh darn it girls. How come my beautiful husband Rodney had to die so young? He was here for such a short time." Aunt Angie looks up at my mother's yellow kitchen ceiling and chuckles. "Yes Lord, I guess it's true; the good die young while the rest of us *Bastardos* get to stay down here and suffer until the end. Ah, Lord, we both know Rodney wasn't perfect. He was an angel without the bottle, yes. But when he hit the bottle, oh Lord, how fast he went to hell." Aunt Angie looks at my sister as if asking for advice.

"Hey Jan, whatta ya think of this; when Rodney used to drink, he'd come home like a damn fool and bust up all my furniture into pieces. Furniture mind you—that I bought with my own backbreaking money working 18 hour days running my beauty salon." Though my sister doesn't know anything about men, she surprises me with a genuine response.

"Ah, that's too bad Aunt Angie; I heard Uncle Rodney was a good father. I know my mother and father loved him very much."

My aunt skillfully blows blue smoke rings to the ceiling— five in a row like magic, mesmerizing my sister and I as we watch.

"Jan, you made some good points. You got lots of common sense just like your old aunt. You're right Jan. Rodney was good, awful, good. And I loved him a lot, but I 'spect…God loved him even more."

I study my aunt's face and realize she's even scarier than Janice with a bulbous nose surrounded by trails of red veins and skin the color of a tombstone. I will say this much about Aunt Angie; the face is scary, but the eyes are kind. It is amazing how much you can tell about a person by looking in their eyes. It is the same with dogs. A few years back my sister and I found a stray dog begging in the backyard. Even though the dog's eyes were glazed over with yellow film and his body showed bones—he still wagged his tail. I was angry because the dog followed Janice everywhere and did not pay any attention to me. My mother was happy that Janice had found someone to love and helped name him Rin Tin Tin. No one could believe it when the dog was found dead the next morning. Gus came over and carried the dog's lifeless body away to bury and said a prayer that made my mother cry.

"Rin Tin Tin, no longer do you have to roam this earth hopin' to find some kind soul. Now you can lie next to the warmest feet and place your head on the lap of the Master Carpenter. Lord, we ask you to welcome Rin Tin Tin into your Kingdom today, Amen."

Aunt Angie interrupts my thoughts when she carries her plate and cup to the sink.

"Oh boy, it's getting late. I better drive you kids to school or your father will have my head on a platter." Before we walk out the door Aunt Angie pauses and looks down at me. "Take a lesson from me kid, make sure the man you love, loves you more than you love him. Trust me; if you never listen to any of your old aunt's bullshit you better listen this time, 'cause it will save you lots of pain!"

Of course I never listened.

My mother ends up staying at The Yale New Haven Hospital longer than anyone expected, leaving Aunt Angie to be the one who wakes me up for school. Aunt Angie and I both have strong-wills with no compromise in sight. Every morning before school, my aunt stands in my bedroom, barking orders like Sam when the garbage man dares to walk across the grass. I try to cover my ears and pretend she is invisible, but it is hard because her backside takes up a great deal of space. As usual, we are fighting over a subject my aunt will never win—my ponytail!

"Ah, Connie Mary, come on kid, you're not going to give your old aunt problems today are you? I got enough pains in the ass at work that can do that for me. Listen kid—we're getting this hair thing cleared up right now: I'm the hairdresser; you're the kid. Your old aunt here has been doing people's hair for more than 40 years. Trust me kid—I know my shit and I'm telling you this—if you keep putting your hair up in those tight ponytails you'll be balder faster than your old man."

I shut my eyes and think if I try hard enough I can wish my mother home. I know if my mother were here right now she would fix my hair in the tightest ponytail and show my bossy aunt that she is wrong!

"See Con, hairdressers like me are like doctors. It's our job to know that hair pulled back tighter than a rat's ass is no good for the scalp's circulation and causes the hair to fall out. Trust me kid; do you want to be bald before your first dance? (Chuckling) *Gesù Cristo* if you keep wearing those tight ponytails, you'll be asking me for one of my wigs before you finish junior high."

I start to scream.

"I WANT MY PONYTAIL! I WANT MY PONYTAIL! YOU GIVE ME BACK MY PONYTAIL!!" My aunt steps back, looking pale and frazzled.

"Okay Connie Mary," says my aunt, clearly flustered but pretending to be calm. She walks toward the steps and braces the peeling banister with trembling hands.

"Okay kid, have it your way." She chuckles. "Sure, you can have your ponytail and have fun doing it, because today— you fix your own ponytail." She descends the staircase smugly, as if she is playing a game of Old Maid with the card hidden in her underwear.

I hug Manfred and think of what to do. I know Aunt Angie has a sneaky plan up her sleeve just like Tom Terrific understands Crabby Appleton's schemes. *My aunt is trying to outsmart me by refusing to make my ponytail. I will fool her and make it all by myself!*

And so I go to school wearing a ponytail made by my own hands. I make sure to smile all day, even when my ponytail turns into a tangled mess looking like string licorice. I love how much I am punishing Aunt Angie, knowing she cannot bear to see my hair in a ponytail.

The next morning before I go to school, my hair is tangled, clumped and knotted and I shamefully have to ask my aunt to comb it out. It is very painful and I cry. I am thankful she does not make a comment about my foolishness and surprised when I hear she wants to strike a compromise.

"Connie Mary, howsa 'bout we make a deal? If you agree not to wear your ponytail too tight, I'll agree to put your hair in a ponytail every single day, okay kid?" My smile seals the deal and my aunt finishes my hair with a ponytail.

"By Jesus, you're Bootsie's daughter all right. But try to remember what your father always says, 'sometimes in life you gotta eat a little crow pie to survive'"

We've been spending every weekend being dragged to Yale New Haven Hospital with my frustrated father. Every Saturday morning, he is uptight and nervous with Janice somehow getting on his last nerve. As we prepare to visit our mother, he is reprimanding Janice again. I do not understand what my sister is doing wrong.

"Stop reading that damn book. Don't just sit there daydreaming all day Janice, get off your ass and help me pack your mother's things. Christ Almighty, can't you do anything right?"

At the hospital we are forced to listen to our mother give a moaning and groaning Oscar-winning performance that would have made Bette Davis pale in comparison. Sitting on the edge of the bed, my sister and I look like two caged birds who, with envy, watch the free birds in the sky fly away.

We are constantly bored until the day Janice devises a great plan. "Con, let's go to that delightful red and yellow coffee shop we passed in the hallway. I saw a delicious gumball machine inside." Very cautiously, holding one hand below her knee, Janice opens a quivering palm revealing two shiny copper pennies. "I saved these for us. There is one penny for you and one for me."

My eyes widen and skin tingles with happiness ignoring my mother talking about her cancer coming back. "Albert, are you sure they got all the cancer out? I'm not going to die from it am I? Am I Albert?"

My father could not be more uncomfortable than if he were sitting on a bed of nails, rising up and down on a hard folding chair. Leaning heavily to one side, he makes a contorted face and releases smelly gas.

"Ah, that's better. Now for the last time Rose—they got all the cancer out. IT'S GONE! How many times do I gotta tell you? Do I need to jump on your bed and sing it to you like Frankie Sinatra? The doctors said you ain't going to die. For Christ's sake Rose, what are you trying to do? Give yourself the *Malocchio?*"

My father wipes his forehead with a handkerchief, leans back, and is soon fast asleep. The room exhales a sigh of relief absorbing the lovely silence. Nevertheless, within ten minutes he is awake looking at me with admiration.

"Rose, did you notice how smart Connie Mary is getting?"

At first my mother doesn't answer. She is happily absorbed with the new magazine we brought and has better things to do like studying a photograph of Marilyn Monroe wearing a gold lame dress with no bra or underwear. Growing tired of my father's constant favoritism of his youngest daughter she responds impatiently.

"No Albert, I haven't noticed." She looks at Janice reading a book quietly in her chair, and her eyes fill with tears.

When my father leaves to use the bathroom we make our escape.

The freedom is exhilarating! We have been gone only minutes when my father, Mr. Angry, Devil-Face comes storming through the coffee shop like a raging bull. You might think Janice had a bullseye on her forehead by the way he lunges at her and shakes violently. My sister's eyes lock and body freezes causing Little Lulu to drop on the dusty floor. The pennies my sister held so tenderly drop and roll across the linoleum floor, disappearing underneath a buzzing soda machine. The people who were in the coffee shop minutes before, eating and remarking how cute my sister and I were, now leave terrified.

My father yells as he slaps my sister's bottom.

"Why didn't you kids tell me you were goin' someplace? Huh? Your mother is worried sick about you!"

The man I see is not a father, but a senseless monster slapping Janice so hard that her head and body snap back and forth like an elastic band. I look helplessly around the coffee shop where empty tables display plates of food and steaming cups of coffee. After my father is done he glares angrily at me.

"Shame on you Connie Mary for listening to your sister and leaving your mother alone."

My sister's face is bright red. Somehow, she manages to grab Little Lulu, knowing my father would leave her behind. Our eyes scan the soda machine where the pennies rolled and I look at Janice. But it is far too risky to chance retrieving them—so she leaves them behind.

The two of us walk into my mother's room like frozen icicles and mechanically sit on the bed without saying a word. My mother looks at us with love while sipping a diet soda through a straw and says, "So, did you girls have a nice walk?"

On the way home Janice sleeps in the back seat rolled into a tight ball clinging to Little Lulu. I look through the dark window at the flashing lights of passing cars and wonder all the way home: *what kind of lucky children will find our pennies and eat the delicious gumballs meant for Janice and me?*

Months pass before my mother comes home from the hospital. When she finally does, our home life starts to darken in ways it hadn't before. My mother has stopped asking if the cancer will kill her because she has worse problems now.

Albert, have you seen Janice's Little Lulu doll? She can't find it anywhere. And my two cats Ginger and Puny; I haven't seen them since I left for the hospital, have you?"

My father's back faces my mother as he sits at his desk paying bills. He takes his sweet time answering.

"Oh. I threw *that* out by accident when I went to the dump." I cannot see my father's face but hear him snicker when he nonchalantly adds, "Besides, *she* was getting too big for dolls." My mother does not say another word and trudges up the stairs.

I stay downstairs and watch television, trying to forget how my sister has been searching for Little Lulu all this time. When I think of Little Lulu having to live alone in the dump I feel an enormous pain and think I will die. That night I decided to tell Manfred my secret.

"Psst Manfred don't tell, but my father threw Little Lulu away.

Don't forget, my father could have thrown *you* away. But he didn't. And do you know why he didn't throw you away Manfred? My father likes me better than Janice."

At six-years old, I am smart enough to know that I am safe and my sister is not.

4

The Sign Of The Cross

"It is one of those magical nights when the moon rises high above Gus's Pond and shooting stars sizzle and burn across the purple sky. There is something surreal and mystical about a night like this. The wind is speaking a language only children can understand. If adults could decipher the language of nature, then they too would know every secret from the beginning of time."

Standing against the blue summer sky is our mother with her hair shimmering in the fleeting afternoon light. It is the perfect time for two little girls to be swinging with someone they love. As she pushes us on the swingset, my mother speaks as though we are adults and understand every mystery in life.

"Girls, you see that rusty, barbed-wire fence stretched across the length of the backyard?" I have no idea what a rusty, barbed-wire fence is but still look in the direction of my mother's hand. "Gus said he's coming home with some pretty pink tea roses to plant in Anna's garden this weekend—and guess what else he said?"

My sister giggles with mischievous joy.

"He said he'd let you watch them grow?"

My mother laughs heartily looking down at my sister with so much love, her eyes water. My mother's laugh produces a happy, boisterous sound that comes from a young mother in love with her two small children.

"Well sure Jan, I guess I could watch them grow in Anna's garden, but Gus said he's going to give me ten rose bushes of my own! On top of that—he's going to have Pinky plant them anywhere I want!" With fierce determination my mother glares at the rust-corroded fence she has come to hate. "No longer will we have to look at this ugly fence. The pink tea roses will grow and hide every bit of ugliness."

My mother goes back to pushing me while my sister glides through the air on a seesaw that is beginning to look too small for her body. My mother pauses to look at the house of Anna and Gus and makes the sign of the cross.

"Dear Jesus, please bless my good friends Anna and Gus. Gus has treated me better than my own father. We both know people like Anna and Gus only come once in a lifetime."

Although Janice and I are still swinging, our mother is no longer with us. She has drifted into the past and is resisting the urge to cry.

My sister admires the sun sinking beneath the pink and purple clouds and lauds joyfully, "Oh Mommy, I love Jesus!"

My mother knows the world is cruel to the best of angels and looks at my sister with a combination of love and fear.

"Oh Jan, you have the most beautiful soul of any child I have ever known."

From a very young age I recognized the unbreakable bond between my mother and sister and this is why I sabotaged my sister whenever I could.

Every spring, birds of every color visit the neighborhood. Some familiar guests are the green and purple hummingbirds, the robins and the crows, and the nuthatches that walk upside down. Gus likes to watch the noisy crows bickering. He says they remind him of people that waste the day away arguing and fussing. My mother enjoys the birds as well and says there are no words to describe the sight of a kingfisher gliding effortlessly across the clear blue water. My sister has a special kinship with birds and feeds them by holding birdseed in the palm of her hand. Her love of birds is not appreciated by everyone and in time will jeopardize the creatures she loves the most.

On Saturday mornings my sister and I always rise early to go outside on our own secret adventure. On this particular weekend, we head out carrying a loaf of crusty bread and little else, slipping across the wet grass. This is the time of day the shadows stretch long and lean while the sun touches the treetops. My sister passes me half the loaf and we crumble pieces across the grass and wait.

"Look Con, here comes a Chickadee!"

We sit on the grass and watch the birds eat, until eventually, I grow tired and go inside to listen to my father complain. Unlike my father, who considers birds to be nuisances who poop and tarnish his lawn, my mother loves birds almost as much as Janice. My father's morning ritual is to read *The Norwich Bulletin* at the kitchen table as my mother cooks breakfast. When my father folds the newspaper he happens to look outside. His eyes angrily narrow at the sight of breadcrumbs scattered across the lawn and then center on the object of his wrath.

"Rose… look at what your daughter did to my lawn. Now the birds will shit on the patio roof. Rose, you better stop your daughter from feeding those birds—or else."

A week passes in an atmosphere of constant fear. Our mother takes us shopping at Mr. Big's department store to divert our attention and on the way home she takes a slow drive on Wawecus Hill Road where we see pigs and cows grazing in the fields. We breathe a sigh of relief upon arriving home because our father's truck is gone. We happily run inside, holding bags of food, toys and clothes my mother bought for us and revel in our new belongings until my sister sniffs the air.

"Ma, I smell gunpowder!"

My mother is the first to see the back door open and runs outside.

"Oh God no," she cries.

My sister and I follow after her and see a sight so horrifying it is hard to believe. The backyard is scattered with birds and every one of them is dead. There on the grass is a magnificent blue jay with a wing crushed underneath its tummy. A few feet away lies an old black crow who still looks alive except for the shocking stare of lifeless yellow eyes that just witnessed a massacre. Janice shuts her eyes and cries silently. My mother walks around in circles looking lost. She incoherently mumbles something about marrying a devil before dashing into the house. After a few minutes she returns holding paper bags and we start cleaning the yard. I help my mother carry the birds to Gus's Pond and we place them underneath a patch of dying bluets.

My sister scatters white pebbles on top of their graves softly crying as she does so. Even though we never speak of the incident again, in time all of us will come to know that certain animals and people living on 93 Fitchville Road will end up dead.

My sister and I have our first big night at school called "Parent-Teacher Conferences." This is my first conference. My sister has attended six conferences so far and always receives outstanding reports. My mother wants to prepare early for the event and picks out my father's best black suit to wear. It is his best suit because it is his only suit. As soon as my father gets home from work my mother is standing at the front door holding the black suit in both arms and smiling sweetly.

"Guess what night this is Albert?" She says. My father looks miserable covered head- to-toe in black grease from cleaning some rich person's oil burner. He responds by giving my mother a look of revulsion.

"Rose, you know I only wear that suit when somebody dies."

I know what Mrs. Hellerman is going to tell my parents tonight. My teacher has given up the prospect of teaching me how to read and is determined to have me repeat first grade. She doesn't know that staying back in an Italian family is considered worse than snitching. Nonno calls it a *dis'face* and says, "When child go down ladder—it shame *famiglia!*"

Intuitively, my teacher is smart enough to know the only one who needs convincing is my father. She knows my father's opinion is the only one that matters. It is too bad my teacher doesn't know she is already on his bad side due to a poorly-timed phone call that interrupted my father's favorite television show, *Gunsmoke*. During that call, my teacher said the reason she needed to keep me back was because of my poor academic skills in reading, writing and **math**.

When my father heard the word math he bashed his fist down and gave Mrs. Hellerman a piece of his mind.

"Listen, Mrs. Hell...er...ah, or whatever the hell your name is; there ain't nothin' wrong with my daughter's math skills! Math is my best subject and the most important subject in school. If a person knows their timetables they can do any math in the world!" and then moves in for the kill. "I'm tellin' you teacha—there ain't nothin' wrong with my daughter's math skills; you think I'm gonna let someone like *you* keep my little daughter back and u-mill-e-ate my family? Sorry, it ain't gonna happen teacha."

He spotted my mother moving in closer to listen and gestured for her to get him another beer before twisting the knife Calabrese style into Mrs. Hellerman's back.

"Huh! You got a short memory teacha... you forget who's payin' your salary?"

Even though my father and teacher have already tangled, my mother still manages to convince my father how important it is to attend our conferences. After supper she bravely stands in front of him as he tries to watch television clinging nervously to a black wire hanger supporting his black suit.

"Albert, you know we have to go... everyone in Bozrah will be there and you don't want them to think you don't care about our little daughters, do you?" My mother stares at my father with big eyes batting long feathery lashes. He tries his best to ignore her by watching *Rawhide* and eating red pistachios that turn his fingers red.

"Albert, if we don't go the next thing you know the Bozrah gossips will be saying we're not good parents. And then you'll lose your job and then the house."

My father gives my mother a murderous stare that would have made any wife run and grabs the suit out of her hands. He walks away growling, "Rose, you always make a mountain out of a molehill.

Dontcha know Rose, Bozrah is one big Peyton Place? All right, I'll go—but first get me a Bromo-Seltzer. That sauce you made for supper was bitter, now I got the *agita.*"

At Parent Teacher Conferences my parents visit my classroom first and sit across from my teacher at her desk. She and my father shoot daggers at each other. My mother tries to remain neutral by sheepishly clinging to my father's arm and picking lint off a green mohair sweater that sways softly whenever she moves. As the adults determine my fate, my sister and I sit in the back playing tic-tac-toe. When I see the look in my teacher's eyes I tremble as I realize that she hates my father even more than me.

"Mr. Falcone, I would be doing Connie Mary a great disservice if I were to send her to second grade knowing how she struggles with reading, writing and *math.*" I can almost see my father's ears point straight into the air like a Doberman pinscher after he hears the four-letter word.

"Math? That's bullshit! You tryin' to tell me teacha that my daughter don't know her math?" He unexpectedly turns to my mother, who despite wearing a size 18 dress is trying her best to disappear inside a teeny-weeny folding chair. "Rose— tell this teacha how you practice math every night with our daughter doing addicshun and subtractshun… go ahead Rose, tell 'er!"

All eyes shift to my surprised mother, especially mine. I want to see how she is going to explain that she is teaching me math when she has difficulty adding and subtracting two numbers. The fact of the matter is my mother's math is worse than mine.

Painfully aware of my father's turbulent green eyes glaring in her direction she stammers, "I…uh, well…ah yes, well of course, we have been practicing, er… Connie Mary's math."

Surprisingly, my father heaves a huge sigh of relief, and more shockingly, he gives my mother a big hug!

Clearly triumphant, he sneers, "See? I told you so teacha!"

This makes my mother decide to go even further with the lie. I am keeping an eye on my mother's nose. I want to see if it will grow as long as Pinocchio's when he told the Blue Fairy lies. Encouraged, my mother smiles big and beautiful, exposing rows of dazzling white teeth. Before executing her next big lie, my mother takes a deep breath and gazes lovingly into my father's eyes.

"I can honestly tell you Mrs. Hellerman… there is nothing wrong with our little daughter's math ability."

My teacher is not amused. She has been teaching long enough to recognize a lie when she hears one and smiles with a crooked grin.

"Oh, is that so Mrs. Falcone?"

My mother must be relieved; her nose did not grow as long as Pinocchio's. She basks in the glow of seeing my father look at her with new respect. And this is why she keeps going, pointing a perfectly-shaped button nose high in the air and quips, "Oh, and one more thing Mrs. Hell…er…ah, or whatever the hell your name is. My daughter and I practice math every single night and I can assure you—there is nothing wrong with her math ability."

To my mother's delight my father smiles and wraps his arms around her shoulders even tighter, causing the hair on the mohair sweater to rise up in celebration of his extraordinary embrace. Like my mother, my father also has beautiful white teeth that compliment his olive gold skin and hair as black as night. When my father looks back at my teacher, his smile changes to an ugly grimace. He chuckles under his breath, determined to win at any cost.

"See? I told you so teacha. There ain't nothin' wrong with my daughter's math a-bill-a-t. She'll stay back the day they allow Khrushchev into Disneyland. In other words, over *my dead body*." I can almost hear the evil words forming behind my teacher's taut smile.

Oh, I'm sure that can be arranged, Mr. Falcone.

Our next stop is to meet with my sister's English teacher. Mr. Pavy is an ancient, bald-headed relic who wears a bowtie bound tightly around a turkey neck. Despite his age, Mr. Pavy dresses better than my father. Everyday he wears an immaculate suit with a white handkerchief tucked inside the jacket pocket. Personally, I think Mr. Pavy looks like a decrepit old book falling apart at the seams, but even the most hardened boys fear him. When he speaks, his face glows with a soft pink light allowing the wisdom of every book to fall from his lips.

"Janice Lynn is my best student. She is my top reader, excelling in every subject. I am honored to have Janice Lynn Falcone in my classroom. She is not only an academic scholar—but a passionate and avid reader as well. She recently wrote the best report I have ever seen from a student. Her work is an example of the highest standard of writing."

Mr. Pavy's rosy baldhead and milky white face begin to blend into a rosy blob like a white and pink crayon melting in the sun. His black-rimmed glasses outline steel blue eyes that reveal his life mantra: reward the good and punish the bad.

On the way home my father calls Mrs. Hellerman bad words in Italian. "*Trola, Puttana;* who the hell does that teacha think she's talking to? —Edward Lillywhite Norton?"

My mother is still thinking how Mr. Pavy praised Janice. "My Janice is very smart. We have a very smart daughter. Don't you think so Albert?"

My father ignores the question and erratically swerves the car in an illegal circle knocking my sister and me to the floor. He speeds all the way to Norwich like a mobster on a mission to assassinate. We stop and give Nonno and Nonna our school reports. Even though my report is not as good as Janice's, we both receive a precious gift of one dollar. On the way home we pass St. Patrick's Cathedral and I watch my father make the sign of the cross on his chest.

When we get home I wait for my mother to tuck me into bed before I ask, "Ma, why does Dad cross his hand over his chest when we pass a church?" My mother is fluffing pillows in blue pillowcases before comfortably arranging them underneath my head. She sits on the edge of the bed looking up at the tiny cross above my head.

"It's called reverence. Your father knows he is passing God's house and shows reverence by making the sign of the cross. Here I will teach you... it's easy."

My mother takes my hand and places it on the top of my forehead.

"In the name of the Father,"—she moves my hand to my heart— "and of the Son," then crisscrosses both my shoulders, "and of the Holy Spirit. Amen. Jesus died after being nailed to a wooden cross because he loved us so much." My mother leans close and covers me with a soft blue blanket. As I breathe in the heavenly scent of Avon's *To a Wild Rose* perfume, I softly kiss her cheek. "Goodnight Mommy, I love you."

Isn't that the way life goes? The moment Gregory and I get recess back and things start looking up, down the hill we tumble and fall. On this beautiful spring day we have been released from detention and flee through the school's cold steel doors. We have one hour of recess and I am trying to convince Gregory to play kickball because Randy needs two more players to form a team. Randy said if I join he'd throw in *the Dunce* for free. Gregory has never played with a ball or bat. He prefers games like Airplanes where he can use his mind to enter a happy place. When I push Gregory toward home plate he doesn't know how to kick the ball.

"Come on," yells Randy, "Kick the ball! I want my up's before

Moby Dick blows 'er top!"

Surprisingly, it will not be Randy who will ruin the day but co-captain Bobby who goes berserk. "Kick the ball, you stupid Duncehead—Kick it!" As the ball rolls past Gregory watches a butterfly dance above his head.

"You stupid Dunce," shouts Bobby. "I'll show you how to play kickball and I'll use your head for the ball!" Bobby grabs hold of Gregory's necktie and spins him through the air. Everyone gasps when Gregory falls in the mud taking on an amazing resemblance to Charlie Brown's friend Pigpen. Bobby is the first to make the connection and laughs with wickedness.

"Hey look everybody, the Duncehead's real name is Pigpen!"

I hit Bobby in the jaw so hard he is on the ground lying next to Gregory.

Some will say I punched Bobby as a result of living in an environment where violence breeds violence. Miss Olive Oyl would call that rationale an excuse and shows no mercy when she digs five bony fingers into my arm.

"Connie Falcone, you bad girl! Shame on you for committing such an act of violence! You march straight into the principal's office this very minute!" and helps by giving me a swift shove toward school. When I look back Bobby is being cuddled and held like a baby with a teacher holding a soda bottle to his lips.

He looks at me and winks.

I have never been to the principal's office before, although I have heard about it from Gregory who is a better liar than Theodore Cleaver. "Watch out Connie Mary, I'm warning ya," he says, wiping a runny nose on the sleeve of his coat. "They oughta put a warning sign on that office door 'cause once a kid goes in, they ain't never comin' out! And you know why Connie Mary? They eat 'em alive."

Despite Gregory's warning I march into the principal's office and plop down on the beat-up sofa reserved for bad children like me. Directly facing the couch is the principal's sweet secretary, Mrs. Goothier who loves children almost as much as Anna and Gus. Mrs. Goothier smiles with the same red lips and white teeth as my mother and reeks of coffee and menthol cigarettes. She has translucent white skin and curly black hair that makes every child believe she is an angel from Heaven. My mother says there are children in the world who do not have mothers and this is why God sends people like Mrs. Goothier to be their guardian angel.

She whispers softly, "What's your name sweetie?"

I never like to say my name because I often see pity in the eyes of adults.

"Connie Mary Falcone."

In that split second when our eyes reveal the truth, Mrs. Goothier travels to a lost and lonely land. "Oh, yes… of course. Now I know who *you* are sweetie."

I forget about Mrs. Goothier when angry voices erupt behind Principal Chester Corporal's door and Mrs. Goothier speaks in a serious tone. "Please stay seated Miss Falcone. Principal Corporal will be with you momentarily." With ample bottom she shifts restlessly and looks down at her candy dish overflowing with butterscotch candy. "Connie Falcone, it's your lucky day! How would you like to try a piece of my delicious butterscotch candy? It will make you feel umm-umm good."

After eating several pieces of butterscotch candy the morning passes uneventfully. Principal Corporal's old couch is a pleasure to sit on compared to the hard oak chairs in our classroom. Lying on my back, I explore the pages of Mrs. Goothier's Movie Star magazine thinking how stupid I was to believe anything Gregory ever said. I am comfortably absorbed by the busy activity of ringing phones and teachers coming and going (if only to sneak a cigarette) and have temporarily forgotten my misfortune. It is interesting to watch Mrs. Goothier monitor bells, type letters and wipe tears from sad children. Everything is beautiful in the office until several visitors enter from the outside world.

The tall boy enters first by hurling himself inside and slamming his books on the table. The boy is wearing a filthy T-shirt ripped into strips exposing a muscular tan belly. He paces around in circles and knows the same swear words as my father. Principal Corporal comes out of his office and looks at the boy with a menacing smile. His voice echoes throughout his small kingdom exalting power, strength and might. "McGillicuddy! Get inside here—now."

The boy is not alone. Coming through the door almost falling to her knees is a worried little woman followed by an extremely angry man who spits salvia between angry words.

"Just wait until you get home!"

Mrs. Goothier smiles nervously. When no one acknowledges, she spins around and starts to sing, "You are my sunshine, my only sunshine. You make me happy when skies are grey." The singing stops and is replaced by the rapid "tap, tap, tapping" of her fingers on a humongous, coal-black typewriter that looks big enough to swallow me whole.

Principal Corporal waits patiently for his prey to enter and throws me a dirty look telling me I am next. The boy and adults foolishly enter the lair bowing in fear. When Principal Corporal slams the door I realize Gregory was telling the truth! I sit on the edge of my seat and listen. When I can stand no more I rush up to Mrs. Goothier's desk.

"Mrs. Goothier! Mrs. Goothier! Gregory McGillis was right! Once you go inside the principal's office you never come out!" Mrs. Goothier refuses to turn around. I resort to stretching my ear like Grumpy the Dwarf in order to learn how the Principal Corporal will eat his prey. When I hear the adults yelling back and forth I feel relief.

"Oh good," and think, "They're putting up a fight!"

When a sound explodes like thunder in the sky, naturally I think the Russians are bombing and look for a place to duck and cover. Seeing no desk in sight I crawl underneath the old couch discovering pieces of chewed gum that magically stick to my hair. As the minutes pass, I realize the boom is not from the sky, but from behind the Principal's door! With my heart pounding, I crawl out and run to Mrs. Goothier pleading—"*Please, Mrs. Goothier you gotta help these people—the principal's eating them alive!*"

After a minute I realize Mrs. Goothier is not answering me because she is in cahoots with the principal and I suspiciously observe her backside, thinking maybe, just maybe, Mrs. Goothier gets all the butterscotch candy she wants for keeping her big mouth shut. Before I get the chance to run, the tall boy spills out of the principal's office like water breaking free and despite his flaming-red cheeks is very much alive. The man comes next and I hear him threatening the boy.

"Wait; if you think this was bad—just wait until you get home!" The woman trails behind silently wiping away her tears. After they leave I peek outside and watch them disappear out the side door.

After eating a few butterscotch candies and planning my revenge on Gregory, I notice the principal standing above me. This is the first time I've had the opportunity to take a good look at him and I will say, he is not very handsome. He is even shorter than my cute Italian father who has to push the seat up in his truck to reach the gas pedal. The only reason Principal Corporal looks bigger than my father is because of the large, flat, wooden stick that resembles a small boat paddle that he holds in his right hand. My father did warn me however, if I was bad in school, the principal would make me good again with a paddle. Principal Corporal holds the paddle menacingly, tapping its flat side on the palm of his hand. He is almost bald with the exception of a few strands of dying grey hair and has eyes that look ready for war.

"Miss Falcone, I have informed your parents of your latest incident. This is not the first time your disrespectful behavior has come to my attention. Mrs. Hellerman has informed me of your unwillingness and refusal to read along with Mr. McGillis, your accomplice in crime. Unfortunately Miss Falcone, due to today's inappropriate behavior you will have your recess taken away for several weeks."

I hold back my tears because Nonno always told me, "When you down, nev-a let 'em see you cry."

"It's a new world out there, Miss Falcone. A world I do not like. It is a sad world when children in first grade resort to violence as a means to settle a dispute, tsk, tsk. I have notified Mrs. Hellerman of your punishment. In a few minutes she will return you to the classroom."

I watch Principal Corporal walk toward his office, tapping his paddle all the way. He pauses before entering and looks back at me with regret.

There are times when the universe comes to a screeching halt in order to tell us the truth about someone's life. This is what happened the moment Principal Corporal decided to look back and see me not just as another brat—but as a child who must be disciplined for the betterment of all children. Principal Corporal is afraid this generation of children will ruin his world. His world that demands little girls become obedient wives and little boys march off to war. A world where children recite the Pledge of Allegiance and respectfully salute soldiers at parades. Later in life, I'll realize: Principal Corporal does not hate me—he fears me. With no further ado, he dashes inside his office and soon smoke is seen drifting under the door.

Mrs. Goothier looks relieved and spins around. "Hey there, little Miss Connie Falcone, now that didn't turn out so bad did it?" The worst is to come when Mrs. Hellerman lunges out of nowhere and yanks me off the couch. Mrs. Goothier waves, "Goodbye, little Miss Connie Falcone. I hope the rest of the day is better for you sweetie," and happily goes back to living in Candy Land where children solve problems by sucking on sweet, butterscotch candy.

It is a losing battle when you try forcing a child to come and they do not wish to go. My teacher pulls me through the same hallway that appeared so joyous on the first day of school. I linger stubbornly, listening to the Mama Robin inside telling me not to go down the hallway. The hallway means no children, no adults and... no witnesses.

It is dark when we reach the middle of the hallway. My teacher stops abruptly and listens for any witnesses. Satisfied by the silence, she peers down at me as if I were the most despicable being on the face of the earth and begins thrashing the top of my head with her hand, seething, "I could have had a good class if not for you!"

I try covering my head and she pulls my hands away. When I feel I cannot take another second I fall to the floor and pretend to be sleeping. I sense someone guiding me now as my teacher tugs at a body turned into a heap of bones. My cheek rests upon the cold linoleum floor where a small puddle of tears form. I listen when she starts to count: "One... two... three...by the time I reach five you better get up Connie Mary."

Mrs. Hellerman breathes heavily as she picks up my ankles and drags me across the floor. I try gripping the floor to slow her down but it is futile, and to my dismay, we are about to turn the corner where teachers and students in the primary grades will see us. What will my teacher do if we are seen? Will she drop my ankles and run screaming telling everyone that Connie Falcone has gone crazy like her mother and needs to be kept away from the other children? Then everyone will know I am a bad girl and I will never be allowed another butterscotch candy for the rest of my life. Not knowing what else to do, I make the sign of the cross.

"In the name of the Father and the Son and the Moldy Ghost—please help me find the beautiful Man on the Cross!" I look at the light only inches away and whimper, "Save me beautiful Man on the Cross." I close my eyes tight, and when I open them again, he comes. Not the Man on the Cross, but Stevie Grillo, the cutest juvenile delinquent in school.

"Let that girl go!" Booms a voice, so strong and fearless it's as if Michael the Archangel has come down to Earth disguised as a teenage boy. Even though Mrs. Hellerman is still holding my ankles, I can turn sideways and see why every female in school loves Stevie. When he walks through the hall, his muscular body sways and every female young and old stops to watch him pass. I have seen this angelic, greasy, slicked-down, platinum blonde-haired, blue-eyed, teenager in the tight white T-shirt many times! Stevie is known for his black Beatles boots, immaculate blue jeans and the heavy metal chain that dangles from his back pocket. Most teachers tolerate Stevie, knowing he goes out of his way to protect the underdog. Mrs. Hellerman releases my ankles and they fall to the floor with a thud.

"Young man if I were you—I'd march straight up those stairs. I am in charge of the situation and do not require assistance from some lawbreaking hoodlum."

Standing firm, Stevie is undaunted. As he moves closer, his voice is astonishingly calm. "Teacha, I know all about *you*. I know you treat kids like shit. I saw the whole thing and I got more bad news fer ya—I know this kid's old lady." He rattles his chain in defiance. "And you know what else I'm gonna do today?"

At the sound of Stevie's rattling chain Mrs. Hellerman grows smaller and smaller until she is no bigger than a mouse begging for cheese. When Stevie smiles it is like the morning sun rising in the

East. "I'm going to this kid's house today and tell her old lady everything I saw." He playfully swings his chain around an imaginary circle.

I have become a liability, encouraging Stevie with hand gestures. My teacher pushes me in the direction of our classroom while yelling, "You get back to the classroom right now!" Clearly frustrated by this new turn of events, my teacher's words hang like sharp daggers above my head.

"Go ahead," she says to Stevie in a high-pitched voice. "Tell her mother! She won't do anything. Did you know she's a patient at the Norwich State Hospital? Need I say more?"

I walk away as fast as I can, triumphantly singing to myself, for I have just been saved from my teacher's clutches. I know I outsmarted her with the help of the Father, the Son and the Moldy Ghost. I charge through the classroom door, victorious, but the children stare at me as if they never thought they would see me again.

When Mrs. Hellerman stumbles inside after me, she moans, "Oh God, let this day end!"

When I arrive home I find my mother already upset, reeling after a phone call from Principal Corporal.

"Connie Mary! — Just wait 'till your father gets home!"

As for Stevie Grillo, he is as good as his word. The afternoon goes by quietly with Janice reading alone in her bedroom and my mother and I watching a television show called *Lassie*. After the show ends, my mother goes into the kitchen to prepare supper and I rush upstairs to use the bathroom thinking how my father always misses the best shows. I plan on playing outside and walk halfway down the stairs when the doorbell rings. My heart jumps for joy! I already know who it is! I sit where I cannot be seen and listen quietly.

"Who can that be?" says my mother, straightening a sauce-splattered apron. She cracks the door open and asks coolly, "Yes? May

I help you?" After taking a closer look at the unusual visitor she changes her tone and purrs affectionately, "*Oh, hell-lo Stevie.*" My heart races with excitement. She knows him! This is better yet! Once again I hear the voice that has the power to make my teacher grow small.

"Afternoon, Mrs. Falcone. I came over to tell you somethin' and I gotta be frank—it ain't peachy keen." I hear the swipe of a match. "It's about your kid, and trust me, Mrs. Falcone it ain't good."

My mother is silent. Now Stevie is too, which causes me to hold my breath. Is Stevie going to leave without telling my mother the truth? Will he turn into Chicken Little and run because he thinks his words will cause the sky to fall? No! Not Stevie.

"Mrs. Falcone with all due respect, do you know what a female dog is called?"

"Y-e-s… I think so."

"Well, that's who Connie Mary has for a teacha. And trust me, this dame ain't Mary Poppins."

My mother's fear is burning brighter than a funeral pyre. I know she wants to run and bury her head inside a spaghetti pot but manages to mumble, "What? Why not?"

"Here's the deal Mrs. Falcone: Today, right this afternoon, I saw that bitch, excuse my French, Mrs. Falcone, but I saw that bitch wailing on Connie Mary. And lemme tell you, it was just as bad as when my old man wails on me. We both know Mrs. Falcone, that Connie Mary is just a dumb kid. How can anyone hit a dumb kid? At least my old man knows I'll take his shit for so long and then I'll turn around and kick his sorry ass. That's not all Mrs. Falcone—I saw that bitch draggin' your daughter by her ankles through the hallway like Farmer Goulot drags his pigs to slaughter. I ain't no Cath-o-lick like you Mrs. Falcone. But we both know even Christ Almighty didn't get dragged by His feet when they nailed him to the cross—did he? I seen it with my own eyes—that bitch who calls herself a teacha was dragging your daughter by her feet like a pig to slaughter."

Despite the silence, Stevie continues. "My old man tells me I ain't the sharpest tool in the box. But I know what I saw. And this ain't the first time I seen that "so-called" teacha pickin' on poor, dumb kids like your daughta. See, Mrs. Falcone the way I sees it is like this—either that teacha's on the rag or she's coo-coo for Cocoa Puffs taking her sorry-ass problems out on dumb kids that can't fight back."

I peek through the banister and watch Stevie pull a cigarette from behind his ear and strike a match on his boot. "I'm sorry Mrs. Falcone, I don't mean to piss off a nice, old, Italian lady like you. I know everybody loves to walk by your house just to catch wind of your meatballs cooking on the stove." He blows smoke into the air and shakes his head in disbelief. "Christ, if you ask me there's gotta be a special place in Hell for a teacha like that."

My mother grasps the doorknob tighter.

"People who hurt children piss me off and if I was you—I'd go down to that school right now and beat the shit out of that teacha! I'd never let anybody hurt my kid."

I hold both hands over my mouth to stifle a giggle and hop up and down on the steps with joy. Stevie's voice begins to fade. "So long, Mrs. Falcone... let me know if you ever need any help beating up that teacha, 'cause I'll be glad to give you a hand! Why, I'll even tie both hands behind my back just to give her a fair shot!" I strain to hear my mother cry tears of remorse—but only hear a calm voice.

"Thank you Stevie, I appreciate what you told me," and shuts the door.

I wait for my mother to take me into her arms and speed me off to school so we can give whatever-the-hell-her-name-is exactly what she deserves, but when my mother never comes up the stairs I start to pee and watch it trickle down the steps in a small yellow stream. Why isn't my mother doing anything? Wait! She is doing something! She is pulling the television knob and watching *The Edge of Night!*

I sit for a long time waiting for my mother to notice me but she never does.

Luckily, Janice finds me.

"What's the matter with you Con? Are you sick or something? Aren't you going to watch *Ranger Andy?* Do you realize it's almost 5 o'clock and dad will be home any minute?" When she steps over me she notices the yellow puddle on the floor and color drains from her face. "Oh no Con, you wet your pants! Hold on and I'll clean it up before dad sees it!" In an effort to help, my sister misses the last step and tumbles across the parlor floor. When she stands, I notice an old wound on her knee has been reopened. Even as she bleeds, my sister lovingly wipes away every bit of evidence and then limps away.

To mend the broken branches in my lonely nest I think happy thoughts like flying airplanes with Gregory. When the aroma of my mother's sauce fills the house, I come downstairs. After my father learns I knocked Bobby out cold, much to my mother's displeasure, he is not upset but proud. "I always said you were a chip off the old block Connie Mary, just like the ol' man!" I was never worried about getting into trouble anyway. I knew what to expect from my father without being told.

That night while saying prayers in bed, I realized my school year is coming to an end and I am still unsure whether I will be going up or down the ladder. So, I asked my mother if the Man on the Cross could help me.

"Yes, Connie Mary, the Man on the Cross can help you. Remember, a church is a nice place to worship. But if you really want to find Christ, that is the Man on the cross, you must look inside your heart."

The nights my mother and I pray together are the holy moments of my childhood. "Ma, who's in charge of answering prayers?"

My mother pretends she has never heard this question before.

"Jesus Christ is in charge. His Hebrew name is *Yeshua*.

"Ma, that's a funny name... *Yesucan*. Where does Yesucan come from?"

"From what I know, before Yeshua came to earth, He lived in heaven with his Father. God the Father saw how bad things were on earth and asked His Son to die on the cross for our sins. Christ is our Savior."

When my mother leaves, I fold my hands and imagine God is listening to my prayer.

"Dear Mr. Yesucan, can you help me get out of first grade? I know I am not very good or very smart, but please, help me get out! Thank you very much."

I lie back down and remember something I forgot to ask.

"Sorry, it's me again...Connie Mary. Please, Mr. Yesucan, can you help Gregory McGillis get out of first grade, too? I am his only friend and he'll be a scaredy-cat if I leave him behind. See, my teacher hates him even more than me."

Feeling satisfied, my eyes grow heavy and sleep is soon upon me. I have always loved the middle of the night. It is a magical time when silence and darkness come together as friends. I have a beautiful dream that Yesucan is walking through each room, and eventually settles in the kitchen where he sits at the table drinking a cup of my mother's muddy Sanka.

5

The Omega

Anna Lorentz, Connie Mary and Janice

"In late autumn the Queen Anne's lace smiles for the last time
in the setting sun. She blossoms no more, her face folded away
as if to say so long."

For a short window of time my sister and I rode the school bus together to Fields Memorial School. It is during these bittersweet years we developed problems with "The K Brothers," a group of boys who sat in the middle of the bus and intimidated other children. For over a year, my sister and I became a target for abuse.

Every morning, as soon as we walked down the aisle, they would taunt us with specific pejoratives. Janice was called Nut Case, Crater Face and Little Lotta. Spoiled Brat and Rotten Ice Cream Cone were names reserved for me. Most of the K Brothers were not much older than me—and every single one of them was younger than Janice. This made no difference. My sister was too scared to say a word in our defense.

Every morning is torture on the Fields Memorial school bus... every single one.

After another day of taunting and name-calling so horrific, I could bear it no longer. I ran off the school bus, into the house and threw myself into my mother's apron weeping, "Oh Ma, I don't want to take the bus anymore! The K Brothers make fun of us everyday!"

My mother lowers the sauce to simmer. I follow her into the parlor where she searches for her coat with eyes fixed and determined. A look I have never seen before.

Where are you going Ma?" The K Brothers' taunting song replays in my head. "*Falcone, Falcone, Connie and Janice Falcone are two rotten, stinking ice cream cones. Your mother is a fruitcake. Doesn't everyone know she's nuts? And your father is just as crazy, driving around in a banged-up truck with bald tires that say, 'WOP, WOP, WOP!'*"

My mother ignores my question and pulls a cream-colored Lucille Ball jacket from a metal hanger and rests it over her arm. When she opens the door and grits her teeth, I realize she is doing something that requires a great deal of courage.

"I'm going over to that house right now to tell those parents everything their boys said about my children. I won't be long. Tell Jan to keep an eye on my sauce." Before I can answer, she vanishes into the wild blue yonder as if the sheriff asked her to join a posse comitatus to restore justice in the world. A world up to now that has shown my mother very little justice.

A loud voice from the dining room interrupts my thoughts. This is not the voice of a tenor, baritone or basso, but someone with the vocal characteristics of all three. Once again my mother has left Enrico Caruso's record playing in the hope my sister and I will understand the famous opera, *Pagliacci*. My mother adores Enrico Caruso and no matter how many times she tells the story of *Pagliacci* we want to hear it again. It is not often we get to hear our mother's voice come alive with animation and joy…

"My dear mother, your precious grandmother Concetta Mazzurra Calanna—how she adored Enrico Caruso! When I was a little girl my mother taught me about Enrico Caruso as I teach you. The humble and great Caruso said the secret to his success was having a big chest, a big mouth, hard work and something in the heart."

If one looks deep inside my mother's hazel eyes they will see a trail of long-forgotten dreams that come alive when listening to Caruso. "Enrico Caruso was born in Naples, Italy. The opera *Pagliacci* was performed in 1892 and is still popular today! Caruso once said, 'I suffer so much in this life. When I sing, this is why they cry. People who feel nothing in this life cannot sing.' *Vesti la giubba* means the conclusion of the first act. This is when Canio discovers his wife has been unfaithful. No matter how bad the pain, Canio must prepare for his performance as Pagliaccio the clown and the show must go on! The pain of Canio is felt in his portrayal of the clown as one who smiles on the outside while crying on the inside. *Si, figliola*—learn about the greatness of your ancestors!"

I am pondering my mother's oft-repeated words about her love for Enrico and his personal suffering as Pagliaccio the crying clown when Janice comes crashing down the stairs. By some miracle she makes it to the bottom floor and then slips on the rug. She rubs her knee and looks at me with a familiar face of fear.

"I heard the door slam. Where'd mom go?"

I pompously ignore her question like she is the little sister and I am the big sister and silently search through the channels on television. "Oh look *Bozo the Clown* is on," I mention before casually divulging— "Ma went to the K Brothers' house to tell their parents what rotten, good-for-nothing sons they have and if they don't stop being mean to us she's going to send Nonno over to kill them."

My sister gasps from fright and limps over to me before sitting in the most uncomfortable chair in the house. I watch her stare at the television screen and imagine her like *Pagliaccio,* suffering on the inside while forced to watch *Bozo the Clown* have fun.

An hour later my mother is home and hurries into the kitchen to check the still-simmering sauce. I follow her, looking like the perfect picture of innocence, with Janice following close behind. We watch our mother dip a wooden spoon inside the cast iron pot and bring a mouthful of heaven to her lips.

"Perfetto. Do you kids want some sauce on bread?" My sister looks at my mother with a face as white as Nonna's sheets.

"Ma, what happened at the K Brothers' house? Did you say Nonno is going to kill them?"

My mother laughs like everything is normal, which we almost believe until she speaks.

"Don't worry Jan. The K Brothers won't be bothering *you,* or *your* sister anymore."

She begins to hum, spreading fragrant red sauce across three slices of crusty Italian bread. Uncertain of our fate my sister and I eat joylessly. After a few minutes Janice can stand no more.

"Ma. Please tell us. Why won't the K Brothers be bothering us anymore?"

My mother knows my father will arrive home from work any minute and fills a large pot with water and sets it upon the stove.

Unable to cope, my sister drops her head on the table and sobs.

"Oh Ma... I hope you didn't make things worse."

My mother looks at us with eyes colder than the arctic snow.

"They promised that every boy who took part in the torment of my daughters will get a spanking and be sent to bed without supper! Believe me when I say this Jan—*the K Brothers won't be bothering you or your sister anymore.*" My mother's voice sounds so ferocious that my sister and I say no more. We never imagined our mother would be so strong! The following morning when we step into the bus we cringe with sickening familiarity at the sight of the K Brothers and prepare for another day of torture. We are shocked when the only sound we hear is the grinding of Mr. Lashinski's brakes and the opening and closing of the bus door. When we walk past the K Brothers we discover not one is looking at us. Every brother appears to be staring at some object in the far distance. Our mother was right! The K Brothers never bother us again and in time lose interest. To this day I cling to the memory of the K Brothers.

It was the only time our mother saved us.

No matter how many times my mother cries or my father yells, I still wet the bed. My habit forms an ugly brown circle in the middle of my twin mattress with a spiraling ring of yucky yellow urine. Even worse, my father says I am starting to smell like cat pee. One morning, after my father sees my soiled bed, he becomes so angry that he picks up my mattress and hurls it through the window. My mother and I watch in silence as the window screen and mattress fall through the air landing on his precious manicured lawn. My mother shows her concern for me by contacting her best and oldest friend Anna Lorentz.

When Anna sees my mother hanging clothes she calls from the kitchen window, "Rose… Rose! I'm coming to see you, my darling Rose!" Even though our yard is less than 50 feet away it is still difficult for Anna to walk because she uses crutches. Still, she makes the journey never complaining, preferring to joke about life's hardships, always comparing her experience to that story about the slow and steady tortoise and the energetic hare.

She finally arrives huffing and puffing and plops down into one of my father's lawn chairs looking exhausted. I would never tell anyone, but I love Anna almost as much as my mother. I jump into her lap, nestling my bony backside into her soft jiggly fat.

"Never forget Connie Mary," she says, breathing heavily while stroking my hair. "The tortoise beat the hare and won the race. See…I use crutches but there ain't nothin' wrong with my mind. And the mind will take you places the body cannot."

Anna never goes anywhere without her two yip-yapping miniature dogs Tinker Bell and Tiny. I leave Anna's cushioned lap to chase Tinker Bell and Tiny through the yard and underneath my mother's pink tea roses. Anna's two dogs are so old that it doesn't take them long to get grumpy and bark at me for teasing them. This causes my father to yell out the window in the upstairs hallway.

"Connie Mary! You teasing them dogs again? Knock it off!"

When Anna hears my father she stops smiling. Unlike my mother, Anna talks back to my father with a stern but motherly voice.

"Al, I'm out here watchin' Connie Mary—and she *never* teases my dogs. Let 'er be."

My father would never sass Anna back and is silent.

Despite Anna's tremendous courage, I still feel sorry for her. I do not think even my mother realizes that sadness is the foundation of

Anna's lonely nest. On the days Anna is not able to come to our house, she sits and stares through a dark kitchen window, watching our lives pass her by. When the loneliness becomes unbearable, she cries out to me as I play in the yard.

"Connie Mary! How's your beautiful mother? Go and tell your mother to come see me!" Because of Anna's loyalty, the friendship between my mother and Anna is pure as molten gold from the refiner's fire and I know it will last forever.

Anna rests comfortably in the sun, enjoying my mother's muddy Sanka, and the two women observe the mattress in the middle of the lawn. Anna pulls a pack of cigarettes from the large pocket of a muumuu dress she sewed by hand and observes my mother with compassion.

"Rose, smoking is when I do my best thinking." She blows a smoke ring in the direction of the mattress. "I see Connie Mary wet the bed again."

When my mother lights a cigarette I know she is getting ready to talk serious and suddenly the scene transforms from two old friends smoking to daughter confiding in mother.

"Anna, I don't know what else to do to stop Connie Mary from wetting the bed. Honest to God, I've tried everything!"

As I watch the purplish blue smoke rings rise toward the sky, Anna gives me a discerning smile. She knows, although it may look like I am playing with her dogs, I am doing something more important: I am listening and learning.

When Anna sees the dogs panting, she lovingly calls, "Come to Mama girls. Come Tiny, come Tinker Bell. Connie Mary will fetch ya some water." My mother hands me a bowl of water to set on the patio and the dogs flock to it, tails wagging. Anna stares at me with apprehension as if I am a delicate glass vase about to shatter.

"Rose, a child who wets the bed, is troubled. See, there's a reason for everything a child does. There's no such thing as a bad child Rose—only children living in bad situations." Anna swallows hard, preparing to discuss a subject that is controversial between the two women.

"Now, let's talk about our beautiful sweet Janice Lynn. I know we wrangled with this issue before Rose, but it just ain't normal for a child to keep falling down! My goodness, my Janice is always banged up with them black and blue marks! Why them little legs and arms of 'ers is cut open like sliced tomatoes on top of a salad. I'm telling you Rose... something ain't kosher and we both know *who* that someone is."

Having forgotten I am listening, Anna glances fearfully in my direction. This is when I glide my hand across the grass pretending to be searching for four-leaf clovers. Anna has steely blue eyes that manifest the inner strength of a hundred men and looks up at the window where my father stood. The only sound left is the swishing of curtains moving in the warm June breeze. With disdain, Anna throws her cigarette on the grass and moves abruptly to crush it with a worn loafer.

"Rose, it ain't normal for a child to do the things Janice does. Did I ever tell you about the day I seen her standing in the front yard looking up at the clouds? She was staring at the wind pushing them poor innocent clouds around till they disappeared. When Al's truck comes rolling into the yard, she jumped a mile high like she saw a ghost or something worse! The next thing I seen was Janice running down the path to Gus's pond and lost sight of her amongst the trees."

Anna nervously examines the blank expression on my mother's face.

"Face it Rose, someday, you'll have to throw away the bad apple that's destroying all the good apples in the bin." Anna cringes when my father's voice comes pouring down from Janice's bedroom window like acid rain.

"You lazy bum! Why do *you* stay in bed all the time? Get up and go outside with your mother and sister."

Unable to do anything to stop the situation, and clearly distraught, Anna blows one more smoke ring and watches the bluish-purple ring rise triumphantly before vanishing into the air. She pauses and looks at me with a mother's love.

"Connie Mary, when I went to school I didn't go up the ladder no higher than the third rung. I don't know any big words like Gus and Janice. But the Good Lord done blessed me by giving me a love for children like His Blessed Mother. Yep...old Anna knows far more than most people give her credit." I never understood why such a loving person as Anna could never have children of her own. Now I know that Anna's lonely nest has enough love for every child in the world. The day ends when dark clouds obstruct the light in preparation for a storm and the two women move underneath the patio to avoid the pouring rain. With each dog protectively by her side, Anna knows there is evil in the world bold enough to invade a little girl's bedroom in plain sight. She looks up at Janice's bedroom window and releases a deep, tired sigh. "Rose, sometimes the biggest danger a child faces in life is a parent."

As a child I never realized when Anna helped my mother she had a much bigger problem...Pinky. "Gus is no problem, why he's a peach," surmises my mother wistfully. "It's her adopted son Pinky that's the problem."

In time, I will trust my mother's wisdom as everything she said came to pass. On a moonlit night in June I will come to understand the depth and weight of Pinky's pain.

My mother and I are on the porch listening to the peaceful sound of crickets chirping when Pinky squeals into Gus's driveway plowing his mailbox to the ground. We see Pinky fling open the door to his truck and fall flat on his face. It takes a minute or two for him to stand before he stumbles into the house and then shouting is heard. My mother looks worried listening to Pinky arguing with Gus.

"Ma, Pinky sounds like a child. How old is he anyway?"

"How old is Pinky? Well, I know when we first moved to Fitchville you were just a baby and Pinky was in high school. But even then the poor child would come home drunk. Gosh, he was such a beautiful boy! He had a round face and flaming red hair. As he grew older, his face turned pink after having too much of the bottle." My mother pauses to listen to Pinky's drunken voice.

"Dad, I tells you— I wasent drinkcan—I wasent drinkcan! Honest to God Dad, can't youse believe me? I wasent drinkcan!"

"Poor Pinky. He has such a good heart. It's too bad trouble follows him wherever he goes. You know Connie Mary, Pinky's real mother, is Anna's sister. When she gave birth to Pinky, she gave him away to Anna and Gus. And you know how Gus is…when Pinky was old enough to understand he told him the truth.

"Ma, do you think that's why Pinky drinks?"

My mother slaps a mosquito on her arm causing blood to splatter. "Gus always said, 'Rose, the truth will set you free. But, first it's gonna hurt like hell and then we'll know how Christ felt wearing a crown of thorns.'"

We think the fight is over when Pinky comes storming out of the house. He has trouble standing and balances by holding the door handle to Gus's brand-new, emerald green Ford truck. Suddenly, he jumps inside and drives recklessly down the dark gravel road toward the pond. My mother sees this and shouts to my father inside the house—"Albert!"

Ten minutes later, I am standing in the moonlight at the center of Gus's Pond along with my father and every upright male citizen in Bozrah. Everyone is looking across the shimmering black water admiring its dark splendor. Pinky is no longer visible, leaving the rest of us to watch Gus's truck sink like a rock in the middle of the pond. Among the shock and awe, one man feels it is his civic duty, for the good of the community of course, to lead the group.

"I saw the whole thing… Pinky backed Gus's truck up to the water and put the pedal to the metal and into the water it flew! Then he swam away like a water moccasin with his nose above the water." The man continues to hold the crowd's attention by pointing his cigarette in the direction of Beebe's Fields. "See that hill up yonder? Up he crawled like a rat disappearing under the fence. If you ask me, I think Pinky did this on purpose."

I stand silent trying to stifle my giggles. Being a girl, I know I must keep my opinion to myself even though I know it did not take a genius to figure that one out. One by one the men confirm the importance of the man's statement by replying, "Ah yes," "Good point" or "Hear, hear" as if they were suddenly hit on the head with a brick called truth.

I look up at the ever-silent Gus who watches the hungry black water devour his truck. The water rises higher causing the truck to sink lower until it is almost submerged. The other men stay silent, but not my father. As usual, he has something to say when no words should be spoken.

"If I was you Gus, I'd break his goddamn neck."

Gus patiently listens to the ominous gurgling sounds and the men gasp when the truck disappears from sight. It is eerie how the Ford's headlights continue to shine beneath the black water allowing us to watch curious pumpkin-heads and catfish swimming through the translucent light. When Gus responds to my father his spirit is sinking as well.

"Violence never solved anything Al. Two wrongs don't make a right."

I know my father loves Gus and Anna very much. I know this for certain because he has no response. Can it be true? For the first time in his life is my father capable of feeling remorse for another person's plight? For who in their right mind does not admire Gustave O. Lorentz? Even with his troubled lot in life, Gus manages to maintain his dignity standing tall and proud like the loyal World War I soldier he is and always will be. My father steps back realizing he isn't fit to stand in the same space as Gus and says in a voice I do not recognize, "All right Gus... he's your son."

Once the last word is spoken the men act quickly bringing Gus's gigantic cement mixer to the scene. They elect two young men and into the black water they plunge toward the murky grave. Within minutes they connect a pulley to the Ford's bumper and the men applaud!

My father and I trudge home over the pond's gravel road that was once called *The Racetrack*. Gus said decades ago, it was a place of excitement, when men raced horses and bet on favorites. Sometimes, when I am walking on the path alone, I imagine I can hear the thunder of hooves pounding the path and excited men cheering.

After I have taken a bath and tucked between blue cotton sheets, I hear my father complaining to my mother. "Gus's new truck isn't worth shit now and it's all because of that damn fool Pinky. Gus thinks he can save him, but he never will."

My mother rarely voices an opinion but tonight she responds.

"Gus knows that boy is hurting. God knew what He was doing when He gave that boy to Gus. No finer stepfather will you see than Gustave O. Lorentz. My gosh, the patience that man has! Albert, sometimes people come into our lives for a reason. Maybe it's not about saving someone. Maybe it's about being there for someone when no one else cares."

On the last day of school, we wash our desks, return our books, and say good riddance to a classroom that can no longer hold us captive. Mrs. Hellerman watches Gregory and I with suspicion as we pull unfinished papers from the desk and laugh.

We rush through our tasks to make it to lunch and then run outside for our last recess. Unlike other days, I choose not to use the bathroom even though I have to pee. I rush outside to play, ignoring the Mama Robin whispering *you'll be sorry!* in my ear. I boldly answer back, *but this is my last recess and I don't want to miss a second!*

The first game we played is one of my favorites. Three children are picked as blind mice and another is chosen to be the Farmer's Wife. Everyone wants to be the Farmer's Wife because she stands by the mice pretending to hold a knife over their tails. The rest of us hold hands in a circle and walk around the mice singing: *Three blind mice.*

The song ends when the Farmer's Wife drops her arm and cuts the tails off the mice. Everyone laughs hysterically falling on top of each other and rolling over the grass. The game ends when the teacher on duty blows the whistle. We don't even care about recess being over because we know we are never coming back. In the meantime, I have foolishly missed several opportunities to use the bathroom and have a nagging pain in my side. I begin to imagine I am swimming in a pool with the water rising higher and higher. For the last time, Mrs. Hellerman takes her seat pulling a large book from the table.

"Children, since this is our last day, I have a special surprise. Instead of social studies, I am going to read an extra-long story to finish the year. The story I have chosen is *Dumbo*. This magnificent tale was written by Helen Aberson Mayer, and I am sure many of you will relate to this story as Dumbo's early life begins with trial and tribulation."

Our teacher slowly sips her tea, demanding with suspicious eyes that everyone understands the privilege of listening. Once confident of our allegiance, her words sail through the air like a grand old ship making peace with the painful past hiding in each corner of our classroom. Though I am listening as intently as I can, the pain in my side is worse than ever. I must use the bathroom *now* or it will be too late. The bathroom door is so close that I could touch it with an outstretched hand. But it does not matter. No one can use the bathroom without permission. I could crawl underneath my desk and sneak inside, but if caught I would be severely punished. I must find the courage to raise my hand and disturb the teacher, I must! Our teacher has strict rules about using the bathroom during class, which is why it is not unusual for my classmates to go home with poop and pee pants and lie to their parents about why they did not use the bathroom.

Gregory is pretending to be listening when he is actually studying the toy trucks and trains packed away in the back of the classroom. He is coming to my house to play after school which prompts me to ask, "P-s-s-t… Gregory, I have to use the bathroom! Do you think I should ask Mrs. Hellerman?"

His eyes grow fearful and he shakes his head silently mouthing N-O. I lean closer whispering louder.

"But Gregory, I have to go ba-a-a-a-d! I can't hold it much longer!" Sensing insubordination, Mrs. Hellerman stops reading to locate the culprits.

"Connie Mary! Gregory! Stop talking—*now*. Or both of you will be sent to the office." Gregory's body turns to stone and I jump at the opportunity.

"Excuse me, Mrs. Hellerman, but may I use the bathroom?"

My teacher gives me the death glare and goes back to reading. My pain feels as though someone is taking a needle and poking holes into my stomach. I don't know what else to do so I pretend I am back at

Gus's Pond studying the bullfrogs that sit in the shallow water and then…release my pee.

I feel a trickling sensation run down my leg and pretend I am invisible. When the tiny stream becomes a tidal wave I know it will not be long before I am discovered. Yellow pee gushed down my legs, soaking my shoes and leaving a small golden puddle around my feet.

Gregory's face is as red as a fireball jawbreaker as he slowly inches his desk backward to avoid getting wet. Then it happens. A voice cuts through the air like a jagged knife.

"Look, Mrs. Hellerman, Connie Falcone peed her pants and left a puddle on the floor!"

Mrs. Hellerman immediately stops reading. All the children look my way and some poke their heads underneath desks to get a better view. No one says a word as the Wicked Witch strides down the aisle on an imaginary broomstick. Step by step, inch by inch, she approaches my desk until she is towering above me like a crooked tree. The room is strangely quiet when she directs the children to come closer.

"Come closer children. Come see what this bad girl did."

The children reluctantly form a circle around my little golden puddle. I close my eyes and pretend I can make myself smaller by turning into a little grey mouse that can run and hide. My teacher does not care that I am a little mouse and hisses—"*Shame on you!*" When no one says a word my teacher's voice rises. "I said—LOOK at the bad thing Connie Falcone did!"

The children nod nervously as if hypnotized.

"Enough! Connie Falcone you made this mess and you will clean it up! And I do not care if you have to get down on all fours and lap it up. One thing is for sure: you will not leave today until every drop of urine is cleaned from this floor." The children scatter quickly and I am left with the problem of how to clean up my mess. Mrs.

Hellerman returns to her seat and smiles triumphantly. I go to the sink looking for paper towels but find none, so I use toilet paper instead. When I am done cleaning, I sit down on my pee chair. I am no longer concerned with its wetness since I am used to wetting the bed. Except for Gregory, all the children point, snicker and stare at me, but I do not cry.

Against all odds, the day ends with Gregory and I running through the prison gates to freedom! On the bus ride home we discover no one wants to sit near us. Many know what happened and snicker at my wet shoes and socks. Since no one wants to be around us, Gregory and I sit in the back seats usually reserved for the popular kids. Enjoying a rare privilege, Gregory throws his feet on top of the seat and shouts—"Hey Connie Mary, look at me—I'm not a dunce anymore—I'm one of the pop-lar kids!"

For the first time, Gregory and I feel special the whole ride home. It is as if peeing my pants has made me famous. When Mr. Lashinski releases the door, we race toward my house feeling the joy of liberation. This is when Gregory stops to reveal a sudden revelation.

"Hey, Connie Mary, you know what? Next year, I'm gonna pee my pants *too!*

6

Staying Silent

Janice at Fields Memorial School (8ᵗʰ grade) courtesy of
Christine Kenney LaBrie

The Picnic Where I learned How to Survive

"When I was eight years old, my father took the family to a VFW picnic at Fort Shantok State Park in Montville, Connecticut for a day of games arranged by men. In each game, children were separated by gender; girls played with girls and boys with boys. I vividly recall a game called *Pop the Balloon*, where little girls aggressively competed against each other to win. First, men tied a balloon around the ankle of each little girl using a nylon cord. The ultimate goal was for each girl to pop the other girls' balloons as quickly as possible using only their feet. Stinking of whisky, beer and cigarettes the men proceeded to push the girls into a circle of flying dust. There was no hope of escape as the strong arms of the men formed a tight circle. The winner, that is, the last girl standing, is the girl whose balloon remained intact. To encourage competition, each little girl's father drunkenly roots for his daughter to win. Frenzied words of encouragement are thrown at the girls like shiny copper pennies at their feet.

"Come on Baby—do it for daddy" or "Make papa proud!"

The game begins with the ominous sound of *pop... pop... pop* that creates a sense of dread and doom inside the heart of each little girl. Those eliminated must leave immediately, deflated balloons dragging behind and stand outside the circle and cry. I recall one father in particular, a red-faced drunk with a bulbous W.C. Fields' nose, who wound the nylon cord so tight around my ankle that red marks lasted for days. In the midst of the noise and confusion I failed to understand what made this game fun. Judging by the terrified expressions on the faces of the other girls, no one else my age understood either.

Nevertheless, I became a fierce Roman Gladiator, fighting for my father's pride! The frenzy and excitement in the men's voices motivated the kill. My adrenaline surged and my heart raced as I listened to my father's sideline encouragement. "Go get 'em Connie Mary! Get 'em for Daddy!" It was then that I knew what I must do. I remember my mother telling me how Satan watched Adam and Eve walking through the Garden of Eden and devised a plan.

I moved slyly toward the far edge of the circle to linger innocently among the competition and was followed by another little girl. I gently nudged her arm in friendship and whispered, "You and me...let's be friends and protect each other." In blind trust the little girl agreed. Together, we merged into the circle—our friendship forged by trust. We were a team fighting back-to-back protecting each other like two soldiers in battle. After the dust from the bloody arena settled there were only two girls left. This was when I turned and grabbed my new friend by the shoulders. With no more care than if I were stepping on an ant, I popped her balloon.

My new friend's face was one of shock and disbelief as I ran towards my father and fell into his arms. Holding a warm beer he triumphantly raised my arm and told the other men, "You did good kid. See? That's my Connie Mary. She's a chip off the old block!"

Every summer my mother's sister Grayce drives all the way from Pennsauken, New Jersey to Connecticut, bringing my cousins Steve and Joey. Joey is several years younger than me and has the most terrible temper tantrums I have ever seen! Grayce (who happens to be my aunt and godmother) looks like a movie star with her jet-black hair, olive skin and luminous eyes that somehow have the ability to see through the darkest of souls.

The day Aunt Grayce arrived I was getting ready to swim in my inflatable pool when Joey ran ahead and belly flopped in the center removing most of the water. I let out a bloodcurdling scream, but Joey paid no attention. Instead, he took my underwater mask to see how long he could hold his breath before I told his mother. When Aunt Grayce came outside, she gently coaxed her little troublemaker out of the pool.

Aunt Grayce is the peacekeeper in the Calanna family. Every time she visits, she brings encouraging words as well as bags of stylish clothes for Janice. My sister is always grateful and gives her a hug.

"Oh, Aunt Grayce—thank you! How did you know I needed clothes?" Holding tightly to the precious bags, my sister runs upstairs, dropping clothes along the way.

My father observes the scene like the dropped garments are cancer cells waiting to spread and grins before he cracks a joke about Janice. My aunt knows my father's jokes are a way of inflicting pain without raising suspicion.

"Hey Gray, if you can get rid of my older daughter that fast, you can bring her clothes all the time."

My aunt does not like my father. The truth is no one in the Calanna family likes my father. Joey and I are upstairs playing with my ceramic horses when I hear Aunt Grayce speaking boldly to my father.

"*Joe.* Don't you ever—ever—talk about my niece that way or it will be the last thing *you* ever do."

At first my father is silent, but then laughs nervously. At this moment, my father and I have much in common. I am trying to hide my favorite ceramic horse from Joey, while he is trying to hide his murder smile from Aunt Grayce. My father knows his sister-in-law is serious and has often said he would rather spend the night with a cobra than piss off Grayce Lerro. There is an uncomfortable silence between the two before he makes light of the joke.

"Ah, come on Gray—get off your high horse. You know I was just kid-din."

Joey and I come downstairs in time to see my father walk out the door. That's when my aunt points an index and pinky finger at his back, sending him the worst curse any Italian could ever receive—the *Malocchio*, the evil eye! She holds the position until my father is out of sight. With an angry voice I had never heard before, my aunt reveals to my mother what she has always known.

"He's no good honey. That man's no good. As long as he walks the earth he will bring misery to anyone who crosses his path."

My mother does not respond to Aunt Grayce's warning and goes outside to fill the pool with water. When the pool is full, I stick my toe inside, but it is too cold to swim and I start to cry. Aunt Grayce cheers me up by tenderly brushing my hair.

"Con-Bon, today I'm going to give you an Italian bouffant like the one Connie Francis wears. It shall be called *'Molto magnifico!'* Now come inside so your godmother can make you look like a movie star!"

My aunt styles my hair at the kitchen table while gossiping about Concetta Rosemarie Franconero and Bobby Darin. My mother stuffs another lemon chocolate into her mouth before gingerly biting small holes into the bottoms of other chocolates.

"Gray, did you know that Connie's father hated Bobby Darin

more than the Italian plague? Gray, I don't blame Connie Francis. That Bobby Darin is so darn sexy!"

Aunt Grayce tugs gently at a knot in the back of my hair.

"Hon, did you know that Connie Francis had to end the relationship with Bobby after her father ran him off from one of her shows with a pistol? Now all Connie Francis has left is a broken heart. I tell you honey, that girl is cursed with the Italian love. And once you got the Italian love for a man—and they know it—you're all done, honey." My mother happily pops a scrumptious looking maple sugar chocolate into her mouth.

"True, Gray, true."

"See honey, instead of marrying a nice Italian girl like Connie Francis, Bobby ended up marrying a polish girl named Sandra Dee after they starred in the movie *Come September*. At the time it was a big scandal because Sandra Dee looked young enough to be his daughter."

My mother nods with enthusiasm trying to look inconspicuous while her mouth is full of chocolate. "Umm, you don't shay, Gray."

"Honey, it's exactly what I tell our niece Barbara Joan. You must marry your own blood. Take your husband Joe, he's a big mouth Calabrese—no class, trash mouth, a liar and a thief, but one thing he's got… he's Italian. See, you and I are both Sicilian, born with gold on our tongue. Not many Italians are like us. The Abruzzese are big mouths with heads of stone. The Neapolitans are dopes and cavones and the Milanese think their poop doesn't stink! The Venetians are weak-minded and the Marceghianos are old-fashioned, wearing skirts to the ground." My Aunt chuckles a deep, hardy growl in the middle of her throat. "Ha, even us, the great Sicilians—the best Italians in the world—some dare to call us 'garbage eaters.' Honey, I'll tell you the truth about Sicilians: out of all the Italians— we seek revenge the best!"

My Aunt stops chuckling and glares at me like a red morning giving warning.

"Connie Mary, never forget where you came from. *Being Sicilian could save your life.*"

Everyday I spend with my cousin Joey is idyllic, unspoiled and magical. In order for him to play with me, he demands that I entertain him by reciting stories from *The Twilight Zone*. Every once in a while, I make up scary stories of my own and sometimes those stories are true.

The sizzling days of summer make us too lazy to do anything except suck on a Kool-Aid ice pop and sit beneath a tree. On this particular day, Joey and I take our time as we meander down the dusty path toward Gus's Pond. We are having a contest to see who can suck the blue out of a Kool-Aid pop the fastest. With the dusty sand rising between our toes and the sun warming our backs, a kind of blissful joy swells up inside of me. It is the magic I taste in my ice pop and the freedom of summer.

Growing tired of walking, we spot a secluded hillside and head there to rest. This is the grassy glen where my father throws his old and broken appliances so we do feel alone. Abandoned washing machines keep us company, looking forlorn and forgotten in the tall grass. We plop underneath a shade tree and lie on our backs, watching clouds drift through the bright blue sky. Growing restless, Joey begins to tap his shoes together and I know this is my cue to tell him a story. I look across the hillside and rest my eyes upon an old abandoned refrigerator that over time has turned the grass yellow and point to the decay.

"Joey, see that refrigerator? I have a story about it. But beware—it's horribly scary! Are you ready? The story is called... *The Little Dead Girl.*" I inhale slowly before continuing.

"One day I was walking along the path surrounding Gus's Pond when I heard the faraway sound of a little girl crying. I stopped and looked but saw no one. I continued to search until I came to this very spot and discovered who was crying."

I pause to listen to the sound of cicadas buzzing high in trees and decide it is time to take out the black string licorice and offer Joey half. Delighted, he grabs it with excited hands.

"Who was crying Con? Was it the little girl Frankenstein killed in the movie?"

"Joe. You have to wait for what I'm going to say next. Trust me— it will scare the pants off you." Joey nods in agreement and stuffs his mouth full of licorice. A plane buzzes low as I point to the old rusty refrigerator standing upright.

"Joe, I was standing in front of that old refrigerator. Do you see it Joe? The one with the door hanging loose?"

Joey looks fearfully at the large cumbersome beast a few feet away and shakes his head as if to say, *yes I see it.* I get the shivers myself when I recall something else.

"Oh, there's one more thing Joe. The door was not broken then. It was shut tight."

Joey stops chewing his licorice and closes his eyes. A black crow flies overhead, cawing so sharply it sounds like a warning.

"I went closer to the refrigerator after realizing that the soft whimpering sounds were coming from inside and knocked on the door three times. I said, 'Hello? —Is anyone there? Are you in there little girl?' I asked nicely so I would not scare her away. To my surprise, I heard a child's frantic voice call from behind the metal door.

'Help me!' she cried. 'Help me get out!'

I yelled back— 'Wait, I'll go get help!'—and took off running, peeing my pants all the way home!" At the image of me peeing myself,

Joey's black mouth bursts open with laughter and he spits his licorice over the grass.

"When I got home, my mother was not there. And then I remembered she had a doctor's appointment with her 'psyeyeatwist' Dr. Baloney. Luckily, Aunt Angie was sitting at the kitchen table smoking cigarettes and ordering supplies for her beauty salon. I could hardly catch my breath.

"'Aunt Angie, come quick! There's a little girl trapped inside one of my father's old refrigerators down Gus's Pond!' My aunt doesn't even bother to look at me. She is too busy thinking about hair color.

"'Ah, gosh damn it, I didn't want Honey Blonde! I wanted Blonde Goddess instead. I have to get Blonde Goddess because the Mayor's wife wants to be the same shade as her husband's girlfriend.'

"I repeated my words—'Aunt Angie, there's a little girl trapped in dad's old refrigerator down at Gus's Pond!' My aunt looks down at me, annoyed as all get out. She takes her wrinkled hands and pulls them nervously through the thin strands of her blonde, grey, white, brown and red hair."

Joey looks horrified as he recalls the memory of my aunt. "Your aunt does have some crazy hair. She kinda looks like Cruella de Vil, don't you think Con?"

"No way! Trust me Joe, my Aunt Angie says any woman who wears the fur of poor dead animals has her brains up her butt! Joe, did you know how they get the fur off those poor animals? Oh, never mind. I can't tell you because you're too young to know the truth. Now, lemme get back to my story. Let's see now, where was I? —Oh, ya.

"'What's all this nonsense about a little girl in a refrigerator?' said my aunt. 'Con, your aunt's too busy to be listening to your Hans Christian Anderson stories. Can't you see that? I got my hands full, got my own business like a man. You know, it ain't easy paying all the bills, just ask your father. That poor bastard not only has you two kids to worry about, but your mother too. He has to pay for your mother's doctor bills, her nerve pills, her Dalmanes, her uppers and downers and inside outers—and on top of that, he has to listen to his wife crying from the bedroom. Gesù Cristo, it's enough to make anyone go nuts. I'm surprised my brother ain't seeing little girls in his refrigerators.'

"No matter what Aunt Angie said, I would not stop talking about the little girl! Finally, making a desperate attempt, I tightened my fists and jumped up and down crying and screaming. As a last resort, I threw myself down on my mother's dirty linoleum floor until my aunt finally told me that if I stopped she would come help me look for the little girl. I run back to Gus's Pond with my aunt following close behind, and when we reach the refrigerator I cannot believe what I see. Somebody else must have been here, because the door is wide open and the little girl is gone! My aunt tries to comfort me but I cannot stop sobbing. 'You had too much sun Connie Mary, that's all. I keep warning your mother. Rose I said, if you keep lettin' Connie Mary run around that damn pond like some wild animal, mark my words—someday when you call her home instead of your daughter, there's gonna be a wild cheetah waiting for you at the door.'

"When we get home, my aunt makes me lie down and take a nap. When it is time for supper, I eat pasta with green peas floating on top of the sauce. When my father comes home, we watch *Gunsmoke* together and then it's time for bed."

Joey stares at the refrigerator as if it was alive and dangerous. "Do you think she died in there, Con? Do you think a wild cheetah came and ate her?" We take a few minutes to study the refrigerator and Joey eats the last piece of licorice.

"Joe, if you stop asking so many questions, I'll tell you more. But it's very, very scary, so be prepared." Joey inches his body closer to mine. I think Joey would have waited an eternity for me to finish. So purposely, I waited longer prolonging the little girl's fate just like Rod Serling does when he tells his stories.

"Joe, after that day, I could not forget about the little girl and began to have scary dreams at night."

"What kind of dreams? Oh, don't tell me, Con—I'll be too scared! No wait! Tell me! Tell me! I want to be scared!"

"I'd be fast asleep but then in the middle of the night, I'd wake up and see this little girl in a long white nightgown standing at the foot of my bed looking down at me with sad eyes. Even though she was a ghost, I could see she had two pink bows on each side of her long yellow hair. Every night, I'd see her. She scared me something awful! I was so scared I pulled the covers over my head. But eventually, I got tired of hiding and asked her what she wanted. Well, I have to say Joe, the little girl told me some strange things. She told me she did not die how people thought she did. She said her father murdered her. I told her I didn't understand because everyone knows fathers don't murder their children. But she was persistent and even knew my name!

"She said, 'Connie Mary, when you're older, you will understand that some fathers *do* murder their children. It has happened since the dawn of time and it is happening as we speak. Someday, you will see, my words will come to pass.'

"Then—POOF! She was gone!"

For a few minutes, Joey and I watch the fading sun fall nearer to the earth.

"But that's not the end of the story. Weeks later, I noticed Pinky and Gus Lorentz pulling into the driveway from work so I decided to ask Gus if he knew anything about any little girls who died in the neighborhood. Both men were unloading shovels and equipment from the back of a cement truck. Gus looked more tired than usual and joked with the little strength he had left.

'Nope, Connie Mary, I haven't heard of any little girls dying lately. But if I do, you'll be the first one to know.' Pinky, however, looked deep in thought and ran his fingers through his bright red hair.

"'No, wait Pop, there was a kid...a little girl about seven-years-old. She died when I was just a kid. She went to Fields Memorial with me. This girl always came to school with black and blue marks over her body. She used to say she fell down a lot. She never made it through the school year. One morning when we got to school, we saw our teacher sitting at the desk bawling her eyes out. Pop, to this day, I still remember the town turning out for that little girl's funeral. I also remember the adults at that funeral saying how her no-good, bastard father beat her up all the time. They said her father should never have been allowed to attend his daughter's funeral, because *he* murdered her.'

"After Pinky told his story, I went into the backyard and picked one of my mother's prettiest pink roses and went to lay it inside the empty refrigerator. Then, I called up to the maple trees watching me from above and said, 'Little Dead Girl? If you stop visiting me, I promise I'll tell your story someday.' The little dead girl never came back. Somehow she knew I would keep my promise."

One week later Joey and his family are gone.

My mother misses her sister so much that she decides to make an appointment with Aunt Angie on the fourth floor of the Disco Building to have her hair done. I tag along to watch my aunt tackle my mother's messy and tangled hair, all the while knowing that she once had the most beautiful hair of any woman in the room. Like an artist starting a masterpiece, Aunt Angie stands back and imagines the possibilities.

"That's it Rose! My little brother is going to go ape shit after I color your hair Romantic Brown! Get ready Rose, Bootsie is going to chase you all over the house!" My mother does not laugh because she is too busy worrying about my grades. Unlike my father who has accepted my bad grades by saying *the hell with it,* my mother takes the blame for my poor school performance.

"Ang'ch, after Janice, I never thought I'd have a child who had trouble in school. Do you think Connie Mary has problems learning because I smoked when she was in my belly? Or do you think it was the nerve pills I took? Do you think I hurt my little daughter Ang'ch? Come to think of it, it never hurt Janice and look how much smarter she is than Connie Mary."

My aunt listens with compassion as she rinses my mother's hair while balancing a cigarette on her bottom lip. The cigarette is hanging so low I fear my mother's cape will catch on fire. Despite the near death situation, my aunt carries on a normal conversation as acrid grey smoke travels up her nose.

"Rose, it's like Pa always said, 'What's gonna be—is gonna be.' When God lays your brick on the wall, He sets it in cement and there ain't a goshdamn thing you can do if your brick is cracked. You get my drift Rose? You smell the espresso I'm brewing here? See, we don't have a choice which brick we get. We take what we get and make the best of it."

Aunt Angie turns the water off and pipes start to rattle and shake like a small earthquake erupting under the sink. She stomps on the foot pedal of my mother's chrome chair and up she pops like George J. Jetson ejected into space. My mother's wet hair covers her face hiding the torment in her eyes.

"So Ang'ch, you don't think it was my smoking or the pills I took that hurt Connie Mary?"

My aunt grabs hold of a hairbrush with bristles that look like porcupine quills and proceeds to brush my mother's hair. Long strands drop to the floor.

"Rose, you can't worry about every little thing in life. Why, look at me, I got a roomful of women just waitin' for me to make them beautiful and all I got is these two hands to do it. But do you see me worried Rose? Nah! Worrying about what coulda been, shoulda been, or woulda been, ain't worth a bucket of wooden nickels. You must trust what I'm saying here Rose. When God lays your brick in the wall he sets it in cement and there ain't a damn thing you can do about it except *take* the brick you've been given."

Every person is born for the purpose of helping someone else. Such was the case of Christine Kenney when she moved to Bozrah and became my sister's only friend. The girls were in the same grade and lived only two houses away from each other. Immediately they formed a bond of soul mates divulging the most forbidden of secrets. I was so used to consuming my sister's attention that if someone had asked what I thought of Christine, I would have said my sister was having too good of a time without me! At eight-years-old I had already evolved into a spoiled selfish brat who wanted Janice all to myself.

One night, Christine comes over to play with Janice. I hide on the basement steps and watch jealously as Christine foolishly tries to teach Janice to dance. They are playing records and listening to Connie Francis sing, *Who's Sorry Now*. I watch them stumble and laugh whenever Janice steps on Christine's feet. Burning with envy, I yell to get my father's attention—"Dad! Janice and Christine won't let me dance with them!"

I knew exactly what I was doing. My father was sleeping on the couch and my yelling woke him from a peaceful slumber. When I yell a second time, he screams as though the house is on fire.

"Goshdamn it Janice, I told you to let your sister play with you!"

I tiptoe into the parlor and see my father give my mother a look that could kill. My mother reaches for a bottle of red Dalmanes knowing she will not be able to see the end of the television show *Sea Hunt*. The ghostlike voice of Connie Francis ominously warns, "Whose heart is aching for breaking each vow, who's sad and blue, who's crying too?" Needless to say the dancing ends sooner than expected when Christine stutters a polite goodbye and runs out the door. Little do I know I am not my sister's biggest concern. There is someone far worse lurking in the shadows called *the night beast*. The night beast comes unseen and with menacing secrecy, slays his prey. The night beast has no fear of being discovered for it knows that evil thrives wherever silence is enforced.

The summer before my sister enters eighth grade, Christine Kenney finds Janice in her bedroom weeping. The night beast had visited the night before and touched the most intimate parts of her body. Once Janice tells Christine, the response is immediate.

"Your father did *what to you*? We must tell your mother now!"

Despite my sister's resistance Christine convinces Janice to tell my mother and leads her by the hand into the kitchen where my unsuspecting mother lives in a world of her own. Christine's voice is urgent as she delivers the shocking news.

"Mrs. Falcone, Janice needs to tell you something." The two girls proceed to sit when Janice suddenly throws herself across the table and hides her face sobbing.

"I can't, Christine! I just can't! I'm so ashamed!"

The brave Christine knows right from wrong. She has a good father and knows a father is supposed to protect his children—not abuse them. Christine is acting more like a mother and gently strokes my sister's hair. "It's okay Jan, just tell your mother. Your mother will help you. But if you don't—I will!"

It is unfortunate for the young girls that my mother is already in a dazed and drugged state by the time she hears Christine's words. "Mrs. Falcone. Your husband *'manhandled'* your daughter. He's been touching her—even when she cries and begs him to stop!" My mother is bewildered. She looks at her 12-year-old daughter stretched across the kitchen table crushed and broken, and looks at Christine with indifference.

"There's nothing I can do Christine, I'm all alone. If I go to the authorities my husband will lie to protect himself as he always does and they will not believe me. My husband works for all the rich doctors in town, what will they think of me? I know what they will do to me. They will lock me away in the Norwich State Hospital and that will be the end of me. I cannot do anything about it... I'm sorry." My mother picks up a pack of cigarettes and walks away.

The kettle of water my mother left behind is boiling and hissing angrily into the air. Still in shock, Christine walks over and turns the burner off. In my sister's lifetime there will be neighbors, friends and relatives who witnessed or heard about the abuse that Janice was forced to endure. It is inconceivable that very few were strong enough to help my sister with the exception of a 13-year-old girl named Christine Kenney.

This is the last Halloween Christine and Janice will spend together. The day begins like most—with my mother sick in bed. Ever since my father started his business, she seems to fall dangerously ill whenever he leaves the house. Having fulfilled his dream, my father is thrilled to have a business of his own. He is desperate to succeed and against his better judgment, asks his brother Henry for advice; the same brother he belittles and insults behind his back and even makes fun of his glass eye. Uncle Henry is thrilled when my father asks him for advice and recommends he hire his best friend Ronnie to be his helper.

I am surprised that my father did not ask his brother Ettore for advice. This brother is college-educated and well-mannered, always giving sound advice that never goes wrong. What my father does not know, though, is when Uncle Ettore comes to visit and goes upstairs to use the bathroom, he opens my bedroom door and my sister's— without knocking. Uncle Ettore is very polite and always apologizes after he peeks inside. My mother, sister and I have learned to compensate for these intrusions by being prepared. Uncle Ettore becomes a subject of humor between my mother and Henry's wife Philomena. Apparently, Uncle Ettore repeats the same scenario when he visits her family. Despite how uncomfortable he makes us feel, in order to avoid conflict, everyone decides to find the situation funny and just laugh. Curiously, once my sister and I reach high school, the incidents involving Uncle Ettore stop and we never speak of it again.

Uncle Henry is the kind of brother-in-law who helps my mother the most and to whom we feel the closest. Under the loving auspice of my mother, my father reluctantly concedes and hires Ronnie. But I know the real reason my father agrees. My father hires Ronnie because he doesn't have anyone else. He immediately regrets it, cursing Henry and whispering to himself, "*Figlio di puttana...* this is the last time I listen to a jackass like my brother. By Jesus, if Henry knows what's good for him...Ronnie better work out."

On the afternoon of October 31st, instead of helping me find a Halloween costume, my mother lies in bed comforted by her pill bottles. To make matters worse, she cannot find my father anywhere. I happen to be sitting on the edge of the bed playing with my rubber figures Gumby and Pokey when my mother chooses me to play detective.

"I'm sick! Oh, Connie Mary, I need you to help me find your father!" It may only be a coincidence that my mother needs my father on the days he is on the road going from house to house. This is good for my father because there is no way my mother can reach him. In a desperate attempt, my mother calls as many of my father's relatives as she can, which takes all day. The afternoon turns into evening as I dial numbers and my mother continuously drops the receiver. My father had an extension phone installed in the bedroom so my mother could answer his business calls and take messages, but deep down, he already knows he is more likely to be picked up by aliens and flown to Mars than have my mother take his messages.

In her drugged and confused condition, my mother takes forever to find a number. The more pills she pops, the more confused she becomes. After much frustration she manages to reach Aunt Angie at the salon. "Help me Angie," she moans. "I'm so depressed today. Please, help me!" Even though I am sitting on the other side of the bed, I can hear my aunt's voice loud and clear amongst the noise and confusion.

"Rose, right now, I got customers up the ying-yang. Now listen to me Rose, call up Pa and see if Bootsie's over there. After work he usually stops to see Ma. Rose, I'd love to talk but the Mayor's wife just walked in and this week she wants to look like Marilyn. And let me tell you, her hair is a bitch to color 'cause it pulls red, and then I have to convince her that she looks more glamorous as Rita Hayworth. Shit, bleached blondes are a dime a dozen anyway. Rose, no kidding, I must go! I know it isn't your fault that you don't understand how it is to work like a dog 'cause you got my brother's money to spend. But nobody is going to pay my bills but me, and time is money—so take care Rose, I love you!" and hangs up.

She calls my father's mother next. "Ma, I don't feel so well today. Can you and Pa come over and stay with me?" I can only imagine what Nonna will say because my Nonna does not believe in eating pills like candy. Nor does Nonna like my mother wasting her time and my father's money going to Norwich every week to see her psychiatrist Dr. Milone.

"Rose! You take-a those crazy pills again? Rose! In Italia...we no take pills. In 'mer-i-ca all da crazy people take-a pill. Rose, why you no throw them pills in garbage like I tell-a you to? And that no good doc-a-ter, he take-a my son's money! His name no Maloney—it Baloney! Listen to Nonna, pills no damn-a good! *Vieni qui, a casa mia,* come over and Nonna teach-a you to make good meat-a-ball!"

"Gee, I don't know Ma. Dr. Milone is known all over the state as a good doctor."

That does it. My Nonna loses patience and quickly adds her two cents before hanging up, *"Ah, baloney!"*

My mother places the receiver down for one whole second before calling Uncle Henry and his wife Philomena. My mother dials three times and still gets the number wrong. Aunt Philomena is my mother's good friend with plenty of troubles of her own. Uncle Henry is good to us but he is no saint; he drinks, gambles and sometimes beats his wife and children.

My mother dials Uncle Henry's number one last time and Aunt Philomena answers.

"Hello, Phil? I don't feel so well today. Can you come over and help me?"

My aunt hesitates. "Rose, I got the overnight shift at the American Thermos Bottle Company tonight...and...I... I..." Scuffling is heard in the background as Uncle Henry grabs the phone out of his wife's hands.

"Jesus Christ Philomena—gimme that goddamn phone!" When Uncle Henry learns it is my mother his tone changes to soft and loving. "Rose—Rose, are you all right Rose?"

"Hen, I'm sick," says my mother, faking a cry like Lucille Ball on *I Love Lucy.*

Without a moment's hesitation, my uncle says, "I'll be right there Rose—hang on!" By the time my mother puts down the receiver and uses the bathroom, Uncle Henry is walking through our front door. He immediately goes into the kitchen and pulls a jar of *Ragu* from the cupboard and starts boiling water on the stove. I assume Uncle Henry is hoping that, when my father sees supper on the table, it will make him happy after working all day.

Uncle Henry continues cooking and everything is hunky-dory until my father walks through the front door. I can tell he is already agitated. As soon as he sees Uncle Henry wearing my mother's flowered apron and boiling pasta on the stove, he flies into a rage, screaming within inches of Uncle Henry's face.

"HENRY! You *cavallo asino*, I'm going to knock your teeth down your throat! You want to know what that rotten, good for nothing, *figlio di puttana, bastardo* you told me to hire—did at work today? I'll tell you what he did! That bastard took off with my truck down Mohegan Park beach along with some *puttana* he picked up! And instead of doing the job I gave him—that son of a bitch was smooching on the beach!" My uncle slowly and carefully steps away from my father and with trembling hands struggles to untie the bow in back of his apron.

"*Figlio di puttana.* I lost a job today because of that *gilipollas* you told me to hire! And now the customer says she can't depend on us anymore and fired me! I should have known better than to listen to my brother who's so damn stupid he doesn't have a pot to piss in!" As my uncle tries to appease my father, I imagine that if fear were alive and breathing it would be hiding inside my uncle's good eye.

"Now Boots, I thought Ronnie changed. Jesus Christ, we grew up with him; he's like my own brother! Now, how'd I know he was going to do that? Wait 'till I see him, I'll ring his goddamn neck." Everyone knows that my uncle adores his best friend Ronnie and has no intention of ever hurting him. My father is good at making people feel so terrified that they lie in order to save themselves. Without saying another word, my uncle gently places my mother's stained apron on the table and leaves without saying goodbye. This is when my mother decides to come downstairs with only one concern.

"Albert, I need you to go down to the pharmacy and pick up my prescription—it's ready."

It is late when he returns. Our house is dark and unwelcoming to the hordes of neighborhood children who are happily trick-or-treating into the fall night. Meanwhile I am in my bedroom, attempting to watch a show on the television set my father borrowed from Constant Brothers, trying not to listen to my mother whine in bed as my father gets ready to blow a fuse.

"Rose, you wants me to bring you to the Backus Hospital? Well, what the hell do you want me to do? Call Ben Casey? Oh, God Almighty—how much more of this life can I take with you? I wish to hell I'd been killed in World War II when the Navy invaded Normandy! It would have been better than living with you! How the hell did I serve in Africa, Sicily, Italy, France and Omaha Beach with the 2nd Naval Beach Battalion, win the Good Conduct and Victory Metal and end up living in this hellhole with you?"

At the worst moment, my sister walks into the house giggling and laughing with Christine and her sister Joanne. The three girls are disguised with black cat masks and carrying bulging bags of candy. As soon as my father hears the joyous sound of the three giggling girls, he flies downstairs with his steel-toe boots banging each step. Though my father cannot bring himself to physically hit my mother at this time, he has no problem hitting the person dearest to her heart. I watch from the stairs as he smacks my sister across the face.

"Why'd you leave your mother alone sick in bed? Why, you selfish, good for nothing tramp!"

With shock and humiliation Janice is unable to look at the other girls. The only choice she has is to curse and run up the stairs. "You bastard...I hate you!"

My father menacingly follows close behind.

"You better run… if I get you, you're gonna be sorry." I breathe a sigh of relief when the bathroom door slams and locks. My father swears under his breath and I feel grateful that my mother lost the key to the bathroom months ago.

After several hours, I creep into my mother's bedroom and open a bottle of Dalmanes. I shake out three pills into my hand and swallow two of them. I settle into a peaceful sleep that allows the horrible images in my mind to fade. Before everything turns completely black, the television delivers its parting words as CBS Anchorman Walter Cronkite reports with a staunch familiarity, "And that's the way it is…"

Documentation to the life of Janice Falcone
By Christine Kenney LaBrie
August 30, 2012

In 1960...

My family moved into a home in Bozrah, Connecticut where I entered seventh grade at Fields Memorial School. Two doors down from my home lived Janice Falcone. Janice and I graduated from Fields Memorial School in 1962. We met in seventh grade and became the best of friends. We shared everything. She lived with her mother, father and sister. We rode the bus to and from school, did homework together, rode bikes, ice skated on Gus's Pond behind her home, took long walks, shared talks about everything and danced to the 60's music as often as we could. Janice had very low self-esteem and at first I thought she was just shy, but I learned very quickly why. There were secrets that she kept to herself but it got to the point where life just got too hard for her to bear and I was there to listen. In seventh grade, when I was first new to school, I had to give a book report in front of the class and was so scared. There were some kids in the back of the room giggling and talking that made me feel intimidated. I thought they were making fun of me, so I dropped the papers and ran from the room. Because I had a Boston accent, was skinny and felt ugly, as all teens back then did, I felt out of place. I was crying in the ladies' room when my teacher tried as he may to coax me out but I couldn't and wouldn't leave. I was horrified. He left and Janice came in and talked me into coming out. I told the teacher what had caused me to leave and we all went back into the classroom to speak to the class. He told everyone that it was time for a lesson in respect. We all listened to him explain why we should all be sensitive to each other. It was wonderful to hear and I had hoped for the best for all of us. Janice and I trusted each other to the fullest after that day. We both talked about this and that's really when the friendship started. I had bought her a friendship ring telling her, "forever friends no matter what." We made a pact and we even pricked our fingers to become blood sisters. We made our confirmation together at the age of 13 when others were making theirs at 10-years-old. We were the oldest ones there and yet we didn't feel out of place, because we had each other. In school we hung out at lunch, PE and recess. Janice hated PE. When in school, we always talked about the boys or what songs we liked, or what was going on with other classmates.

We went on our eighth grade field trip to New York City. Janice, I, and another girl were roommates at the hotel we were staying at. We had a blast. We were away from home and felt like adults and just having fun on our own. It was such a great feeling. We would have the giggles as teens would, knowing that we could have our own party, even if it were only for a few days. On our first day there I lost my wallet and was devastated. I worked so hard to earn the money to take with me. Every time that we would leave the hotel Janice would ask if I would like to borrow some money but I did without until the return trip home. That's when Janice gave me ten dollars so that I could buy each one of my brothers and sisters something from the big city. She tried to share what she had throughout the whole time we were there. I repaid her once I earned enough babysitting money.

We would do homework together after school either at her house or mine. She was so much smarter than I when it came to schoolwork. If her father were not home, we would go to her place but if he showed up we would both leave and head to my home. Many times we would go to her basement, play the record player and dance until it was time for me to go home. We totally enjoyed that time with our music. At school, it always seemed like I was defending her from the typical teenage jokes that were said to all of us, the ugly hormones of teens. We were awkward, with pimples, moodiness, changes in our bodies, learning the ropes of the opposite sex and it wasn't easy then. Some of us girls would cry at the drop of a pin let alone someone calling us names and the boys seemed to do a lot. Because Janice was well developed, in those years the boys always seemed to tease her and I was always sticking up for her. She would never speak up for herself and it was that way at her home. She would rather clam up than start an argument, fight or be assertive. She always found a way to get out of speaking up. We would have to stay after school for something and she wouldn't want to go home. We would be at church for confirmation classes and she would ask to stay longer so that she wouldn't have to go home. It got to the point that she would do anything to stay out of her house. Whenever we would get together we would always have trouble with her younger sister, who was five years younger than Janice. She wanted to be with us or do what we were doing. We tried to do our own thing without her and found it impossible. Because there were quite a few kids in our neighborhood that she could play with, we would tell her to go visit with them but there were times that she just would not leave us alone. I was always telling Janice to stand up to her but she would tell me that she would pay for it if she made any effort to correct her. At first I couldn't believe it but as time went on sure enough one day it happened. Janice and I were up in Janice's room experimenting with trying on makeup when her sister came in. I told her that we were talking and wanted to be left alone and when she left, she went to her room to play by herself. We thought that was easy; there was no fuss or talking back. We didn't see or hear from her for hours. We heard her father come downstairs and out of the blue she screamed, started to cry and ran down the stairs. Janice and I just looked at each other, I shook my head and Janice shrugged her shoulders. Her father started to scream for Janice to get down stairs.

We both went down and he smacked her across the face. I was shocked and left quite shaken up. He was in a rage.

The next day Janice said that her sister told her father that we were mean to her and that I wasn't allowed over for a week. Another time we were studying for a test upstairs in Janice's bedroom and her sister came in and punched her in the arm. When Janice got up to chase her out, she began punching Janice in the stomach over and over for no apparent reason. When she was finally out of the room Janice locked the door and her sister started pounding on the door. I wanted to know what that was all about and I was told that all she wanted was attention. When we didn't respond to the noise, she started to sing her favorite "song" through the door at us: "Fat and skinny had a race up and down the pillow case." I was 5'8" weighing 87 pounds and Janice was slightly overweight. Anything that was said to her youngest sister would always be told to the father, so Janice would tell me not to say things that would or could be repeated in front of her sister. If Janice tried to defend herself to her father, her father would tell her not to talk back and he would scream at her more. Many times her sister would be standing right next to her mother or father while the father was yelling, laughing and pointing. Once when we were in the bedroom and Janice had already locked us in the room, her sister began the "song" and her mother came up, as she calmly took her downstairs to be with her. Her mother never did any yelling, at least not when I was around. Janice also told me that if her mother ever reprimanded her sister her mother would pay for it. If her mother did anything at all to upset her sister, her sister would always tell her father and then the yelling would start for the rest of the night and Janice would hide in her room. When I was there and the father came home from work his youngest daughter would always run to him and hug him. I never saw him once greet Janice or hug her. It was rare to see him even talking to her. There never seemed to be a normal conversation, ever, between Janice and her father. But her sister was his princess and there was nothing she could do wrong. If something did go wrong it was always Janice's fault. If the house wasn't clean, if something was out of place, if the sister wanted something Janice had to get it for her, if dinner wasn't made, if laundry wasn't done, it was all up to Janice because her mother was too sick or in bed. If something wasn't done just right Janice got the abuse.

I had gone over one day when just she and her mother were there and when I knocked, her mother answered the door to say that Janice was upstairs and that I could go up. I found Janice crying in bed with the door open and as I walked in, she sat up. When I asked her what happened, she wouldn't tell me, but after a while she opened up to say that her father had manhandled her. She never went into great detail but I told her that she needed to tell her mother. She didn't want to but I took her by the hand and brought her to the kitchen table so we could talk. Her mother was sitting there and I said, "Janice needs to tell you something."

Janice starts to cry and puts her head down on the table. I told her we should tell her mother what her father has done to her so that she can do something to help Janice. But Janice's mother tells me that there is nothing she can do, that her husband will beat her if she did go to the authorities. She tells me that he would lie to protect himself and in the end she would be the one that would end up in the Norwich Hospital. I was in shock and in disbelief. Her own mother wouldn't and couldn't do a thing to help her. Her mother was always ill, at least it seemed that way to me. She was in bed or sitting in a chair with her hands holding up her head. The next day there was silence between us but we hugged and knew we had each other. "True friends forever." We had secrets and those secrets were never told. We would go out on long walks or bike rides just to be alone with our secrets. She was hurting but it seemed that there was nothing either one of us could do. And so we both blocked it out. It was a man's world in the 60's and who would believe two teenage girls? My account would be "hearsay" and hers, a daughter who was rebelling? What recourse did we have?

A few weeks before the end of our eighth grade graduation day we were coming home from school on the bus when her sister decided that she was going to sit between us. There were plenty of seats but she wanted to sit between Janice and me. I told her to leave and Janice said, "Oh, it's ok," and I said, "No, it wasn't." I told her to find herself another seat. She made such a fuss and ruckus that I moved to another place. The next day at school I wouldn't speak to Janice and when we got home her mother came over to ask if I would come to her house because Janice was so upset. As I went to her room her mother and sister were both there as I tried to calm Janice down. She thought our friendship was over and now that her mother had forced me to come over, things would change. I was upset with this and I told her mother that her youngest daughter caused this whole thing. It was time for her to leave us alone and to find her own friends. She had interfered with us once too often and that she was a spoiled brat. As teens we sometimes treated her sister as if she were the same age as we were, when in reality she was only eight years old, something we did not comprehend at the time. I had whispered to Janice that true friendship never ends and we would always remain friends forever. Nothing could ever break up friends.

When high school came along we went to Norwich Free Academy. It was so big, with close to a thousand students in our class alone, that we never saw each other in high school. I had different classes and I was probably in a lower academic grade level than she. Janice was so bright. We had no classes together. The only time we would see each other was on the school bus trips to and from school or on weekends. I joined different activities, loving sports, playing music in the school band and singing in the choir. But Janice didn't. She was more of a girly girl, kept to herself and was afraid to step out on her own, afraid of what others may say or do. Janice was always reading; she loved paperback books. She would love to listen to music, and loved to draw, so much so that I thought she would become an artist. She was so good at drawing and she even took art classes at Fields Elementary School. Her art was her way of expressing herself and I had hoped that she would pursue her talent. She drew quite a bit and I wish I had some of her art. We would talk whenever possible but we saw less and less of each other and at the end of our second year at NFA my family moved to up-state New York where my father transferred to a new job. I wrote and wrote, but never received any letters back. I had wanted to stay in touch but there was no way of knowing what was going on if she wouldn't write back.

Janice was the kindest person that I ever met. She never had a bad word towards anyone that had crossed our path. She was very close to her mother, that is they could talk, knew what each other were feeling and hurting. Because her mother was suffering more than what we realized as teens, Janice became her mother's source of love. Her mother had such love for Janice in her heart, as any mother would for her own child. She suffered so much to see Janice being abused that their bond was special in its own way. Janice suffered in silence, with so much love in her own heart to give and yet she felt no one accepted her. She's at peace now but my heart still aches for what she went through. Our friendship will never end.

Your Best Friend Always,

Christine Kenney LaBrie

7

Snitches End Up In Ditches

"Why do some people live their entire existence in poverty, while others bathe in privilege and wealth? When observing the losers of the lottery, many believe a person's lot is chosen, but have forgotten that nothing happens perchance, for even the stars above align to some divine mission. In the end, we will be judged by one question: what did you do to help the losers of the lottery?"

Dr. Milone's dark office is located on the second floor of the Hanover-Curland Building in Norwich. My father calls him "a headshrinker" and a "thief" because he charges too much money. My mother used to see him alone. Then something happened and Janice started coming along too. I do not want to come to his office, but my mother says I am too young to be left home alone. Whenever we go, I try to make the best of it by drawing pictures of our cats, Ginger and Puny. After my mother went into the hospital, the cats disappeared. My mother cannot stop thinking about them. *"Girls, cats do not just vanish into thin air. Something bad happened to them. I just know it."*

Of course, everyone knows my father hates cats, especially ones that have babies. Ginger would prepare to give birth by slinking into the basement to find the old rug by the furnace. My mother always said giving birth is holy and encouraged my sister and I to sit on the basement steps and wait for the kittens to arrive. Once Janice told me a story to keep me from getting bored and even illustrated it on the cement wall with a piece of chalk.

"I know you like robins," she said, while drawing a perfectly detailed nest with a Mama Robin and babies sitting inside. She wrote *The Lonely Nest* beneath it.

"Con, did you ever hear the story of how Mama Robin received her orange breast? One day the Son of God was carrying a heavy cross along the road to Calvary when a Mama Robin flew above and saw the suffering Christ. The robin felt compassion and glided below pulling a painful thorn from His head. In return, Christ blessed the robin when His blood touched her breast turning it a passionate orange-red. In that moment, the robin felt an abundance of love and flew home to place the thorn inside her nest. From that day forth, a lonely nest would always be filled with love and sadness, as one cannot exist without the other."

Janice accidently dropped the piece of chalk and I cringed as it shattered across the cement floor. My sister's mouth started to twitch and she looked terrified.

"Oh, Con, I'm sorry! Please, don't tell Dad I dropped your chalk. Please don't tell Dad!"

At first, I was angry that my sister broke the chalk that I stole from the teacher's blackboard. But all was forgotten when my mother beckoned us to follow her into the basement to check on Ginger. We were happy that Ginger gave birth to a litter of wet kittens and they were all drinking from her belly. After the kittens were born, my sister and I would go into the cellar everyday to pretend to pick out a kitten to keep. We both knew this was only make-believe and that we would never be able to keep the kittens we chose. Very soon, within a week or so, the kittens begin to have shiny hair, beautiful eyes and fluffy tails...this is when my father takes them away in a burlap sack and we never see them again.

My thoughts are interrupted when the door to Dr. Milone's office opens and my sister exits with a foolish smile. My mother follows behind with a strained expression, looking as though she aged a hundred years in there. Both hold tight to slips of paper, prescriptions to help them cope with what Dr. Milone calls *the result of living with a man unable to control his compulsions.*

My mother always seems to feel better after we leave the doctor and often treats us to lunch at Mr. Big's department store in Taftville. The three of us pick a booth with cracked red seats and then order food from the deli. This is a special time because my sister and I learn everything bad my father does to our mother. We ordered three pizzas the size of a large pancake and three tall cherry Cokes. My mother gives Janice two quarters for the jukebox and she chooses H1, E9, L8 and P9. Within seconds, everyone in the crowded deli is humming along to the Beatles song, "Nowhere Man." When our pizza is served I notice how with every one bite I take, my sister takes two. Soon, my sister is looking at her empty plate with disappointment.

"Ma, I'm still hungry. Can I get another pizza?"

My mother tries not to be obvious as she observes my sister's double chin and bulging belly. Not knowing how to say no, she reluctantly digs inside her pocketbook and pulls out a few wrinkled bills. After closing her purse she unabashedly shares adult conversation with her children, displaying little to no emotion.

"The doctor says your father likes bad, not good women. Bad women make your father feel superior and good women make him feel less. I guess that's why your father does not want to have relations with me anymore."

I watch my mother take a long and deep inhale on her cigarette. I force myself to look away, choosing to read the handwritten signs above the cash register. *Specials of the day: Liver and Onions $2.50, Delicious Melted Cheese Sandwich $1.50, and Hamburger with Fries, $2.50.* I wince in pain as the pizza I ate burns in my tummy like a small fire.

I do not understand the word "relations." It was only last week I asked my sister what it meant. "What do people do when they have relations?"

My sister answered coldly. *"It's what men do to girls in the dark."*

Dissatisfied with my sister's answer, I asked my good friend Jodi Rajotte for his thoughts on the subject, as he had already told me everything I needed to know about the birds and the bees. Grinning and pointing to his zipper, Jodi said relations happen when a girl kisses a boy's private. Shocked beyond belief all I could say was—"Where you pee?"

I also asked Jodi what girls liked about relations. "I don't think it matters much to girls," he said, "because only boys like relations."

The whole relations thing is very confusing. If girls do not like relations, then why does my mother want my father to have relations with her?

"Girls," said my mother, sucking noisily on a straw full of air, "I think your father's problems began a long time ago when he served in the military in those Godless, immoral countries that sell girls to men."

My sister is shocked. "Ma, no! Really?"

My mother angrily blows smoke at the ceiling. "You're darn tootin' Jan! Girls, I'll tell you one fact about men right now. Men will hide their sins together and go all the way to Hell before they tell! It used to get me so upset until I asked Gus about soldiers taking advantage of young girls in those faraway countries. Gus is a distinguished World War I soldier you know. And furthermore, everyone knows Gus never learned how to tell a lie." My sister, forever the provincial Bambi, stares at my mother with a mouth full of pizza. "What'd Gus say, Ma?"

"What's a good soldier like Gus going to say anyway?" laughs my mother. "It was the day Gus and I were watching a kingfisher skim across the surface of the pond when he gave me his answer.

'I don't deny it never happens in the military, Rose. But I reckon, it's kind of like when you go into First National and buys one of them nice, big boxes of juicy strawberries. You see, those strawberries looked real good in the store didn't they? But when you brought them home and opened the box, you spotted a few rotten ones mixed in with the good ones. But you still kept the box of strawberries didn't you Rose? You kept them, because you knew, *a few bad strawberries won't spoil the whole bunch.* They'll always be soldiers that take advantage of poor females in them far-away countries, but by God, and I truly believe this, there are far more *good* soldiers who don't. So Rose, don't let a few bad strawberries spoil the whole bunch.'"

Janice places a hand on my mother's shoulder and tries her best to console. She is speaking to my mother like two best friends sharing a soda. "Why doesn't *he* want to have relations with you, Ma? You're so pretty and cook good spaghetti sauce."

Filled with regret, my mother downs the glass of Coke and asks the waitress to bring another. And now our mother has something worse to tell us.

"Girls, I have a confession to make. Your father doesn't want to have relations with me because he is in love with the next-door neighbor, Mrs. Banell."

Upon hearing my mother's words, my sister coughs violently, spitting pieces of pizza into her plate. My sister and mother share the same fear.

"Ma—does she love him back?"

My own body feels frozen and strange. I like Mrs. Banell, who smiles so sweetly, along with Mr. Banell who works in his vegetable garden every afternoon. But no matter how nice Mrs. Banell is, I do not want her for my mother.

"Oh no," laughs my mother, "A good woman like Mrs. Banell doesn't even know your father exists!"

Janice's elbow begins to twitch, which causes her third glass of Coke to fall over the edge of the table. The three of us watch the broken glass and brown bubbling syrup travel across the deli floor. My sister's eyes fill with tears as the jukebox plays the last song: *Do you want to know a Secret?* "Oh no Ma! What are we going to do?"

My mother looks like she's about to cry when she looks inside her pocketbook and forces a smile. "I don't know, girls... but who wants another pizza?"

My sister shouts with joy— "I'll have another! This time I want anchovies, what kind do you want, Con?"

Thank goodness—our excursion is over. After giving a generous tip, my mother stands and looks in the mirror behind the counter.

She frowns at the reflection of the plump woman and touches her protruding stomach. She lowers the wispy veil attached to a green chiffon hat and gathers short white gloves over her hands. In defiance, she takes one last drag of her cigarette and blows ugly grey smoke at the back of a man's head. Her words slide out like venom from the jaw of a dead snake.

"Now girls, we go home."

When you're like me and go to school, there are always dangerous obstacles to avoid. Sometimes you can maneuver around them, but other times it is impossible. One day, during lunch, I notice a group of boys tormenting Gregory as he tries to eat his tomato soup. The boys steal his oyster crackers and take turns tossing them into his soup. Gregory wisely ignores and eventually the boys leave in search of another victim. Within minutes they spot Francis and his younger sister Lilian trying to hide in the corner of the lunchroom. They make their way through the long rows of tables and sit facing them. In a mocking gesture, they belittle Francis by pulling their ears up and down, which causes the two siblings to huddle closer.

One sneers, "Hey, look at me. I got big ears! My name isn't Francis—it's Dumbo!" The teachers on duty glide by, clearly hearing and seeing but saying nothing. At this time there is a shared belief system where everyone believes *boys will be boys* and should not be held to the same consequences as others.

When I talk to Aunt Angie about Francis and Lilian she looks angry. "It's a piss-poor fact of life that some children come into this world with feet already knee deep in shit left behind by their parents. If life is hard for us, imagine what it's like for people like Francis and Lilian, whose shit is up to their eyeballs."

I have troubles of my own. I am in sixth grade with a teacher that hates children. When I tell Nonno about Mr. Hubris, he says it does not matter whether a teacher is good or bad. All that matters is going up the ladder to the next grade because it is better to *morire di* (die of shame) than have to crawl back down the ladder.

This is the year my father loses his business and has a nervous breakdown. He decides it is far safer to stay in bed than return to a world that hates him. Everyday after school I run upstairs and find my father in bed staring through the eyes of the insane. No longer does our mother dote on us when we arrive home from school. She is too busy running up and down the stairs in an agitated state, constantly checking on our father. I worry about my father never leaving his bedroom. I visit him often to let him know that he doesn't need someone like Ronnie to be his helper. There is someone better.

"Guess what, Dad? I'll be your helper!"

My father does not acknowledge me and stares gloomily out the window. When he decides to talk, he sounds like a child forced to read in front of the class.

"I...lost my...business Con..." He throws his face into a pillow and sobs. "I had too many doctor bills from Milone that I couldn't pay, and then...there's Janice. I made a lot of mistakes with Janice. Now, she's getting worse and I don't know what to do."

"But, Dad, why do you stay in bed all day? You still have time to get up and start another business and I'll help you! I'm a big girl now!"

My father's mood suddenly changes and his eyes grow large and excited.

"Doctor Milone told me to stay in bed and think good thoughts. I'm thinking of the days I had a pilot's license and flew a Cessna 150. I used to fly right over the house! Do you remember that Con?"

How could I ever forget my short stint as my father's co-pilot? The one time he took me up in his airplane all by myself. As soon as we rose high as the clouds, I cried so hard my father had to take the plane down. I lied that I was sick to my stomach and about to throw up. Without saying a word, my father brought the plane down, making a perfect landing at the Patchag Airport in Voluntown. When he opened the door, I jumped out and pretended to vomit behind the fuel pumps. My father never asked me to fly again.

"Connie Mary, I got all day to think about the times I flew a Cessna and was happy and… and…" My father's pills make him so sleepy that he falls asleep mid-sentence. When I hear him snore, I go into my bedroom and watch television. Soon, my mother pokes her head into my room.

"Con… I have to go over to Nonna's house to help make the meatballs for Sunday's dinner. Your father will be home with you kids. Please be very, very, quiet okay? I'll be back shortly."

After my mother leaves, I fall into a restless sleep, dreaming that I have fallen off a cliff and hanging by my fingertips, when Sam, loudly barking and scratching at the front door awakens me.

Irritated, I yell—"Jan! Can you let Sam out?"

My sister does not answer even though I can hear the sound of her radio crystal clear. I go into her room to investigate, only to find her holding a pair of scissors in one hand and the remains of a decimated wig in the other. I am shocked. My sister is completely bald!

At first she did not acknowledge my presence.

"Jan…why are you destroying that wig? Didn't mom just buy you that?"

She answers in a mocking, jeering tone. "I hate the way I look! I'm ugly!" and looks at me with sadness. "I want to be like you, Con. I want to be pretty like you. You don't know what it's like to be *me*." She steps towards me. "Con, when a girl is fat, she is invisible to the world."

I don't know what to say. I do not understand why my sister

thinks she is so ugly, so I leave to let Sam out. With a flash of his tail, I watch him disappear like a warning signal into the night. I decide to follow him watching my body blend into the shadows created by the moon. I discover him lying underneath a tall pine that separates our yard from the Banells. Someone else is here as well, disrupting the beauty of the night. It is the outline of a man climbing an aluminum ladder and cursing at the innocent branches blocking his way. Sam pants as he watches the dark figure climb higher and higher. Upon reaching the top, the man emits a pleasurable moan as light from the Banell's house illuminates the darkness. I peek through the branches and see Mrs. Banell walking through her bedroom wearing a full-length white slip. The light also reveals the identity of the man. It is my father.

I know that most children would have kept quiet that day about what they saw. They would have been too frightened to tell, but not me. I wait for my mother to come home and the second she steps inside the house—I tell her what my father was doing. Within minutes loud voices erupt from the kitchen and my sister locks her bedroom door. I sit on the steps to listen and it is not long before my mother is screaming hysterically.

"You good-for-nothing-peeping-Tom! *Sei un maiale* (You're a pig)!"

I do not recognize my mother's voice when she screams like an animal being hurt. "I KNEW YOU WANTED HER ALL ALONG!"

I hear the familiar click of a beer bottle being opened and listen for the bottle cap as it's thrown across the floor. My father's voice is flippant with no sign of remorse.

"Connie Mary told you this? Why, that little snitch… my own daughter told on me? Doesn't she know that snitches end up in ditches?"

My mother lunges with imaginary claws that helplessly swipe the air. "Don't *you* dare blame that child! Why you good for nothing peeping Tom!" I never heard the phrase "Peeping Tom" before this night. But I will never forget it. The fight rages on as my father insults the memory of my mother's beloved family.

"All your sisters are a bunch of *bagascias* (harlots). When you met me, you were starving. Your father was nothing but a *Cosa Nostra criminal* and when your mother died, he threw you and your sisters out on the curb on Millick Street in West Philly! All of you, left to roam, like a bunch of hungry dogs! Then the *bastardo* moves his young *puttana* in to take your mother's place. Your whole family is no good. None of them ever gave two shits about you. Your sister Sadie is half nuts. Rosalie is a rich *figlia de cagna*. Josephine, I can't say anything bad about…but Mel is a selfish bitch! The only one with half a brain is Grayce."

My mother weeps uncontrollably as she pleads for my father to understand. "My father didn't leave us…my father didn't leave us— he didn't! He gave us an apartment to live in and helped us! My father helped us!" My mother collapses to the floor in a helpless ball of pain.

My mind becomes saturated with guilt and I close my eyes. If only I hadn't snitched…if only I hadn't snitched! Unable to silence a tormented mind, I look underneath my rug to where a box is hidden and take two pills from it. Several hours later, at two o'clock in the morning, I am awakened by the sound of bottles crashing to the floor and my mother's voice shouting, "Help me, Connie Mary, Help me!"

When I try to stand my body falls to the floor, groggy from a drug-induced sleep. I move carefully and head downstairs, the walls spinning. I stumble into the kitchen to find my father standing inches away from my mother with his hands wrapped around her neck. My mother squirms like an insect stuck to flypaper with her eyes rolled back. Without thought or apprehension, I run behind my father and yank his hair with all my might, causing the little bit he has left to come loose in my hand.

Immediately my father lets go of my mother and I stare at the red indentations on her neck. When I open my hand, precious black strands of hair fall to the floor. With a look of disbelief, my father looks down at the fallen strands of hair and begins to cry. He feels his head and begins talking to some imaginary person.

"Why, I'll be damned. My little daughter pulled out the last of my hair." He continues to feel his head as tears stream down his face. He has forgotten all about my mother collapsed in the corner gasping for air.

"I didn't have much hair left—why did my little daughter have to pull out the rest?" Stumbling and sobbing, my father heads toward the door.

"She pulled out my hair… my little daughter pulled out my hair." In a few minutes the roar of a truck is heard speeding down Fitchville Road. My mother feels her way back to the kitchen table and manages to sit. Her hair is greasy and she is wearing the same apron and ragged dress as the day before. My eyes gaze at the broken glass scattered across the floor. No longer in exile, Sam licks my mother's hands folded awkwardly across her lap.

"Ma, what are we gonna do now?"

My mother looks down at her shiny gold wedding band and chuckles with remorse. "This ring came from Joseph Lerro, the famous Philadelphian Jeweler. Listen to what your father told Joe to inscribe: *To Honey, All My Love, Forever, Bootsie 7/19/47.* Go to bed, Connie Mary," says my mother. "We'll think of a way to get your father back tomorrow."

The next morning my sister and I both miss the school bus. When I go into the kitchen to make something to eat, I am surprised to find my mother quietly sitting at the kitchen table, smoking a cigarette with her coffee. I am even more surprised to see that she washed and curled her hair. I know my father returned before sunrise because I heard the front door slam on his way out.

"Ma, is Dad coming back?"

My mother stirs the beautiful red sauce whose aroma has the power to make people stop and smell the air. "Remember what I told you about making the perfect sauce? You have to fry the paste in garlic and olive oil and wait until it turns a deep orange-red before adding the tomatoes. This is what gives the sauce its rich, fragrant taste. Now *figlia*, come and sit and taste a bit of Heaven."

One week later my father has still not returned. In his absence, a strange sense of peace washes over the house. Instead of being locked away in her room, Janice lounges on the couch and watches her favorite television shows. The more time that passes, the stronger my mother's fantasy of my father returning as a changed man.

Even though my father is gone, the destruction he left behind is a permanent consequence of his actions. When I go into my sister's bedroom to visit, I find her destroying another radio. When my mother buys my sister a radio, she understands what she is really buying is an innocent object onto which Janice can transfer her rage. After the radio is destroyed and has served its purpose, my mother buys her a new one.

I watch Janice take a hammer and pound the radio with a vengeance.

"Jan, is it broken yet?"

My sister brings the hammer down one last time, which causes the radio to collapse. She exhales a sigh of relief, "Now it is!"

When one entire month passes without my father, the tranquil silence almost seems normal. Just as we started to anticipate being able to sit in front of the television set without fear for the foreseeable future, my mother brings words at the breakfast table that cause my sister's blood to run cold.

"Today is the day Nonno brings your father home!" My sister and I exchange worried glances as we both struggle to swallow our cereal.

When my mother goes into the cellar to gather tomatoes, I whisper, "Jan, do you want dad back?"

My sister begins to cough so violently that her wig becomes lopsided. The wig serves Janice in similar ways as the radio. Janice will not allow her hair to grow. She prevents this by spending time each day cutting it into short, spiky pieces. Embarrassed by what she has done, she asks my mother to buy her a wig. Now, instead of her own hair, she begins chopping the wig to pieces. I guess Janice finds it easier to destroy her own hair and then the wig, than to stop the person who is causing the pain. My mother continues to supply her with wigs, knowing Janice needs to destroy something in order to survive.

Janice rises from the kitchen table and looks at her reflection in the mirror. She clasps a handful of belly fat and seethes with disgust.

"I don't want him back! I don't...I hate him!"

The high school bus comes earlier than the elementary bus and we both startle when Mr. Lashinski blares the horn. "Con, do *you* want him back? I don't. I hate him!"

Trying to apply a crooked line of lipstick, my sister moves closer to the mirror. "I almost forgot Con, after school today I have a job interview at Pike's Plaza in Norwich. I won't be home at the usual time—can you let mom know?"

After Janice leaves, I think to myself, *another job interview. I wonder how long it will be this time before she is fired?*

They say all good things must come to an end, and later that night Nonno drags my father home from the Norwich Motel. I am in the parlor eating a tomato and mayo sandwich when they arrive. My father is wearing dirty clothes and clutching a banged up valise. At first I do not even recognize him, but the moment our eyes meet, I scream— "You hurt mommy, I wish you never came home!"

My mother, who is in the kitchen frying hot dogs and potatoes, hears me scream and comes running with wide-open arms to welcome my father home. My father does not see my mother. He looks as though he stepped inside the wrong house and drops his valise to the floor with a thud and runs for the staircase. Nonno is watching the scene unfold with scorn and rolls his eyes in disgust. Having seen enough he walks to my father's liquor cabinet and pours himself a shot of whisky. I follow my father up the stairs and watch him fall upon the bed sobbing.

"My little daughter said I hurt her mommy! Connie Mary didn't want me home... my little daughter didn't want me back."

Life goes on with our secrets concealed like the precious agates a child hides inside the ripped lining of a spring jacket. During this time, I often think of something Gus said to me. "A secret is never content to stay quiet. Secrets aren't good, Connie Mary—none of them. We're only fooling ourselves if we think we can keep a secret hidden. A secret will find its way out, even if it has to bleed through our own skin."

8

Nonno's Justice

Nonno Falcone and Sam

"I said a prayer for all the troublemakers in the world who were labeled bad. Now I know there is no such thing as a bad child, only children living in bad situations."

It is the magical hour, when the arms of the clock reach far past midnight. My mother and father take refuge in their bedroom like two lost souls seeking redemption. Safe in my father's arms, my mother is content to take part in a nonverbal agreement where she has the privilege of hearing his secrets. When the creaking of the bedspring disturbs the silence of the house, it fills the memory with a lost forgotten love. Once upon a time, my father's lonely nest evolved from the tender branches of a young sapling blossoming in spring. With the passing of time, my father's secrets tangled the branches, preventing light from entering his soul. When a secret is released into the world, a strange phenomenon occurs. The secret grows smaller and is no longer powerful.

I am in my bedroom, lying in the dark, listening to my father tell my mother secrets from long ago. "Every Friday afternoon Ma would stand on the porch and wait for Pa to come home from work. It was payday and the old man had money. When Pa finally came stumbling up Talman Street the neighbors locked their doors and Ma yelled— 'Corsa, fare una (run, hurry)! You papa come—hide Bootsie, hide!'"

He takes a drag on his cigarette. "I was just a kid watching my father stagger up the road, giving his middle finger to cars trying to pass. I ran into the house and watched Pa though the window. When Pa came up the steps, he saw Caruso tied to his chain. Caruso is wagging his tail, happy to see him when the drunken bastard punches him in the head. Caruso did not live long after that." My father takes short gasps of air.

"From the road our house looked like paradise. We had this fancy cement fountain in the front yard with blue water pourin' out of it making every neighbor shit green with envy. My mother used to feed the birds and they'd shit all over the yard. When she wasn't looking and we were hungry, my brother Henry and I used to shoot 'em and cook them over a fire."

My mother dares not speak lest the magic disappear.

"Pa came closer and looked in the window calling for me. 'Bootsie, you little *bastardo*, I come-a for you!' Geez, I was only a little kid and cried to my mother, 'Ma, where am I going to go? Where can I hide where Pa won't find me? Because Pa knows all the good hiding places.' My mother's face turned white and she slapped me across the face.

"*NASCONDERE* (Hide)! *Corsa fare una* Bootsie! Your Papa is coming. Hide, Bootsie—HIDE!"

"My face hurt like hell, but I ran up the stairs in search of a new hiding place. It was useless though, Pa plays hide and seek with us kids and knows all the good places. I hear him now, rumbling through the house like some rogue elephant busting up everything in its path. When he pauses at the stairs, Ma tries to block him, but with one wild-ass swing, he knocks her down the steps. But Ma's strong and pulled out the rosary praying, '*Guida alla Beata Madre, aiutami* (Help me Blessed Mother—help me!)' There I was, watching all this shit from the top of the stairs, already knowing I'm a dead duck. My brothers and sisters had enough brains to hightail it down the road when they saw the old man coming, but it was me Pa always wanted.

He laughed, 'Bootsie, You son of a Bastardo, I come for you.' And up the stairs he stomped with steel-toed boots banging each step. Ma polished the steps real good for a reason. And the old man slipped and fell. He didn't notice the silver dollars spilling out of his pockets, coins rolling down like manna from Heaven. On her hands and knees, Ma picked up every last coin and hid them between a crack in the cellar wall. But nothing could stop Pa from reaching the second floor. I was desperate and crawled underneath a pile of dirty clothes, praying that every part of me would be hidden. I gagged when I inhaled the stench of my father's clothes: the piss, whisky and shit so thick I could hardly breathe!

He stepped into the bedroom and I could immediately smell whiskey. I covered my eyes, thinking how I've been playing this game with Pa too long and never won. When Pa stood over me, he howled with laughter. "Bootsie, you little *asino* (jackass) I can see your little black-a boots!"

I looked up at him and said, 'YOU BIG DIRTY BASTARD!' His face went from laughter to rage and he lunged at the clothes pile, grabbing shirts and socks and tossing them into the air. When he unbuckled his leather belt I thought he was going to beat the crap out of me, but then a miracle happened. The old man wavered with glazed eyes and seemed to droop in front of me. I held my breath when he unzipped his pants, pulled out his manhood and peed on my head. With warm pee dripping down my face, I ran as if the devil was after me. When I looked back, Pa was falling over like an enormous tree, crashing down upon his knees and about to pass out face down in the clothes pile."

Having a sixth-grade teacher who hates children becomes intolerable. After a particularly brutal day at school, I cope with failure by walking around Gus's Pond until the sky turns midnight blue. When I returned home, I noticed a plate of burned lasagna on the counter. I knew this piece is meant for me and that my mother has another piece of lasagna warming in the oven for Janice.

I could hear my parents in the parlor listening to Walter Cronkite talk about the architects, inventors and contractors involved in the making of *The New York World's Fair*. After learning the World's Fair is within driving distance, my father shouts at my mother sitting only a few feet away. "Did you hear that Rose? The World's Fair is going to be right next to your sister Rosalie's house in New York! They even got that marble statue made by that famous Italian guy. What the heck is his name? You know who I mean Rose, the one who carved a statue using a slab of marble." My father grew increasingly agitated at my mother's silence.

"Jesus Christ, Rose—the guy who laid on his back and painted the church ceiling!"

My mother, never one to be quick on her feet, fails to answer fast enough.

"Christ Almighty, Rose, don't you know who I mean? The one who made the statue of Mary holding her dead son! Honest to God Rose, you can't remember anything I ever say. Even if you had two brains, you'd still be a nitwit."

My mother appears mildly dazed by my father's pejoratives and answers with a voice so soft, you can hardly hear her response. "You mean *Michelangelo* and *The Pieta*?"

"Yes! —That's him! Next time we go to New York to visit your sister, you and me Rose, we're gonna see that statue!"

I joined my parents in the parlor to watch the *Million Dollar Movie* on WOR-TV Channel 9. I think my mother is anxious for Janice to arrive home from work. I see her wringing her hands and fidgeting while she watches television. My mother does not have many happy days and neither does Janice. When the two of them are together, they find a happiness that no one else can understand. After an hour, the room is filled with a thick hazy smoke, but no one dares open the window. Every year, as soon as the weather grows cooler, my father declares the same commandment: "Thou shalt not open a window." There is nothing that makes my father angrier than the sound of the oil burner rumbling because he sees dollar bills flying out the window.

During a commercial my mother rambles on about Janice to my father, who is barely listening.

"My Janice just needs to find *the right job,* that's all. It takes time to find the right job."

Almost immediately after my mother turns back to the television, Janice rushes into the house and heads towards the kitchen, banging the door against the wall on the way in. My father, who is dozing on the couch, slurs a warning without opening his eyes.

"Janice, we only got one front door. Don't break it off the hinges."

Like magic, my mother suddenly has the energy of a teenager and joins Janice in the kitchen. Soon, the aromas of hot lasagna, antipasto and garlic bread celebrate my sister's arrival. The two laugh and talk about old times, old movies, and everything else I could care less about. I slither into a dark shadow and watch with jealousy as my mother lovingly unfolds my sister's napkin and pours her another glass of milk. I remain silent but seethe with envy at their stupid comments.

"Oh, no Jan, I think Liz Taylor really loves Richard Burton, don't you?"

Annoying giggles follow.

"On the other hand Ma, don't you think Eddie Fisher is such a dud?"

It is only a matter of time before the colors of the rainbow dissipate and the gaiety fades when my mother brings up the subject again.

"Jan, do you think they can give you more hours at Pike Plaza? See, it's your father. He only wants the best for you and hopes you can earn more money."

My sister trembles with fear and speaks very slowly, as if she is unsure of what words to use.

"Ma, I don't think I can…they already said there are too many people on payroll and some will *have* to go." What my sister doesn't mention to my mother is that she had already been given two pink slips for poor job performance and for accidently pricing down an entire shelf of loafers. Feeling satisfied, I tiptoe back into the parlor and turn my attention to my father who is innocently lying across the couch. A commercial for *Lay's Potato Chips* begins with Bert Lahr dressed as a devil trying to tempt his audience when he says, "Betcha can't eat just one."

Upon seeing this, my father's immediate reaction is to sit up and light a Winston.

"Huh! Look at that," he says. "My mother says Americans like to dress up like the devil and pretend he's not real. In Italia—*noi sappiamo meglio*—we know better."

My father waits for a response and smiles at me.

"So... what do you think kid? How's life treating you anyways?

I avoid my father's question and tell a terrible lie. "Dad, did you know that Janice doesn't want to ask her bosses for more hours because she likes staying home?"

My father's face explodes like a crushed tomato. He leaps from the couch and rushes into the kitchen. I know when my father is talking to Janice because he never says her name.

"What the hell do you think I'm going to do, support you forever? Tomorrow you ask those Jew bastards for more hours—or don't come home."

That same week my sister asked for more hours and was promptly fired. Later, I found her hiding behind her bed, sobbing to some imaginary person. "What's going to happen to me? What's going to happen?"

When I told my parents, they came upstairs and my father surprised everyone by his reaction. "What the hell do you care about that penny-ante job anyways? Tell those Jews to shove it up their ass—you don't need them. Don't worry, you'll find another job," and then walked away. For a few minutes I stayed and watched my sister sob on her bruised knees. She looked like one of those homeless dogs, waiting so long for someone to love them but not realizing until the needle pricks and life drains out that no one is coming. Feeling terribly sad, I left, knowing my sister would not be finding another job for a long, long time.

Italians have troubles for sure, but there is nothing more glorious (or risky) than celebrating an Italian holiday. At family gatherings, the whisky and wine flow as dangerously as whitewater rapids that trap innocent people beneath the water. On *Vigilia di Natale* (Christmas Eve) the Falcone family seeks sanctuary at Nonno's expecting a feast cooked to perfection.

The women began their work a week before, rolling what seemed like miles of cookie dough. The tables are set lavishly, one with Italian cakes and cookies, another with pasta dishes, meats, swordfish, calamari, and the famous Italian classic—salted cod, known as *baccala*. The most anticipated event of the night is the unveiling of Nonna's famous sauce. No one has ever been able to replicate the magic in the old woman's sauce.

This year, we all dine to our heart's desires, eating and drinking with no sense for danger, only a hunger for pleasure. After enjoying a lavish dinner, I walk into the parlor to admire Nonna's two white aluminum trees and a rainbow color wheel that seems to illuminate the entire room. Around me, the men settle jovially around the kitchen table playing cards and gambling. As the bottles start to go from half-full to nearly empty, dark thoughts overpower the men changing the mood from happy to deadly. Troubled by a restrained restlessness, the wives shuffle about, serving in a robotic fashion as the men consume bottles of Johnnie Walker Black. My sister drowns her loneliness with plates of pasta, mindlessly swallowing and choking on a nagging secret. I grow bored and wander up the massive staircase where, in the polished mahogany, my reflection looks back at me. Once on the second floor, I look below and catch the contemptuous sound of men arguing. This is when a flicker of light catches my eye and I move closer to Nonno's bedroom.

I stand in the doorway and peer into the semidarkness, wondering what light caught my eye. Nonno is in his rocking chair holding a cigarette, unaware of sparks dropping on the floor. The stench of whiskey and smoke forces its way down my throat and causes me to cough, yet even then, I do not perceive danger. I am taught that strangers mean danger and family is safe. Nonno welcomes me by batting his hand in the air like a bear waving its paw.

"*Nipote*, come. Come, see."

As I approach Nonno, I see thin red lines spreading through his glossy eyes that make him look like a monster. As fast as lighting strikes, I am caught unaware when he lunges toward me and pulls me on his lap. With bewilderment I look down at my legs dangling and think this must be happening to someone else. With my back facing Nonno, I feel a burning hand reach inside my underwear and rest on my backside. I feel my body fight and shake as it tries to get out of his grasp and then finally with one strong kick—I jump from his lap! I fly down the stairs and try to enter the raucous crowd as casually as possible. I place myself near the kitchen table where my father and Uncle Henry are arguing.

"You cheated Bootsie, I saw you!" With greedy hands my father pulls a large pile of silver dollars to his side and laughs in his brother's face.

"And whattaya gonna do about it, Mama's Boy?"

Aunt Philomena appears out of nowhere and tries pulling her husband away but he shoves her against the plaster wall. Everyone in the room witnesses this but remains silent and moves out of the way. Uncle Henry, humiliated to the point of sobbing, slinks out the door while his terrified wife and children trail a safe distance behind. The family that gathered so happily now scatters like thieves in the night. The women frantically scrub pots and pans moving rapidly to erase another beautiful celebration that always seems to turn into something ugly.

I find my mother in the dining room placing Nonna's dishes inside the cabinet. I casually walked up to her and revealed, "Ma, Nonno put his hand in my underwear."

My mother's first reaction is fear. She looks at my father's relatives who are circling Nonna's leftovers like vultures and repeats a familiar narrative that absolves all Falcone men from wrongdoing. "If we ever needed help, I have no family that lives close by. All we have is your father's family." She sighs and looks up at the elaborate gold-painted ceiling for guidance. When no words of enlightenment come, she solves the problem by squeezing my arm…hard.

"Connie Mary, don't ever go near Nonno when he's drunk! You cannot trust him when he's drinking!" Taking a deep breath, she allows the Mama Robin in her lonely nest to release a forbidden secret: *"Connie Mary, Nonno has done this before!"*

I stand amazed, suddenly recalling the day my mother and Aunt Philomena laughed about Nonno's "Roman" hands and how no grandchild should ever sit on his lap. When she releases my arm, I notice how our reflections in the cabinet's glass look distorted, like two creatures lost in a world they do not belong to. Once again, my mother finds the tolerance that allows her to continue living in a man's world.

"Anyway, it doesn't matter. We're going home soon and this will all be forgotten. Don't tell anyone about this, you hear me Connie Mary?"

I nod yes, knowing I am good at hiding secrets because this is not the first time a man has put his hand down my pants. The other incident happened last year, when my father drove our family to North Carolina to visit my mother's sister Carmella. Along with having a lovely home in the city, Aunt Carmella and Uncle Genoa have a retreat in the mountains and invited us to spend the weekend. On the first day, my father and Uncle Genoa began the process of drinking all day and into the night. Long before Uncle Genoa was drunk, I knew he wanted me in *the bad way*. Even though I was only nine years old, I was very aware of Uncle Genoa's lustful eyes watching my every move and did my best to avoid his presence. After swimming, my mother was helping me remove my bathing suit in the bathroom. She did not know Uncle Genoa was peeking in the doorway. Uncle Genoa is cunning and knows how to appear normal by joking with my mother while lewdly winking at me. The tighter I held my towel, the harder my mother pulled, unaware my uncle was waiting for the towel to fall. My mother laughed, "Honest to goodness Connie Mary, when did you become so shy?"

I remember feeling ashamed the moment the towel dropped and my uncle's eyes widened with glee. On Sunday night, we returned back to Aunt Carmella's home in the city. After dinner the adults laugh and joke in the kitchen and the only voice missing is Uncle Genoa. When I go to use the bathroom, I almost bump into Uncle Genoa dozing in a chair like a crocodile ready to spring. I was caught unaware when he grabbed me and pulled me against his legs. Then it happened—the sweaty male hand groping inside my underpants with no remorse. Somehow the days I would wrestle with my father came to mind and I surprised my uncle by using a familiar tactic: an elbow in the stomach. He released his grasp with a painful "Ugh" and I escaped.

When my mother heard what happened she made choking sounds in her throat.

"We...we're...leaving tomorrow. Your uncle had too much to drink Connie Mary. Don't tell anyone about this!"

And I never did. I hid my secrets deep inside my lonely nest where it hurt me far more than it hurt those who committed the crime against me.

When my father receives the phone call from Mr. Hubris and hears that he needs to attend parent-teacher conferences to discuss my retention, he does what he always does when he's in trouble: he calls Nonno. A week later Nonno pulls into our driveway, already beeping the horn before he has even parked the car. My father wakes from his nap on the couch and sits up. His eyes darken as he says with a vengeance, "Let's go Connie Mary. School's over for that teacha."

My mother cautiously waves goodbye, her lips trembling. "Albert, you better be careful what you say to that teacher. I don't want to visit you in prison." I blow my mother a kiss but my father enters the car like a soldier heading for battle and doesn't look back. Nonno adjusts the rearview mirror with fingers that sparkle with diamond rings. He glares at me with sternness and pride.

"How's my fav-o-rite *nipote* today, *Buono*?"

I admire Nonno's flawless black suit and hair that shines like a white cloud floating across a summer sky. Next to Nonno, my father looks like a lump of coal wearing the same grimy clothes he wore to work this morning. Nonno has aged differently than my father, whose bald spots have spread like a malignancy through what used to be his thick black hair.

Once in school, I happily show Nonno the way to my classroom. The halls are filled with the chatter of excited children and their parents. Nonno walks like a proud swan with my father trailing behind like a lost specter. I point at Mr. Hubris behind the desk and Nonno takes one look and enters the classroom without knocking. My father follows behind, slamming the door. I choose a seat in the back of the room, folding my arms to hide my face but leave one eye exposed. Mr. Hubris glowers at Nonno and says in a forbidding tone, "Excuse me, but I do not remember any of *you* having an appointment."

Forever the ticking time bomb my father angrily bangs a powerful fist on his desk.

"If you think you're gonna shove my daughter down the ladder teacha—*you got your head screwed on backwards!*"

Quickly, Nonno moves forward and taps my father's shoulder. "*Silenzio*, Bootsie... in-a time, in-a time. We have-a appointment with Mr. Teacha," says Nonno, standing six foot two like a Calabrese Giant facing an ant. "We here to discuss my *nipote* and 'er future."

From the back of the room I quip, "*Nipote* means 'Granddaughter' in Italian!" which immediately prompted my father to turn around with a mad monkey face and warn me not to speak again. Thinking it would be in his best interest, Mr. Hubris politely offers Nonno his hand.

"Nice to meet you, Mr. Falcone."

Nonno looks away in disgust leaving Mr. Hubris looking embarrassed. "Let's get down to bis-a-ness Mr. Teacha. The ladder in education go up. The ladder in education go down. My *nipote* no go down ladder. She goes up ladder. *Si? Tu mi capisci?* You understand me?"

Mr. Hubris typically speaks to his students in a condescending manner so I am delighted to hear him squeal like a little pig. "Do you realize, Mr. Falcone, that your granddaughter has great difficulty in every subject? Personally, I think it would be a great disservice to pass Connie Mary to seventh grade."

My mouth drops because I have never heard Mr. Hubris say my name before!

Then, very slowly and deliberately, Nonno slides a black and ivory switchblade out of his pocket. He collects switchblades and this one is called "White Death" and came all the way from San Giacomo d'Acri, Italy. Nonno takes delight in tapping the small button causing the switchblade to spring open and shut. The look on my teacher's face tells a story when Nonno begins trimming his fingernails on the razor's blade.

"Mr. Teacha, I did a little chicken up on-a you. You dunna mind, do you Mr. Teacha?" Nonno is laughing, unconcerned with the huge gap in his front teeth. He lost that tooth in a gang fight in San Giacomo d'Acri and likes to add the most important detail of all, "You should-a seen da other guy."

Nonno stands behind Mr. Hubris causing him to glance nervously at the door.

"What exactly do you mean—you did a little "chicken" up on me? What exactly are you insinuating, Mr. Falcone?"

Nonno stops smiling and a thin line of saliva rolls down the corner of his mouth.

"You damn well-a know what I find out 'bout you…dun you Mr. Teacha?"

Mr. Hubris foolishly looks into Nonno's eyes and the green meadows of San Giacomo d'Acri curse his existence. "There must be some mistake, Mr. Falcone. How did you arrive at such misinformation? I have no record with the police—*why, you can ask the police yourself!*"

Nonno leans his face toward Mr. Hubris exposing a jagged scar where a broken bottle came too close and whispers, "What did you say to me, Mr. Teacha? To ask-a the pol-lease?" and spits in the wastebasket as he remembers his people, the lost Italian immigrants.

"NEVER tell-a me to ask the pol-lease. Pol-lease one step up from criminal!" then bows his head in reverence choking on his words. "Me no forget you Sacco an' Vanzetti. My people come-a here for betta life only to die in fire chair. Want me to tell-a you what I know 'bout you Mr. Teacha? Shame on you! *Vergognati!*" I should putta you lights out!"

The only sound in the room is the tic, tic, tic of Nonno's pocket watch booming. The karma in the room is thrilled at a teacher being given a taste of his own medicine. Nonno's intimidation tactics are interrupted by a group of parents impatiently banging on the door.

"I am sure there has been some mistake Mr. Falcone," croaks Mr.

Hubris. "I actually had no intention of keeping your granddaughter back in sixth grade and only wished to bring it to your attention. In fact, I have come to recognize the validity of your point."

Nonno grins. "Why, just look at-a us! We two diff-er-rent peoples from two diff-er-rent coun-a-tree, but *si, si,* look how our hearts *comprendere.* Eh, Mr. Teacha?"

My teacher does not look well. When he stands his face is as white as chalk.

Nonno offers his hand to Mr. Hubris and with hunched shoulders my teacher reluctantly grasps it, only to recoil in pain. I watch his knees buckle as the commanding grasp of a Calabrian hand still recalls the days of moving boulders to make wells. After a few more agonizing seconds Nonno releases his grasp, causing Mr. Hubris to stumble back.

"*Grazie,* Mr. Teacha, *Grazie,* I happy we all in 'greement—my *nipote* go *up* da ladder. The ladder 'portent in life, 'cause if ladder break, somebody get hurt." Nonno tips his Stetson and walks out the door. The three of us walk silently past a group of angry parents demanding to know who is next.

No one speaks on the way home. When my father goes into the house Nonno looks at me with mischievous eyes. "*Nipote...* no need to tell-a the Mama 'bout *visita* with teacha? It secret. Capire?"

"Sure Nonno, but can you tell me what you know about my teacher? I mean, if you don't have to put my lights out." Nonno laughs heartily.

"I finda no-a-thing wrong wit' you teacha. See Nipote, we all have-a skel-a-tin in closet. Mr. Teacha, *si,* he hide some-a-thing for sure, but Nonno no find. We hide our secrets in closet an'-a hope, an'-a pray, no one find!"

Later in bed, when the house is silent and dark, I think about what Gus Lorentz will say when I tell him that Nonno got the best of Mr.

Hubris. Gus told me there is a way to solve every problem in the world, even though I didn't understand it when he said, "*There's more than one way to skin a cat.*"

9

Goodbye Gregory

"I know the day is done when Gus returns home, carrying the scent of black oil and tar after paving the roads in the hot summer sun. Before entering his house, he lights a cigarette and waits for Farmer Beebe to call his cows home."

162

On the last day of school Mr. Hubris torments us by pretending to grade papers, knowing we are all waiting with bated breath to see who goes up the ladder. Our teacher gains pleasure from our pain, as witnessed by the occasional smirking grin. I envision Mr. Hubris, as a small child, playing far from the discerning eyes of his mother, studying a row of ants before methodically determining which ones will live and which ones will die. As he grows older, I imagine him secretly forcing a cherry bomb in the mouth of a toad before striking the match. Nonno has a saying about people like Mr. Hubris: "A bad apple is rotten from the beginning."

After the report cards are distributed and the day is over, I lose sight of Gregory but eventually find him waiting for the bus.

"Where the heck did you go, Gregory? I've been looking five whole minutes for you!"

Gregory is busy kicking a small rock between his shoes when the tears flow.

"Connie...I ain't goin' up the ladder with you. Too bad I wasn't I-tal-yan like you. If I was, then maybe Nonno Falcone could have helped me, too. I never had nobody help me like you Connie Mary. Why, you're the only friend I gots in the whole wide world. Even my first grade teacher hated me."

"Greg," I say very gently, "Every teacher hates you."

Gregory shakes his head. "True, true," and wipes his nose on his sleeve. "But I gotta tell you something before the sun goes down—I love you Connie Mary!" He kisses my cheek before disappearing into the crowd of children.

I stood motionless, before hearing Mr. Lashinski calling me through the orange doors.

"What cha plannin' to do Connie Mary, wait here 'till next year?"

The cracked leather seat on the bus is hot from having absorbed the rays from the June sun and I wonder if Janice ever sat on this seat.

I stare at the sad reflection in the window thinking my childhood is slipping away and know there is only one person who can help me.

Anna and Gus never lock their doors. Gus believes if anyone needs to steal anything that bad, they must need it more than him and are welcome to take it. When I step inside the house, I find Anna in the parlor sitting on the daybed that Gus built, sewing little toy clowns for poor children. The minute I sit next to her, and tell her my thoughts about childhood slipping away, I discover she believes quite the opposite.

"Oh, Connie Mary, there ain't nothing about childhood that's ever lost," she says, wiping my tears on the hem of her flowered apron. "Honey, you ain't losing your childhood! Don't you know? Childhood days are stored inside the heart where you can pull 'em out whenever you need to remember." She places my hand on her heart. "See? I got you and Jan right here. Whenever I can't see or be with you, I know you both live inside my heart."

When I return home I encounter my father holding a bloody rag to his mouth. Then I remember my mother and father had their teeth removed and replaced by false ones. When I ask my father why he wanted false teeth instead of his old beautiful teeth, he stares at the kitchen table and winces from the pain. "I didn't take care of the teeth I had Connie Mary, so in the end—I lost them all."

The evening is quiet with Janice working late at *The Central Shoe Factory* in Norwich. She only has a few days left of working there. Last week, she brought home Desert Boots for my father and me. This did not go well. First, she had to exchange my boots because they were the wrong size. Then, my father's heel became unglued. Not long afterwards she was given a pink slip. Distraught with my sister's downward spiral, my mother believes Dr. Milone is not helping anymore. Rather than confront the real enemy, she decides to take Janice to see a psychiatrist at the Norwich State Hospital.

Summer passes quickly with my mother and sister attending so many doctor appointments there is little time for anything else. When my mother hears the katydids echoing in the night, she knows it is time to go school shopping at Mr. Big's Department store. This year Janice is a senior at the Norwich Free Academy and my mother believes wearing attractive clothes will help her attract a nice Italian boy. On one of the last days in August, we pick through the piles of clothes on wooden tables and find a few outfits. On the way out, we enjoyed a pizza at the deli.

Once my mother makes the last turn up Fitchville Road, the mood in the car turns grim. Even as the motor dies, we sit silently in the driveway, unable to reach for the door handle. We expect to hear birds singing, but instead, hear a high shrill sound. When we step from the car, the yard looks as though a tornado came through leaving a path of destruction with piles of broken branches spread across the grass. The pink tea roses that once camouflaged the barbed wire fence have been destroyed with hundreds of pink petals discarded across the grass resembling a little girl's broken party dishes. Then the slaughterer appears with sweat dripping down his face. He walks menacingly, swinging a chainsaw in his hand. We step from the car into the malicious mind of a madman and I reach and touch Nonno's switchblade inside my pocket. I have been preparing for this day. The day I must fight my father.

My father notices my mother and barks— "Rose! You and your kids get a rake and clean this mess up."

Looking dazed, my mother picks up a rake and hands it to Janice. She ignores the look of terror on my sister's face and points to a pile of leaves. And together we spend the rest of the beautiful summer day picking up broken tea roses, chopped forsythia branches, and innocent flowers, all annihilated by my father. I am unable to speak. I have been forced to swallow my rage like a lump of poison meant to make me violently ill. The only way I am able to continue is through every word I seethed between my teeth. *"Someday Dad,* I'll kill you for this. I swear to God, Dad...*someday I'll kill you."*

Entering junior high means there is a whole new wing of the school to explore, as I am no longer sequestered in the safety of the elementary wing. Mr. Pavy has not changed since my sister was his star pupil wearing the same pinstriped suit and bowtie. Mr. Pavy believes every child has the potential to read and considers books to be society's most valuable tools for changing lives for the better. My mother holds Mr. Pavy in high regard and praises him often.

"Mr. Pavy is the voice of a thousand poets and the heart of a true teacher."

After a few weeks of school, Mr. Pavy announces he is calling our homes to introduce himself to each parent in the hope that they might volunteer with his students. When the phone rings on Monday evening, I assume it is Mr. Pavy, especially by the way my mother smiles when she answers. My father has been on the couch for most of the evening, pretending to be sleeping. When he hears my mother answer the phone, he leaps up to turn the television volume to its lowest setting. I want to hear the conversation as well, so I sit near my mother.

"A very good evening to you, Mrs. Falcone. It is such a pleasure to talk with you again. I am calling every parent in the hope they may consider volunteering to read with some of my more troubled readers." My mother is mesmerized by Mr. Pavy's voice. Living in the Falcone family, it is rare to see men with such manners.

"I am advising my students to take a trip to the library and choose a book for silent sustained reading. As you know Mrs. Falcone, I consider reading to be as important as oxygen cursing through the blood."

My mother looks at me and suddenly realizes I am not Janice Lynn.

She takes a deep breath and says, "Um...did you remember Mr. Pavy, that Connie Mary *is* Janice Lynn's sister?"

There is a long silence before my father begrudgingly mumbles in the background.

"Ya, tell 'im if he likes Janice Lynn that much, to find her a job."

My mother turns the receiver away.

"Oh, yes Mr. Pavy! I am sure of it! Connie Mary *really* is Janice's biological sister! No Mr. Pavy, Connie Mary was not adopted. Oh yes, Mr. Pavy, Connie Mary had a normal birth. No birth defects at all. What's that you say? Yes—of course! I will tell Janice Lynn that you said she should become an English teacher. Oh my, you would write my Janice a recommendation for college? Thank you so much Mr. Pavy! Connie Mary is so fortunate to have you for a teacher! Yes, Mr. Pavy, good night to you too and sweet dreams."

My mother places the receiver down and stares at it. My father is stretched across the couch and wants to hear the news. "What the hell was that all about?"

My mother moves cautiously to the chair with worried eyes.

"Nothing really... Mr. Pavy found it hard to believe that Connie Mary and Janice are sisters. I guess their academic levels are so different." My mother inhales a cigarette with grey smoke curling around her nostrils. My father did not hear one word my mother said.

"Rose, turn up the volume on the television, and while you're at it, go get me another beer." My mother silently carries the glass into the kitchen, leaving my father and I alone in the parlor. I am sitting behind my father wearing the same blue skirt I wore to school this morning when my father does something so reprehensible I can never trust him again. Slouched across the couch with his head upright, my father swivels his head around like one of those bobbling dogs you see in the back of a car window. I am focused on the television when I notice my father looking at me with dark wicked eyes that travel to my blouse and my skirt and then rest upon the forbidden entrance between my legs, all the while grinning like Howdy Doody.

Immediately, I blamed myself. I had not been aware that my legs were slightly relaxed. *Mom's right. You never sit like a young lady! You should have realized your underwear was showing. What a bad girl you are Connie Mary!*

My father listens for the whereabouts of my mother, and I wonder, where did my real father go? After forcing my paralyzed body to rise, I ran upstairs to lock my bedroom door, stuffing a piece of Kleenex into the keyhole. I sit in the semi-darkness, looking at my image in the full-length mirror feeling disgusted by my developing breasts. Curious about what my father will do next, I open my door and listen.

I hear my mother return to the parlor and question my father as if something is wrong.

"Where did Connie Mary go?"

My father's voice reeks of power and dominance and quickly extinguishes the conversation. "How the hell do I know? What do you think I am—your daughter's keeper?"

Seventh grade is a constant reminder of how girls must be careful. Girls cannot walk alone in certain places without dire consequences, whereas boys can walk beyond the eyes of the teacher without giving it a thought. On any given day it is not uncommon for a mischievous boy to pull the back of a girl's bra like a slingshot. The sound is loud and embarrassing and the boys laugh. Another so-called harmless joke girls endure is called the "Titty Twister" game. This is supposed to be hilarious when a boy grabs a girl's tender breast and twists it forcefully in a circular motion. And just when you think you have endured all the pain you can possibly stand without fainting, someone in the crowd shouts, "What's the big deal? It was only a harmless joke. You girls are such babies, you can't even take a joke!"

I have often wondered what boys would do if girls invented a game called "Penis Twister." I wonder how funny that would be? Another problem in seventh grade is never being able to express an opinion without condemnation if it runs contrary to a boy's belief. This is when boys coin that old familiar phase that has worked so effectively to stifle a female's voice.

"Don't listen to her—*she's on the rag.*"

Recess in seventh grade is no longer fun as girls stand around in cliques listening to boys heckling other boys who do not measure up to certain athletic standards. Boys love to compare other boys to the lowest standard of sportsmanship by jeering, *"You play like a girl."*

Returning to the classroom after recess requires a long walk through a dark hallway. This is where girls must be very attentive to their surroundings, as some boys will automatically start grabbing at a girl's breast or reaching underneath her skirt as soon as the shadows fall. Generally, girls who fall victim to these assaults are usually the quiet shy ones. After such an assault, an odd phenomenon often occurs; the victim is suddenly branded a "whore" and the predator receives praise.

School is a dangerous place and to survive I learn to take risks. At home I help myself to my father's gin and then water it down so he doesn't notice the crime. I never steal Nonno's liquor, knowing the consequences would be far worse. There is something about Nonno that is far more dangerous. He will be sitting at the kitchen table and suddenly slip behind a door to answer the telephone. Then there was the day he invited our family to lunch, offering to drive us in his black Cadillac. Janice did not attend. It seemed she had fallen out of bed in the middle of the night and was too bruised to go out in public.

When the Cadillac approached with its dark windows, my parents were already outside. Nonno cannot tolerate people who are late and rolls down his window to give specific instructions: "Make-a sure, no one move my floor mats. And shake-a you dirt-t-feet before you climb in."

Nonna was next to Nonno patiently combing her bright blue hair. It was Aunt Angie, of course, who convinced Nonna that blue hair is all the rage: "Ma—all the doctor's wives get their gray hair tinted blue and I can make you beautiful too!"

Before my mother got in the car she asked Nonno a question. "Pa, could you open the trunk so I can put my pocketbook back there? It's too big to hold in my lap."

Nonno laughed heartily, "Rosie, how you gonna put you pock-e-book in the trunk when I gotta dead body back-a there?"

Not knowing how to respond, my mother carefully climbed into Nonno's car clutching her pocketbook for dear life. I looked at Nonna who heard every word and continued to apply lipstick. I looked to my father, who chose to ignore Nonno by staring blankly out the window. When Nonno turned around and saw the look of terror on my mother's face he threw his head back and laughed.

"Imma jokin' with-a you Rosie! Dunna you know? It's not murder unlessa you find-a the body. And, you no want to be the one to find body, eh Rosie?"

My mother agreed by nervously shaking her head.

Nonna is a woman of very few words yet possesses the mental ability of Albert Einstein. When she speaks, Nonno listens. She looked sternly at Nonno and whispered low, "*Nunzio, lascia che sia* (Let it be)." Nonna felt sorry for my mother because she knew the branches supporting her lonely nest are not strong.

"Rosie, my Nunzio, he kid with you no more. I make-a sure."

My father said nothing. Either he knew it to be true or had heard

Nonno's joke too many times to be funny. He preferred to look out the dark window, enjoying the anonymity of seeing without being seen. And as the saying goes—*this too comes to pass*—as most of the Falcone Family cruised down Fitchville Road in a car with the cleanest floor mats in town. In the last moments of the setting sun, Nonno's silver rims sparkled stupendously, likely reflecting envy in the heart of every man in Bozrah. As for my mother, she never complained about the size of her pocketbook again.

Uncle Henry continues to be a bone of contention for my family. My father is repulsed by the fact that his brother cannot control a gambling habit and almost lost the deed to his house in a poker game. Despite the animosity between my father and uncle, there are occasionally happy times. Like when their wives get creative about the ways the brothers can tolerate each other. The process is called "double dating," and proves love can be revived under the right circumstances. The double dates always take place on a Saturday night, which is when I get to witness my mother transformed from frumpy to glamorous. My sister expertly applies her makeup and then stands back to lovingly admire her handiwork and my mother's beautiful face.

"Oh Ma, tonight you will be the prettiest woman anyone ever saw!"

We help our mother slip into a slinky, gold lame dress and place a gold necklace with rhinestones around her neck. Janice adds one more dusting of powder and my mother looks in the mirror and sighs, "I used to be so young." It is hard for my mother to accept her loose false teeth, gray hair, and added pounds. Less concerned is my father, who walks into the room with his shirt buttons straining to hold a bulging belly. Despite an obvious decline in attractiveness, my mother worries my father will find another woman.

"Mark my words Connie Mary! The minute I'm gone, your father will bring another woman into this house and she will be younger and prettier than me!" I used to laugh at my mother. I was unaware that she saw the deceit hidden deep in my father's heart while I merely judged the surface.

After my parents' night of dancing and drinking, I hear the door unlock at two o' clock in the morning. I tiptoe down the stairs and watch from behind the banister. The couples are laughing and joking, with my father and uncle talking like real brothers. Uncle Henry is gushing with affection rolling off his tongue. "Boots, next week, I'll comes by and helps you wit' that oil leak in your truck."

"Oh hell no, Hen," says my father. "I'll comes by youse house furst, and help youse chop down them trees."

The couples gather around my mother's Philco Solid State Stereo record player and Uncle Henry asks my mother a question. "Rose puts on Bobby's Darin. You gots that record, "Beyond the Sea?" My mother is thrilled to hear my uncle's request and hops blissfully over to the stack of records. "Sure Hen, I got it right here!" What happens next absolutely astounds me! The couples push the furniture against the wall and begin gliding gracefully across the floor! The night ends with shots of Sambuca and the approach of dawn.

The next day my parents slept long into the afternoon. It is an unusually warm day for November, so I decide to walk through Beebe's Fields. Before crawling underneath the barbed wire fence, I stand at the top of the embankment remembering when Beebe's Fields did not have a steep precipice surrounding its terrain. Before I attended school, the fields were level and sloped in lovely grooves and valleys. It was during the 1950's, when men excavated the land in order to prepare for Connecticut Route 2. It was through eminent domain the land was acquired by the state, and a hole, roughly a quarter-mile deep and a half-mile wide, was hollowed into the belly of Farmer Beebe's fields. Mr. Beebe knew for his cows to survive they must drink from the Yantic River on the other side of the highway and asked the state to make a stipulation. The state agreed and dug a tunnel underneath the highway so his cows could reach the water. The tunnel is dark and foreboding and one I have often walked through. It can become dangerous during a rainstorm as the water rises quickly. I found this out once when the rain came suddenly and the water rose above my knees. I struggled to reach the end as the current tried to pull me down.

My thoughts are interrupted by a strange sight; below the embankment, where Mr. Beebe's cows graze in the tall grass, lay my mother's beloved figurines broken and scattered. One figurine is of a mother and child, now with their heads decapitated. The others are unrecognizable. I think I know who stood above and hurled the statues below.

"I hate you Dad!" I shout. "You destroyed what Mom loves best because she ruined your business!"

When I run into the house, I find my mother sleeping on the couch with a lit cigarette hanging between two fingers. It is a familiar scene, me removing her forgotten cigarette and crushing it out. I shake my mother's arm.

"Mom, come quick…Dad threw your figurines over the fence. Come, I'll show you!"

My mother stares into space with the catatonic stupor of someone gravely ill. A confused whisper rises from her voice, "*What?*"

I take hold of her hand and frantically tug—"Get up Mom, I'll show you!"

My mother is able to stand with my assistance and we wobble to the back door. She stops briefly in the kitchen to stir a pot of meatballs simmering on the stove, then continues, walking slower than Anna Lorentz with crutches. When we reach the fence we avoid touching the sharp barbed wire and I point to the massacre below. "Ma, look what Dad did!"

To truly judge my mother one must understand my mother's ambition in life was to get married, be a good wife and cook for a house full of happy children. The truth is my mother did not know what to do with the two choices she faced in life, which was to choose between protecting Janice and being loyal to an abuser. It was not possible to do both.

My mother is unconcerned by the destruction below. "Oh, look at the Mama cow and baby. Isn't that cute?" The little Holstein stays close to its mother for protection. The Mama cow senses danger and slowly moves the baby away.

"Ma, Dad didn't do this, did he?" My mother stares below at the yellow withered grass.

"No. It was not your father."

She leaves and the sky is overcome with impending doom. A rain begins to fall and I do not seek refuge even as the cold water drenches my face and clothes. Another day on Fitchville Road has come to an end. A day of fear, horror and inexplicable beauty.

10

The Lost Souls Of Kettle

Once abandoned and lost, misguided, and scorned, the suffering angels
of Kettle Building now reside in a place where love shines eternal.
The Kettle Building (2014) one year before being demolished.
Photograph by Concetta Falcone-Codding

When spring bursts forth in New England, it boasts splendor in field, wood and valley. Not everyone appreciates it here due to the harsh ice and snow. My father's siblings left for warmer climates, leaving my mother alone with him. My mother does not recognize the implications of living without witnesses and laughs, "Con, I could never leave Bozrah." My mother's insistence of not leaving home eventually formed a noose around her neck.

Bozrah does give my mother one gift: she develops a natural talent for photography. My mother spoke of death as imminent and was determined to leave evidence behind by photographing my sister and I at every stage in our lives, always explaining how a photograph is far more effective than words. Her words echo in my mind. *You can try to convince people of the truth and they may not believe you. But show them a picture and there is no denying the truth.*

Inspired by poetic visions of spring, my mother imagines she is painting the parlor robin egg blue or creating beautiful flowerbeds, when instead, she is sobbing in a dark bedroom. Day after day, I ask my mother why she cries. When the days turn into weeks I become a broken creature weeping on my knees by her bed. "Please Ma, why do you cry all the time? Please Ma, I need to know!" Cloaked in fear, I held her sweaty hand listening to the same answer.

"I can't tell you Connie Mary. It's something your father did. And it's very *bad!* You wouldn't understand—you're too young!" I begin to wonder why I am the only one who notices my mother crying in bed. Where are my father and sister? And why do they tiptoe past her bedroom pretending not to see.

The day comes when my father asks his family for help.

"Rose, won't you please get out of this bed?" begs Uncle Henry. "Please, Rose? For me?" My uncle resorts to bribing, promising my mother a new set of pink tea roses to replace the old ones my father butchered. Uncle Henry and my mother both adore flowers. They are so close that sometimes I think they met each other long ago, at a better time, in a better place.

Growing frustrated, my uncle makes one final appeal, "Rose, if you get out of this bed right now—I'll have your roses planted tomorrow!"

My mother moans, *"Hen, go away and let me die!"*

Uncle Henry leaves with tears in his eyes.

Next comes the big *Capo* (boss) striding through the front door as if he were Douglas MacArthur leading his military forces into battle. Nonno marches up the stairs, skipping every other step and with one swift kick opens my mother's bedroom door.

"Rosie! Tell-a me why you cry-a all the time? You tella you Papa who make-a you cry anna I snap hissa neck in two!"

My mother turns away. "Pa, go home… I can't tell you."

Nonno says he needs a drink and leaves with a red face.

Holding a cigarette in one hand and a can of Tab soda in the other, Aunt Angie calmly strolls into the house, dropping ashes all the way up the stairs. My aunt is clearly flustered by having to leave her beauty shop in the middle of the day. Make no mistake, though. Aunt Angie would let the beauty shop burn to the ground if it meant helping my father.

She sits on the edge of the bed and stares at the dusty floor. "Rose, I'm tellin' you kid, shit happens. You can't hide underneath those blankets forever," and chuckles with the usual hacking cough. "Don't cha know? Trouble knows where you live. You get my drift, Rose? None of us are getting out of this alive."

My mother stares into a parallel universe only she can see. My aunt tries a different tactic. "Hey, Rose, you want Angie to make you a beautiful blonde like Marilyn?"

My mother is familiar with Aunt Angie's beauty treatments and remains unresponsive. On the way out Aunt Angie passes my father coming up the stairs and lowers her voice.

"Boots, you know it's got to be done."

The next day, my father committed my mother to the Norwich State Hospital in Preston, Connecticut. He speeds down the highway all the while ignoring my mother's constant moaning. Nonno is in the back seat with me, straining forward in order to rest one hand on my mother's shoulder.

"Rosie, all you do is cry inna bed all day long! You go hospital, anna get betta. You cry too much Rosie—no good, no good!" Janice wanted to come, but she was told to stay behind with specific instructions from my father. "*You* better clean up this pigpen and have supper ready for us when we get back."

Soon the endless rows of macabre brick buildings appear before us. Our destination is reached. My mother sees as well and cries harder, but no one seems to hear. My father is looking for the signpost up ahead that could easily have read *The Twilight Zone*. Moments later, with no more care than if he were batting away a mosquito, he flatly declares, "Kettle Building, yep. That's it. Your mother's going there. "

The Kettle Building is dark and lifeless and we have trouble finding the elevator. Everything about this building is barren and grim and when the elevator shuts I think I may never see my mother again. My thoughts are confirmed when a grim-looking man wearing a white uniform appears on the other side of the steel door. After a polite interrogation, the man in white leads us through an endless hallway where every so often he stops to unlock another barred door. He struts briskly with eyes accustomed to the dark. In the distance, more men await our arrival with uniforms that glow like ghosts in the shadows. At one point my mother begins to scream. Nonno tries to encourage her to keep moving, but in the darkness and confusion he stumbles and cries out in a desperate voice, "Rosie, please, come!"

My father draws back and his eyes fill with fear—*not for my mother—but from someone learning the truth!* Upon reaching our destination, the men take my beautiful mother and, before she can say anything, administer a long needle into her arm. Within seconds she is subdued into complacency. One grim-looking man looks back and warns, "You cannot go any further—she will be fine." And before my heart breaks into a thousand pieces, he tenderly whispers at a volume no one else will hear, "Don't worry kid, the first day is always the worst."

The men lead her through the last door and when it slams shut, the three of us are left alone, peering through a window that tells the hard truth about my mother's new life. Nonno cannot bear to look and turns, wiping his tears away. With palms pressed against the glass, my father watches my mother disappear inside a massive room filled with dozens of other patients. They stand immobilized, watching with curiosity as my mother is led away. As for me, I cannot believe what I see and continue to stare at a room that is larger than my school's gymnasium! Later I discover this room is called *the day room.* The people I see are clearly not well. Some laugh hysterically as others sit restrained with cloth belts tied loosely around their waist. Some women have white hair even though they are no older than Janice. Others look like the living dead, wandering lost and forgotten. They all wear bathrobes and blue foam slippers.

Nonno cannot stand anymore and pulls my father away, knowing my mother's life will never be the same. In the last few seconds before the elevator door closes to a world few will ever see or understand, I strain my neck to catch a last look at all the crazy people that will become my mother's new friends.

"**O**ut of all my family," says my father matter-of-factly, "Angie is the one I'd trust with my life." Several weeks have passed since we brought my mother to the Norwich State Hospital and as unbelievable as it sounds—life is better. It is Sunday evening and an extremely rare event is occurring: my sister watching television in the same room as my father. As we wait for Aunt Angie to arrive my father starts a conversation.

"My poor sister works up to fifteen hours a day in that sweatshop she calls a beauty salon with no help from anyone. When Rodney was alive he was one hell of a husband... as long as he wasn't drinking." He inhales a cigarette. "Hell of a good guy, that Rodney. Your mother loved him too. Hell, we all did. It was too bad he dropped dead right on top of Angie's front lawn. Yep, remember it like it was yesterday. 1958. The day Angie was hosting a barbecue."

Remembering the day makes my father forlorn and I guess he forgets that Janice is sitting a few feet away. "Hell, maybe Angie can straighten your sister out. She offered to come here after work to help us," and added proudly, "If Angie can't straighten Janice out—nobody can!"

Soon enough, a weary and exhausted Aunt Angie stumbles through the door carrying bags of beauty supplies she says a girl can't live without. She drops the bag onto the floor and out fall bottles of emerald green *Prell* shampoo, blonde hair dye and *Cover Girl* makeup.

My father laughs, "Holy Shit, Angie, what-cha do, bring the whole damn beauty shop with you?"

Aunt Angie plops into my sister's hard swivel chair and rests her head to look up at the painting I did of Christ praying in the *Garden of Gethsemane*. My aunt is feeling His loneliness.

"Oh sweet Jesus, some days I don't know if I'll get through another second of this life... and then I remember everything you went through. Lord, I know my dilly-dally shit don't compare with all the suffering you went through for us fools."

My father looks admirably at his sister and suddenly becomes a philosopher.

"Angie, you got to put one foot in front of the other and keep on walking. Some days that's the only way I make it: one foot in front of the other and keep on walking." Not having my mother to boss around, my father gets up to change the television channel himself. He is delighted to find the movie *From here to Eternity,* starring Frank Sinatra and laughs with excitement. "Hey Ang'ch, look! Here's that movie I was telling you about. It's got that wop Frankie Sinatra in it. Frankie always gets what he wants. First, he gets a contract with Tommy Dorsey. After that he's too big for his wop britches and wants out. But Dorsey won't budge. Humph! Dorsey's no slouch, he would of gotten one third of the little wop's earnings for the rest of his life. By Christ, that Frankie is one smart wop! He goes and cries to the Mafia to lean the Black Hand on Dorsey—and ha! Just like nothing, Dorsey has a change of heart and lets the little wop go free for a few thousand bucks! Did ya know Angie, that Frankie's middle name is Albert, like mine?"

Aunt Angie laughs heartily. "Ah Boots, don't-cha believe all that Hollywood shit! Eh! True… the little wop always gets what he wants and the little shit even won a Academy Award for playing Maggio." She is laughing so hard that tears slide down her cheeks.

"Goshdamn wops…they sure know how to make the green *denaro* (money)."

Louder than my father's big mouth is the sound of my sister banging pots and pans in the kitchen with the song "*Georgie Girl*" blasting on the radio. For some reason my father no longer hears the noise my sister makes. Aunt Angie leans toward the kitchen and grins with a new set of false teeth. "What-cha doing Jan, burning down the house so your mother won't have to clean it when she gets home?"

To our surprise, Janice pokes her head out of the smoke-filled kitchen and replies, "Oh yes Aunt Angie. I want to make her life easier."

Everyone laughs at my sister's joke and if anyone entered our house they would think a normal family lives here. After my sister bakes what she calls a cake, each one of us eats a small portion and my father pretends to like it. After the movie is over, he offers to go to Club 41 and bring us back a pizza. The three of us settle around a kitchen table that balances on three legs. Aunt Angie displays the products she brought as if they were the answer to every problem in the world, and then brings up the past. Of course, she has not forgotten Gerard Frederick Valentine, AKA: Rodney Valentine, the love of her life!

"Goshdamn Rodney. Damn fool drank too much and died too soon. But lemme tell you girls, when my Rodney wasn't drinking, you couldn't find a better man." She blows smoke at my mother's yellow ceiling. "Rodney was my Heaven on earth girls. I guess God only made one perfect man, and Connie Mary rightfully painted Him. See girls, that's how it is in life, everything comes back to the cross, always the cross. At least we can have a little girl talk now with my big mouth little brother gone."

The happy atmosphere in the room fades when Aunt Angie grows teary. "Your father, my kid brother…Hell girls, I ain't blind. I know the way your father acts and it ain't right. I want both of you to know that your father wasn't always like this. When my little brother was young and single he was the most 'happy-go-lucky,' guy in the world. Always smiling and helping someone."

Aunt Angie cannot adequately tell my father's story without exposing an ugly secret from the past. "When Pa was drunk he always went after Bootsie. Bootsie was the one who suffered the most abuse. I think that's why he hollers, bosses your mother around and picks on poor Jan here." This causes my sister to stare at the floor.

"Girls, I'm going to give it to you straight… just so you know the other side of the story. Don't you believe a word those Sicilian gangsters on your mother's side of the family says about my kid brother. You ought-to know by now girls, *one thing I am not is a liar.* My little brother, your father, does the 'crazy-ass shit' he does because he's weighed down with all the baggage your mother's carrying. You poor girls got a Mama that's the most beautiful, sweetest woman in the world and the nicest sister-in-law anyone could have, but she's not well. And girls, you can tell those Sicilian gangsters I said this. Ha! They know better than to mess with a Calabrese hairdresser holding a pair of scissors in her hand. The truth is my brother's marriage to your Mama is what made my kid brother go '*pazzo*' in the head."

Aunt Angie leans toward Janice with the sad bloodshot eyes of *Droopy the Dog.* "Girls, as you get older, I may not be around to help you. And I don't see many relatives from your mother's side of the family running to help either." Her hands begin to tremble. "See, I got the feeling that both your lives are going to be damn tough. I want you girls to promise me you'll remember that your father was once a happy, carefree boy. As children we're born into the thick of it by taking on the sins of our Mama and Papa. My brother married your mother expecting she was going to save him and quickly found out—she couldn't save herself. See, when we get married, we don't expect our spouse to be the biggest heartache in our life. Rodney never did all the cussing and swearing your father does, but when he died I wanted to jump into the hole with him. Hate makes you strong, *but it's love that kills you.*"

My sister answers without hesitation. "Yes Aunt Angie, we promise to remember."

Aunt Angie pulls the wrapper off another pack of cigarettes. "Cancer sticks are what Bootsie calls 'em." My sister and I know something is wrong when Aunt Angie jumps for the sink. "Oh-no!" she cries—"Shit, not again!" and vomits red and black guck into the sink. After drenching her face with cold water she looks like she aged a hundred years.

"It's the damn disease. Yep, and now you know girls— I got cancer." Our aunt is soon restored to her cheerful self and looks at Janice with a sorrowful kind of love.

"Jan, I was just thinking. Maybe, we could bleach your hair a little bit blonde, so you could drive the guys wild. Ha! My brother Bootsie would be waiting at the front door ready to beat the hell out of 'em with one of his monkey wrenches."

In a few hours my father returns home with a giant pizza. The three of us watch television laughing and talking until midnight. When I think back to this moment, I never remember anyone mentioning my mother.

It's back to school on Monday with Mr. Pavy putting everyone to sleep with his lecture. We are awakened when Jodi Rajotte comes bounding into the classroom, yelling as if everyone were deaf. "Hey, did you clowns hear what that jackass McGillis did at recess? He jumped inside the dumpster and it took three teachers to pull 'im out!" The children roar with laughter.

Mr. Pavy responds by cracking a yardstick across the desk. "*Enough of this foolishness*—how dare anyone call Mr. McGillis such insidious names!"

Jodi grins mischievously with silver wires wrapped around his greenish-yellow teeth. "I didn't call him an ass, Mr. Pavy. I called him a *jackass*. You must admit, Gregory McGillis belongs in the Norwich State Nut House locked inside a booby hatch. He could be dangerous."

Mr. Pavy places his hands on the desk in an attempt to steady himself and his trembling voice. "Mr. Rajotte, please gather your personal belongings and march straight to the principal's office. We shall continue this conversation later this afternoon accompanied by your parents."

After Jodi leaves, Mr. Pavy sits on his rocking chair surrounded by rows of books. It is the time of day when the daylight filters through the dusty blinds and a unique stillness fills the room. He removes a white handkerchief from his pocket and wipes the sweat from his brow reciting words that make no sense to us. "G.K. Chesterton, may your words give me strength. 'The fascination of children lies in this: that with each of them all things are remade, and the universe is put again upon its trial…we ought always primarily to remember that within every one of these heads there is a new universe, as new as it was on the seventh day of creation… In each of those orbs there is a new system of stars, new grass, new cities, a new sea.'"

Mr. Pavy's expression changes when he looks at the oak tree in the center of the playground. "Oh my goodness, I did not wish to believe! The grand old oak is showing no signs of life," and sighs. "After all these years, our magnificent oak has died." He bows his head in reverence.

Even though the afternoon has almost passed, the birds continue to sing. They are accompanied by the sound of the buzzing black and yellow bumblebees that collect nectar from the daffodils below the window. Unlike people who take a day for granted, God's creatures know this day will never come again. There may be other days, but never this day, never this hour. Never will the world turn upon its axis in the same way as this moment in time. Mr. Pavy straightens his wire glasses and carefully tucks his watch and chain neatly into his vest pocket. His eyes search longingly towards somewhere beyond this world. No longer is his voice laced with anger, but peaceful resolve, as he prepares to give the final lesson.

"Soon all of you will be leaving Fields Memorial School. Lucky children to be graduating with an education, a precious gift indeed. Out of every lesson I have ever taught you, I want you to remember this day." He stretched forth his arm to point a finger at each one of us.

"If not for the Grace of God, you, you or—YOU—could be Gregory McGillis. The only difference between Gregory McGillis and the rest of you is the slight wave of God's hand."

No one says a word. Some look at the floor. The room is still except for a single hummingbird hovering near the window flying from flower to flower. For a moment, the hummingbird peers inside the classroom before becoming a blur of greenish-blue as it flies away. And even though we hear the buses rumbling in the parking lot, everyone remains silent. For this is the day every single one of Mr. Pavy's arrogant, self-centered students came to realize—*anyone one of us could have been Gregory McGillis, if not for the slight wave of God's hand.*

W̲henever I visit my mother at the hospital I find her crying in the day room, surrounded by patients asking for cigarettes. I learn quickly there is no such thing as privacy at the hospital; the bedroom my mother shares with ten other women makes that clear. But the women are not as scary as first imagined. As in the case of my mother, I learn most women have been committed by their husbands. After the women live together for several weeks, a strange phenomenon occurs. Their eyes brighten and they learn to laugh again. This is when I question if the person locked up is the crazy one after all.

Several months into my mother's stay, my father and I arrive at the Kettle Building to visit, but cannot find her anywhere. After hearing my father curse impatiently in front of the nurse's station, a nurse comes to help.

"I have good news, Mr. Falcone," says the nurse. "Mrs. Falcone is working at the canteen as a cashier! Isn't that grand?"

A disgusted grimace turns my father's face to stone. "My wife don't know nothin' about money. What the hell is a canteen?" The nurse explains very nicely how the canteen is the cafeteria located on hospital grounds where patients work for therapy. Needless to say, he walks away without saying thank you.

We arrived at the canteen just in time to see my mother giving back the correct change from a ten-dollar bill. I am too flabbergasted to speak, having heard my father tell my mother numerous times: "Rose you're the stupidest woman I ever knew. You don't even know that 2 + 2 equals 4!" After the initial shock, we find a small booth and watch my mother in awe. Now, instead of my mother, I am stuck listening to my father complain as I take bites out of a dry, Genoa grinder that is slowly choking me.

"What are we going to do about your sister?" moans my father, spitting provolone and salami into the air. My father is no longer concerned about my mother, but with a larger, more urgent problem he alone created. "Your sister gets fired from every job. Can't you help your sister, Connie Mary? You're a winner like the old man, a chip off the old block. You and me kid, we know how to survive, don't we?"

I turn away in disgust to instead watch my happy mother take cash from customers. One customer is a handsome doctor who gives her a compliment. "My goodness Mrs. Falcone! Did anyone ever tell you that you have the most beautiful eyes? Hazel, are they not?"

My mother beams brighter than a summer day. "Oh thank you, doctor. Yes, hazel. How'd you know? Thank you so much!" As I watch my mother have a second chance in life, my thoughts are interrupted by a purring voice.

"You want some more milk, little girl?"

When I look up I see a waitress with two large breasts hanging over my father's shoulder. The waitress is a patient and quite young, although her body looks worn and tired like a car driven fast by too many reckless men. She resembles Bozo the Clown with white face powder and two circles of red blush painted on each cheek. Looking at her bleached blonde hair is painful due to several inches of black roots trying to recover from the trauma. The uniform is most disconcerting of all. It looks several sizes too small with seams around the breasts ready to bust! She hovers near my father's lustful eyes like a forsaken doll wearing the highest high-heels I have ever seen! She spins around, revealing a backside as plump and firm as a Vidalia onion on the shelf. Before I can answer her question, my father places his cup underneath her breast and smiles from ear to ear.

"I'll take some more of that good milk Miss—with coffee please. By the way, what's a good-looking dame like you doing in a place like this?" Clearly, the waitress is years younger than my father. This does not matter at all, for the waitress is a hungry feral cat, desperately looking for a place to rest. She has mastered the breathless voice of Marilyn Monroe that promises all the pleasures of paradise.

"I'd ask you the same—what's a good-looking guy like you doing in a place like this?" Of course, my father always has the right response when it comes to pretty young women. *"Honey—ask me no questions and I'll tell you no lies."*

Within minutes the young waitress is sitting uncomfortably close to my father drinking coffee and wisely taking his advice to not ask questions—but tell plenty of lies!

"What? I can't believe you're a day over 30! Gosh Joe, you sure do keep yourself fit."

She inches closer. "A man with a body like yours must exercise all the time!"

My stomach begins to feel queasy.

"Dad, I'll be right back, I'm taking a walk outside, okay?"

The waitress gives me a conniving smile, showing yellow teeth dabbed with red lipstick.

My father looks suspiciously around the room.

"Don't go too far… this place is full of crazy people, you hear?"

After several minutes of walking around the grounds, I go back inside, but quickly realize I entered the wrong building. The building is bleak and empty surrounded by steel doors. I continue until I come to an open door and a stairwell. When I walk down the steps I sense a guiding force as I plunge deeper into a forgotten world. I step into a dark space and walk carefully around pieces of broken glass. I hold my nose due to the stench of mold. The only light comes from two dirty windows and I startle at the sight of two black chains hanging from the ceiling. The chains are long and reach a torn leather chair cemented to the floor. The chair is fitted with a leather belt and handcuffs on each arm and I realize that someone could scream for hours in this dungeon and not be heard. Suddenly, as though someone has been listening to my thoughts all this time, the translucent outline of a woman appears floating above the chair with tears flowing from her eyes. With chills running up and down my spine I run up the stairs and out the door into the life-giving sunshine. I believe that I had stepped into some lost, forgotten world, when patients were given lobotomies and shock treatments in dark secret places. It is a sad fact of life that even the angels lose their way and the rain falls on the just and the unjust.

As the weeks turn into months, life is different without my mother. The biggest surprise is seeing Janice working hard in the kitchen, wearing my mother's apron and cooking supper every night. Who would have thought my father would yell less with my mother gone? There have been other surprises as well. I came home from school early one day and discovered my father and sister were home alone. I thought this was very strange, as I did not think either one could stand to be around the other. When I first walked into the house I thought no one was home, but then I heard my sister and father whispering upstairs. Minutes later, my father comes rushing down the steps, avoiding eye contact and mumbling about having *to work outside*. As a child I did not pay close attention to what may have transpired on this day or any other, as I was not taught to believe what was in plain sight. After he left, Janice came downstairs to prepare supper and was silent for the entire night. I was afraid to mention this incident to my mother and never did, even when she was released from the hospital.

Returning home is hard for my mother. The biggest surprise is finding out that my father wants to change for the better. For a brief period of time (and I do mean brief) to make my mother happy, my father plans a vacation to Long Island to visit the two people he hates the most: my mother's sister Rosalie and her husband Joe. Bunch of "rich bastards" and "show-offs" is what he calls them, even though everyone knows my father is jealous of anyone with money. Rosalie and Joe live in a fabulous house with two daughters, an older son, and a dog named Queenie. During the two-hour drive my father does not curse or yell, which makes the trip actually enjoyable. Upon arrival we discover a welcome note taped to the door.

> *Dear Chickie and Joe,*
> *Come inside and make yourselves at home. Meatballs and sauce are on the stove. We are at work. See you soon. Love your sister,*
> *Rosalie*

Aunt Rosalie lives in a luxurious split-level home with a sunken living room and green shag carpet that glistens like dew on the morning meadow. Elongated gold-framed mirrors create an illusion of endless space where sunlight is reflected through clean, shiny windows. Immediately, my father falls asleep in front of the television, moments after reclining in a blue La-Z-Boy chair. With my father asleep, my mother is ready to give the house a thorough inspection. My first intention is to taste the thick sauce in a pot brimming with meatballs and sausage. As I reach for a slice of Italian bread, my mother calls from the basement, "Con, you're not going to believe this! Come down and see!"

I walk down the basement steps and stop halfway to look at an enormous room that resembles a well-stocked department store. My eyes cannot fathom the quantity of dresses, coats, suits, furs and gowns hanging from movable racks. The basement looks like a furniture showroom with its lamps, Oriental furniture, marble coffee tables, and everything else my mother has always wanted but will never have. One wall is lined with over a hundred shoeboxes and my mother is elated when she discovers size 10. "Hurry, Con! Hurry before my sister comes home! We must get *my* things into the station wagon and hide everything before your father wakes up!"

After we have everything loaded and hidden underneath blankets, my mother leans against the car and casually opens a box of Tastykakes. She is unconcerned when the plastic wrappers fly into the soft breeze and rest underneath Aunt Rosalie's rosebushes. After consuming her fill, my mother casually asks, "You want one Con?"

Later that night, after the adults have been up half the night drinking and eating, I hear my mother and aunt whispering in the hallway. My aunt is questioning my mother and trying not to laugh. "Chickie, do you happen to know who opened my box of chocolate Tastykakes? I found several empty wrappers underneath my rosebushes."

Not missing a beat, my mother replies, "Oh gee *Nin,* (short for *ninny* which means breast in Italian) my girls were playing in the basement and took them. I told them not to eat them, but you know how kids are, they never listen to what their mothers tell them."

I soon discover Aunt Rosalie's home is the central headquarters for the Calanna family. There is something tragic when you see the Calanna sisters all together. It is like standing in a room surrounded by the most beautiful broken toys that never leave the toymaker's shop. The only sister missing is Josephine Calanna Bevilacqua whose mysterious and premature death at age 38 plagued the family. The sisters speak of Josephine in ways that fail to include the truth. They know who killed Josephine. It was a monster called domestic violence.

We stay at Aunt Rosalie's house a week or more. On one of the last nights, at about two in the morning, I hear my mother's footsteps coming down the stairs. I slip out of bed and lie next to her in the soft darkness of the parlor. I take comfort in the coolness of her menthol cigarette, knowing she feels safe enough to tell me her secrets.

"You don't get what you deserve in life, Con. God knows my life wasn't easy—*I never had any luck.* In Philadelphia, I had to quit junior high. Dummy me. Connie Mary, remember, the older you get, the less opportunity you have in life."

"Ma, how'd you meet dad?"

My mother's soul shifts to a higher, brighter place. "Albert Joseph Falcone was the most beautiful man I ever saw in my whole life. It was love at first sight! When I met him, I thought he would help me, and my family wanted me to get married. I was tired of working in filthy factories with old men who thought they could put their hands on me whenever they felt like it. They would reach over my shoulder and touch my breasts. I always had such big breasts and felt ashamed of them."

A chill passes through the window and I reach for a lime green afghan to cover my feet. My mother kicks away her dirty slippers revealing enormous crooked feet with ugly bunions on each side of her big toes. "I met your father after he got out of the Navy. He was going to school at the *Philadelphia Technical Institute* majoring in refrigeration engineering and rented an apartment from my sister Grayce's boyfriend Joe Lerro. Grayce told Joe that my refrigerator wasn't working and he sent over a plumber named Albert Falcone to my apartment. I was sitting at the kitchen table with my hair in rollers, unaware that my life was about to change in ways I never imagined. Grayce liked your father at first—but then drastically changed her opinion, warning me not to marry him. It didn't matter though, within six months we were married and I learned the meaning of living in Hell."

With only a few days left of vacation, my mother wants to visit the World's Fair. It's Saturday morning and the coffee is brewing while the adults are bickering in the kitchen. Aunt Rosalie has the most persistent voice of all and always gets her way. "We must take my sister and her hubby to see the World's Fair. Have you heard about the World's Fair Honey?" and turns to her husband Joe. "Joe, show my sister a picture of the Unisphere."

Uncle Joe is too much in love with his wife not to do everything she asks, and patiently sifts through *The New York Times*. "Look Honey, here's a picture. It says the Unisphere is two stories high and made of stainless steel. It represents man's achievement on a shrinking globe in an expanding universe."

"Albert, I want to go! Do you want to go?" My mother looked at my father with hopeful eyes. Unfortunately, if looks could kill my mother would be dead.

"Rose, you know I want to go. Can't you remember anything I said? I'm the one who told you about the fair in the first place! Jesus Christ Rose, if you had a brain you'd be dangerous."

"Well, you both came at the right time," says my uncle, politely ignoring my father's crude remarks. "The World's Fair runs from April to October, $2.50 for adults and one dollar for children. You can't beat those prices, cheaper than going to the local moviehouse. But you better wear walking shoes, the fair is over two miles long." That night I happily drift to sleep thinking I am going to the World's Fair tomorrow. In the other twin bed, my sister is listening to the radio. She is not excited about the fair, because no one has asked her to go.

The next day I wake up hearing my favorite cartoon show *Quick Draw McGraw,* blaring downstairs. I look at the clock and panic. "Oh no—it's 8:30! I'm late for the fair! Still in my pajamas, I slide down the banister and into the parlor. I am delighted to find my cousin Waynie Ormston sitting in front of the television chugging soda out of the bottle. I tiptoe and give him a surprise tap on the shoulder. When he jumps, the bottle drops and soda flows like a tiny river through the green carpet.

"Aw-w-w, what'd you have to go and do that for? Aunt Rose was hiding three bottles of soda in her closet and that was the last one."

The sweet scent of honey buns drifts into the room when Waynie's mother comes around the corner wearing a knitted cap and shawl. Aunt Sweetie is the baker in the family and with a mischievous grin searches through her purse with gnarled fingers that are never without a cigarette. Her voice is raspy and deep like a bullfrog croaking in the night.

"Hey there, little Connie Mary, ain't you gettin' perty? Your mom and dad left early this morning for the World's Fair with Aunt Rosalie and Uncle Joe. Now, I want you both to be good little children, ya hear? Your sweet sister Janice is sleeping upstairs, so be nice and quiet all right?" She glares suspiciously at Waynie. "I'll be right back. I have to go to the corner store and get more supplies to make my sweet rolls."

Waynie and I exchange smiling eyes and watch his mother walk out the door. In less than a minute, she returns, peeking her head inside the house. "Don't forget Wayne...Aunt Rosalie does not like her things touched." and with great reluctance, she shuts the door.

Waynie and I sit on the floor watching *Snooper and Blabber*, but Waynie grows bored and starts picking crumbs off his undershirt that barely covers a round belly. Even though we never discussed our fathers, I feel a special bond toward Waynie because his father looks as mean as mine. The best part about Waynie is that he believes everything I tell him. The worst part is that he is sick. For some time now, I have been listening on the phone to Aunt Sweetie tell my mother that Waynie is sick. This is hard to believe. I am looking at Waynie right now eating a large plate of pasta and he doesn't look very sick to me. I am more upset that my parents did not take me to the World's Fair.

"Waynie, are you upset that we didn't get to see the fair?"

Waynie's response is to fall on his hands and knees and sniff the carpet like a dog. He crawls to my feet and pretends to polish my shoes with an imaginary cloth and I smile knowing the *real fun* is about to begin.

"You're not fooling me, Shoeshine Boy. I know who you *really* are underneath that magnificent blue cape. You're that Cosmic Hero of the magical world!"

Grinning, Waynie backs away and steps into Aunt Rosalie's coat closet. When he slams the door, it sounds as though he is fighting against a hundred metal coat hangers. I must prove I am just as wild and jump up and down on Aunt Rosalie's couch. When the closet door finally bursts open, it is not Shoeshine Boy, but the most famous dog in the world—*Underdog!* Using his undershirt for a cape, Underdog makes his grand entrance by leaping on top of Aunt Rosalie's coffee table and tries to sing the song from his favorite cartoon show: "*Wah-oo, Wah-oo, Wah-oo... when bad people in this world appear, the cry for help comes far and near—Underdog! Underdog! UNDERDOG!*"

I fall to my knees and beg for mercy. "Oh Underdog, I am the lowly Polly Purebred! Save me from the evil likes of Simon Bar Sinister, Riff Raff, and Overcat!"

Underdog jumps to the floor. "There's no need to fear, Underdog is here! It is my duty, sweet Polly, to serve and wipe out evil that has plagued Dogkind for ages. We shall go forth, fighting evil, side by side." He kicks open the door to the back yard. "After you madam."

Together we hold hands and walk across the lush green lawn. When Underdog notices a ladder leaning against the roof of Aunt Rosalie's garage, he bravely faces danger. "Polly, you stay here. I will climb this roof and see if any intruders are lurking in the bushes. Your mission, Polly Purebred…is to…ah…hold the ladder." Underdog stands on the roof placing one hand over his forehead to scan the neighborhood.

I call up in my sweetest voice, "Are we safe yet?"

"Yes, Polly Purebred, it looks good. You can climb up now. No appearance of evil appears on the horizon."

I answer slyly, "Good." and pull the ladder from the roof to rest across the grass.

Underdog cries foul play. "You fiend—YOU traitor! —I should have known not to trust Polly Purebred! I should have realized you're not a Purebred at all—you're just a mongrel!"

I stick out my tongue. "Underdog, let's say you and me, we make a little deal. You tell me who you're in love with at school and I'll be a good little doggie and put the ladder back… okay?" Feeling the pain of defeat, Underdog lies on his stomach and hangs his head over the roof. The Great Underdog is deep in thought. The only sound heard is his stomach growling. Underdog must risk giving in or starving to death.

"Hmm… how about we make a deal? I'll tell you the juicy details, if you tell me if you ever kissed a boy. How about that?" I tuck one hand behind my back and cross my fingers. "It's a deal. You go first." When I plop down on the grass to hear Waynie's confession, I see a neighbor watching us from his front porch.

Underdog rips off his cape. "Okay Polly Purebred, I'll spill the beans and I'm not ashamed to say it! I'm madly in love with a girl named Patricia! She's the most beautiful girl in the world!" and looks at the sky all lovey-dovey. "One day when we were at recess I kissed her smack-dab on the lips and whispered, 'I love you, Patricia!'"

Screaming and laughing at the same time I shout— "Oh, Waynie, YOU BIG DOPE!"

Underdog hangs his head in shame. "All right, Connie Mary, cut the bullcrap. You won. Now tell me about your first kiss." Before I run, I look at Underdog's trusting face.

"Ha! I fooled you! I fooled you again Waynie Ormston! I was never planning on telling you anything and never will!" Waynie can no longer contain his frustration.

"Ah, gee whiz, gosh dang it, she did it again."

I run into the house laughing so hard my stomach hurts. I lock the doors and watch my cousin jumping up and down on the garage roof saying worse swears than my father! I hide behind the couch and hold my hands over my ears. When it is quiet and I think he has given up, I peek outside to see Waynie taking off his clothes and throwing them up in the air. There goes his belt, sneakers, socks and pants— and that's enough for me! I run outside just before he is about to pull down his faded underwear with the yucky brown spots.

"Waynie—STOP! Okay, okay—I'll put the ladder back… geez…ok." The next twenty minutes is spent trying to find Waynie's missing sock until the same neighbor I saw watching us calmly walks over dangling Waynie's sock between two fingers. Without smiling, he drops the sock on the grass and asks a question. "By the way, WHEN are you two kids going home? Sooner than later—I hope?"

197

When we enter Aunt Rosalie's house, we find Janice sitting alone at the kitchen table eating a plate of meatballs. This is when Aunt Sweetie comes prancing through the front door and plops two brown bags on the kitchen table. She goes right to work banging Aunt Rosalie's new pots and pans around. When she first notices Janice her eyes look sad. But she quickly changes her expression and smiles with love.

"Hey Jan, you're welcome to stay here with me. You can keep your old aunt company while I bake my finest sweet rolls." She chuckles as if she is planning on poisoning us instead. My sister smiles through red teeth.

"Oh thank you, Aunt Sweetie, you are a wonderful aunt!"

Aunt Sweetie sees Waynie standing next to me wearing only his underwear and laughs.

"Ah, ain't that cute. Were you two kids having fun playing *Underdog*? Well, does Polly Purebred and Underdog want some of my prize winning sweet rolls? If they do, they have to be good little children and go into the parlor and watch television."

The three of us are already transfixed by *Alvin and the Chipmunks* when Aunt Sweetie strolls in carrying steaming plates of gooey sweet rolls. Waynie is the first to grab a bun and shove inside his mouth. Aunt Sweetie pretends not to see and giggles, "Kids, I'll tell you a secret. If everyone in the world ate my sweet rolls there'd be no more wars, no more hate, and no more crazy people running around. See kids, I got a secret ingredient in my rolls. And you know what that is?" We don't answer because our mouths are stuffed with gooey sweet rolls, so Aunt Sweetie answers for us. *"It's love kids, pure love."*

The next morning I am very sad to be leaving Waynie. To protest my departure, Waynie climbs to the top of Aunt Rosalie's highest tree and will not come down no matter how many times his father threatens to *"break his goddamn neck."*

I stand below the tree, listening to the Mama Robin in my lonely nest weep. We both know I will not be seeing Waynie for a long time and cup my hands together and yell.

"Waynie! I wanted to say goodbye! I'm sorry I tricked you… *again*. I'll never tell anyone you kissed Patricia on the lips!"

Waynie looks down with the face of an 80-year-old man trapped inside a child's body.

"Oh sure…do you realize you just told the whole neighborhood?"

In the distance my father calls my name and I rush my words. "Waynie, don't forget me, and I promise I won't forget you!"

The dark, tangled web of branches cannot hide the light shining on the innocent face of a child. "You promise? This ain't another one of your tricks, is it Connie Mary?"

I hold up both my hands. "See, no crossed fingers. I promise I'll never forget you, Waynie Ormston. Never!"

My mother waves goodbye from our car and we drive away, Aunt Rosalie's house growing smaller and smaller until all that exists is the memory of what it looked like. We are less than a mile away when my father's eyes darken and he starts to confess all the thoughts he was forced to hide.

"*Hai detto a tua sorella, che Puttana, che non ero un idraulico buono.*" (You told your sister, that whore, that I was not a good plumber). My mother's eyes open wide with fear. She is shocked at my father's allegation and maybe a little guilty.

"Oh no, Albert. I didn't say a word about you!"

In the back of the car, my sister sits shaking but still has the courage to say, "Stop it, Dad! Stop this fighting! You'll kill us driving so fast!"

Out of the corner of my eye I see my father's fingers twitching like the tail of a rattler. He lets his foot off the gas and slows the car, looking at my sister with dark eyes. I know this is the warning that comes before a large unconscionable fist moves covertly, clandestinely, like death sweeping across a battlefield and makes a direct hit crushing my sister's nose. There are moments in life that are so horrific that time must stop to catch its breath. Pain, shock and horror spread across my sister's face as bloody-red gunk shoots from her nostrils. My mother can do nothing but scream—"What have you done Albert? What have you done!"

And then comes the greatest lie of all. When a seasoned abuser feigns remorse. My father calmly watches my sister's blood spill and her hands claw the air. The abuser's rage has been defused by transferring his pain to the victim and slowly turns into the parking lot of a Howard Johnson Restaurant. After removing the key from the ignition, the abuser lowers his eyes and gently gives his handkerchief to Janice. He clears his throat to show humility and with all the remorse of a serial killer carrying the victim's head in a suitcase meekly utters, "Janice, I'm so sorry. I didn't mean it. I lost my temper, forgive me."

My father ends up taking us out to breakfast and promises to stop at the next store to buy Janice a radio. On the ride home, I close my eyes and remember Waynie. I did not know then that Waynie would die from Leukemia and never grow old. To keep my promise, I dedicate this chapter to Waynie Ormston, who was born on October 25th, 1953 and died on January 4th, 1975, long before he could save Dogkind.

Documentation to the life of Janice Falcone written by cousin Lynda
Schnurr
January 6th, 2011

Dear Connie,

First of all, how could I forget you? You are my cousin. We played
together as children although I was closer with your sister, my sweet
cousin Janice, since we were closer in age. Because we lived far
apart—your family in Connecticut, mine in New York—we were not
able to meet up very often. And, quite honestly, my father was not
too keen on your father. That brings us to the subject at hand. I am
going to be as blunt as I am comfortable being. You might be
offended, but then maybe not. Some of us probably know something,
but not "a lot" as you put it and I cannot speak for anyone other than
myself. At the time, those of us who remained were all very young,
lived far away, and the stories about Janice's abuse came from second
hand sources—the main one being Aunt Grace—after Janice died.

The fact is your father was a vile creature. Sorry, but there it is, if
you want to see him as a victim, that's up to you. But adults have
choices, and he had to know that the things he did were wrong. He
seemed to be obsessed with heterosexual sex. He was even caught as
a peeping tom, looking in on the neighbor. Then there was the story
about your mother walking in on him with Janice in bed. He was
"touching her intimately," shall we say? Whether your mother told
my mother or Aunt Grace told my mother, I can't remember. I didn't
hear this story until after Janice had died. But it is obvious there must
have been more. I do not blame Janice in the least. She was driven
mad by guilt and rage; not only by her father's actions, but by her
mother's turning a blind eye. Janice visited Aunt Grace one time and,
upon leaving, being alone with her aunt, she turned to Aunt Grace
and said, "Aunt Grace, I hate my parents." She may have said that

she wanted to kill them. This was her cry for help.

Whether your mother participated in the abuse, I cannot say. But, Janice once had an opportunity to leave and get married. There was a fellow who wanted to marry her. She wanted to. They would not let her. I believe she would be alive today if she had. It wasn't the abuse that drove her mad. It was the powerlessness. I do know your mother would call my mother and tell her things. This story about the father in bed with his daughter may have come from a direct conversation between Aunt Chickie and my mother. My mother would tell her to get out or do something and she would cry and say, "Where would I go, how would I live?" Women then did not have the choices we have today. Your poor mother was a victim as well. Even Aunt Mel wondered about your mother's death. I have even wondered if your father may have murdered your mom (I told you I was going to be blunt), through her medication. Aunt Chickie was never a strong person and was young when she married Joe Falcone— He liked them young even then. I do believe he kept your mother drugged, as well as Janice. Thinking back, I believe the abuse of Janice may have started as young as 6 or 7. I remember one visit in Amityville. We were really little and she convinced me to hide and tried to show me how to masturbate. My mom caught us and broke up the scene before we did anything. But, I think this indicates that she already had some sexual knowledge beyond her years. Calanna mothers never taught their children anything about sex, leaving us hugely unprepared for life when the time came. It seemed odd that Janice already knew so much. Who taught her that?

I also remember when we were in Massapequa, we little girls used to love to dance (silly really, like modern dance, no gyrating or anything) in the big living room because we had a wall to wall mirror in there. When your family would visit, we would all dance: Janice, Carol, me, and maybe you, too; a nice memory, really. None of the adults would notice us at all (they'd be in the kitchen talking and eating!), that is except for your father who was very interested and would try to watch. Once he even told my mother that she shouldn't let us do that. It was "indecent." To him I guess it was very sexualized. They say that abusers were abused as children. Whether your father was or not, we will never know. But I do know that abuse in any form is about power. And, your father certainly had his own little kingdom that he ruled like Vlad the Impaler. Did he bother children in the neighborhood? I always wondered about that. You sent a picture of Aunt Chickie with bruises. That is so sad. He must have added physical trauma to his list of activities, but I never heard of it or saw any indication of it till now.

What a tragic story. Did he bother you? I don't know. You were the favored, golden-haired child. We never heard anything about you being violated. Was she not believed? I think my mother may have tried to encourage the removal of your sister from the family, but if the parents weren't permitting it, what power would an aunt have? And, the Falcone family—did they know? They were right there. Your mother's family was far away. It is all such a great tragedy, but isn't it late in the day to figure it out? All the major players are gone. You alone remain. You have survived, made a good life for yourself, and your beautiful children. So there you are. That is everything I know. I do remember watching Janice go further and further downhill on each visit. We would see one another about every two or three years. She had been such a pretty girl. Toward the end she cut off all her hair and retreated completely from reality. I am glad she is at peace.

Love always, your cousin,

Lynda

11

Farewell Good Soldier

The last photograph of Gustave O. Lorentz, taken by Rose Falcone

The last time I see Gus Lorentz it is spring, the season when the leaves open lush and green and the skunk cabbage reeks of life. I sense Gus has one foot left in life with the other getting a head start into the next. I am sitting beneath the little maple tree that Gus planted when I was born, when he walks toward me wearing an olive-green work shirt with *"Lorentz and Howard"* embroidered over the pocket. In his hands he carries his WWI helmet. When he stops, he looks up at the little tree with a sad face.

"Connie Mary, I planted this tree over a decade ago and now look how big she's grown."

The rays of the afternoon sun radiate behind Gus, making him look more like an angel than a man. "I was going to dance underneath this tree the day you got married." His eyes fall to his helmet. "See this helmet? This helmet protected me in World War I and was my loyal friend. I want to give it to someone who will take care of it," and lay the helmet by my feet.

"I'd like you to have it, Connie Mary. It would be 'portant to me if you would keep it. Maybe someday when you is a sophisticated college girl you can write something about my helmet and me. The good Lord knows I've told you and Anna enough stories to fill a book."

I gently picked up the helmet. "I'd be proud to keep your helmet, and someday I'll write a story about it, I promise Gus." After Gus leaves, I bring the helmet inside my house. I am surprised when a folded piece of paper that was tucked inside falls to the floor. I open and read the bold printed words: **"At the end of the day, when two soldiers from two different battlefields put down their guns, all that's left is two brothers standing side by side."**

One week later, Gus dies.

From the parlor window, through the pouring rain, my mother watches the ambulance workers roll a stretcher out of Gus's house and makes the sign of the cross.

"Oh no—no! It's a skinny body!" she cries. It's Gus! Oh, Jesus! The blanket is covering his face! Oh, our beloved Gus is gone! Oh dear God, what will we ever do without our dear Gus Lorentz? Poor Anna."

My father comes rushing down the steps seconds after using the bathroom, still trying to buckle his belt and shouts—"Who died?" When he learns it is Gus he has no desire to go outside and talk to the neighbors who swarm the scene like a drove of cattle. Despite the pouring rain, the old and faithful neighbors hold black umbrellas and silently weep at his doorstep knowing *there'll never be another Gus Lorentz.*

My father is at a loss for words and stumbles to the couch with a vacant expression. He has known Gus Lorentz for a long time. Their paths crossed the day my father signed the mortgage to our house in 1948. I can honestly say Gus Lorentz was the only man who truly loved and respected my father. When my father needed help, Gus did everything to come to his rescue. I am paralyzed by my own pain and cannot even cry. All I can do is whisper, *"Goodbye, Gus. I love you."*

One month later, Anna calls my mother sobbing. "Pinky's demanding I give him money for the bottle! He says if I don't I'll be sorry! Oh, Rose, what should I do?"

And what can poor Anna do? Anna is alone in the world, with the exception of Pinky's ex-wife Shirley who brings the grandchildren Debby and Chris over to visit on a regular basis. The oldest grandson Gustave (Cookie) Lorentz III is missing from these visits. When I ask Anna about Cookie she starts to sob.

"Oh, my poor baby Cookie! He's got trouble. They took him away and locked him up in one of them reform schools. Gus wanted everything we had in life to go to Pinky's children. They are our *only* grandchildren, you know. Gus knew those grandkids would never have much in life and said, 'Anna, if I go first, make sure the grandkids get what rightfully belongs to them.'"

Anna had no idea that greed and corruption were listening in the shadows or that Cookie would never live long enough to see his inheritance. If Anna had only known, she would surely have signed the deed over to Shirley that very day.

A week later, I exit my house and look over at Anna's place with curiosity, wondering why Tinkerbelle and Tiny are not outside. At this time of the day, the two dogs should be sleeping across Anna's driveway. I have a bad feeling as I walk toward Anna's house and before I reach the door, a frantic voice calls from the kitchen window.

"Connie Mary, I need to talk to your mother! Please tell her to come over—now!"

"Anna, where's Tiny and Tinkerbelle?"

Never in my life have I heard Anna cry with such sorrow. "Pinky took my babies away. I wouldn't give him money, so he sold them to a family with seven little chillrens."

When I visualize Anna's poor dogs in the rough hands of young, mischievous children, I know they are never coming back. That night while pouring a boiling pot of rigatoni into a colander, my mother vents angrily. "This would never have happened if Gus was alive. It is a sad fact of life Connie Mary, when Christ sends someone to protect us we think we will always be safe. But we should never forget: the Lord giveth and the Lord taketh away."

My days at Fields Memorial School are coming to an end. On a warm June morning I enter the school bus with little understanding of how the choices we make in life change our lives for the better or the worse. Soon enough, my school day begins with math class. As soon as Mr. Gagnon sees me, he lets out a sigh of exasperation. "Please try to behave today, Connie Mary."

He hands out worksheets and for the next 20 minutes, I sit embarrassed, having no idea what to do, and eventually decide to make a spitball. My eyes scan the room for the perfect victim and spot Frances scribbling circles on his paper. I wait for Mr. Gagnon to turn his back and then aim for my target. I make a direct hit between the eyes! This causes Francis to glower at his archrival Randy, who is innocently working at his desk. Francis repeats my process, but his spitballs include a tack with the point sticking out. Before all hell breaks loose, Mrs. Goothier's sweet voice comes over the intercom.

"Excuse the interruption Mr. Gagnon, but is there any way you could take a phone call in the office?"

"Sure thing," answers Mr. Gagnon. "I'll ask Mrs. Bucason to take my place."

The second Mr. Gagnon steps out of the room, Francis hurls the spitball at Randy and smiles when blood trickles down his victim's face. Outraged, Randy retaliates by throwing a chair against the wall.

Francis and Randy face each other with Francis standing a head taller. The boys in the class join in and egg Randy on. Francis is one of the strongest boys at school, yet cannot punch his way out of a paper bag, so when he takes a swing, Randy effortlessly blocks his fist and slaps him across the face. Randy begins punching Francis with such a force that Francis can do nothing but use his arms to protect his face. The other boys add to his misery by kicking his shins as hard as they can.

Mrs. Bucason enters the classroom and is horrified to see Francis being beaten. She cries out in a heavy foreign accent, "CHIL-WREN! Why you up in de seat fight-ting? Sit! Or I call Prin-ci-bull!"

No one is afraid of Mrs. Bucason, everyone is afraid of Mr. Paddle. The boys return to their seats and everyone is quiet except for me. I act bolder than any boy when I look Mrs. Bucason in the eye and say, "Why don't you go back to Russia with all the other commies and stop bothering us American kids over here?"

I am suspended that morning and my father is called from work to pick me up.

As I wait for my father, I stand in the silence of an empty playground and watch the clouds drifting by, wishing I could go with them. Finally, my father pulls up beside me in his old truck. When I climb in my father will not look at me. I plead, "Please dad... I'm sorry! It wasn't my fault!" I would have said the teachers beat me and I went insane if I thought it could have saved me. The short mile back home is extremely painful. My father is not speaking. He is waiting.

As soon as the key is pulled from the ignition, I run for the house, my brain screaming with fear. When I reach the kitchen my mother is nowhere in sight and my father comes up fast behind me. I seem to die of shame when he pulls down my jeans and exposes my underwear. Then he pulls the belt from his pants and yells in such a vindictive voice you would have thought I murdered someone.

"Bastard! I'll teach you to get into trouble at school!" and proceeds to whip his belt across my backside and legs. The pain is excruciating! And just when I think I cannot go on, I imagine Christ and the beating he took before He was crucified.

"Jesus. Help me, Jesus," I whisper.

With pain burning like fire, I see my mother standing behind my father with tears streaming down her face.

"Ma!" I yell. "Help me—help me!" But my mother cannot help me. As I am about to faint, I see, standing in the corner, the most beautiful vision of Christ who is somehow taking *the beating with me*. His spiky crown of thorns drips scarlet red and His heart flows tears of blood because Christ is *weeping with me*. I look at His precious image and feel no pain. When the beating stops, the beautiful vision disappears and the pain returns. Hours after this incident, I walk to Gus's Pond and gaze above at the stars lighting the black sky. When I hear the crickets chirping in the tall grass and feel the warm breeze moving through my hair, I know what happened to me today was a miracle.

The next morning, while still in bed, I hear my father's loud, angry voice. For a brief second, I think I am only dreaming. "Your daughter is just like you—a lazy bitch! She graduated from high school and now what is she going to do with her life? She's going to do what her mother does. Stay in bed and let me support her. I'm not going to do it. I'll kick her out of this house first. Think, Rose. If it wasn't for Janice we could be happy."

Hours later, I sit in the parlor, trying to ignore my mother crying in the kitchen. Janice stays upstairs as long as possible knowing our mother is waiting for her. When she finally comes through the parlor, she pauses at the image in the mirror.

"Oh dear God, why am I so fat?" In her quest to ease the pain, she heads for the refrigerator forgetting about my mother who is waiting patiently.

"Oh Jan, I'm so happy to see you! I'm so alone. Let me tell you all the bad things *your* father said to me today."

The tone in my mother's voice has a way of making my sister twitch and shake. It is no surprise, then, to hear a bottle smash on the floor. I clench my teeth at the sound of glass shattering and my mother's desperate plea— *"Why, Janice why?"*

With uncontrollable rage, I jump from the couch and run into the kitchen. I lunge and in one quick moment, slap my sister across the face and rip the wig off her head. The three of us watch in silence as the wig floats on top of a milky puddle of shattered glass.

My sister picks up the wig and says with calm resolve, "My sister is turning into *that* monster." She attempts to make a dignified exit but slips and falls into the milk and glass. Unable to contend with another Albert Falcone, my mother becomes hysterical, slapping my head and shoulders.

"CONNIE MARY—NO—NO! I won't let you do that to your sister!"

I escape out the door and run down to Gus's Pond. When I reach the massive oak overlooking the pond, I climb as high as I can. The stillness of the pond reminds me of the day I waded through the water as my mother watched. She thought the pond was safe and was shocked to see my legs covered in leeches when I stepped out.

That evening she asked Gus if he knew his pond had leeches. Gus hesitated before answering the question.

"Yes Rose, I knew my pond had leeches. I seldom talk about it 'cause people don't like to hear that something as vile as leeches exist. They also don't want to know that snapping turtles and water moccasins live below the surface killing innocent creatures. There will always be leeches in the world Rose. You just don't see them until they do something bad to you."

I stayed on the limb long after dark thinking about what lives beneath the dark water, trying to determine how I became my father.

My sister becomes more confused as each day passes. This is why she accepts the hospital's diagnosis that she is mentally ill rather than admitting her father is a rapist and having her family destroyed. The treatment plan includes partaking in a series of medication trials using Thorazine, Valium, Haldol, Lithium, Depakote, and Phenobarbital. Endless needles stab and prick her skin while her brain and body are subjected to endless tests. When medical tests confirm no evidence of a physical illness, a lifetime of psychotic disorders is stamped upon my sister's records. Due to an inability to control gross motor skills, Janice is repeatedly tested for Parkinson's and Huntington's disease, both of which prove negative. With all the trials and tribulations my sister had to endure during her lifetime, one question remains unanswered. Why was there never a connection made between my sister's deteriorating condition and the environment she lived in? There were reasons…

Underneath my sister's happy and cheerful disposition was an iron will committed to protecting my mother and me. I witnessed my father's physical and verbal abuse toward Janice, but did not learn about the incest until decades after her death. I have often imagined the words my father used to seal my sister's silence: *if your mother finds out, it'd kill her! Do you want me to go to jail Janice? And if I do, what will happen to your mother and little sister?*

As atrocious as this sounds, during my teenage years, I witnessed my father calling my sister a *whore*. This confused me, as I did not understand my father's motives at the time. Now, I understand that shaming is how a rapist keeps their victim quiet. Some readers will conclude that my father got away with all he did because very few knew about the incest. This is false. In every social network there are family members, neighbors, or even friends that know bits and pieces about the abuse yet fail to report it, as was the case with Janice. My father got away with all he did by appearing normal in his daily contact with clients, doctors, and family, while abusing the weakest link. In many ways I was stronger than my sister. This strength helped me survive, as it did the day the Bozrah Fire Marshall came to our home.

I am upstairs when I hear my father arguing with someone in the parlor.

"It couldn't have been my daughter, she don't even know how to light a match!"

The other voice is undeterred. "I'm sorry, Mr. Falcone, as hard as it is to believe, we have proof it was your daughter who set the fire, the older one with the black hair, kind of heavyset right? We have eyewitnesses who say it was Janice Falcone who set fire to the tall grass surrounding the pond owned by the late Mr. Lorentz."

My father emits an unholy growl.

"Mr. Falcone, may I give you a word of advice? In my experience, people who set fires tend to be troubled and it's a cry for help. That being said, maybe you should get your daughter some help?" I tiptoe past the men and go outside. When the voices subside and everything is quiet, a bloodcurdling scream strikes the air—

"Con! Help me! Your father's going upstairs to kill your sister!"

I rushed inside to find my mother blocking the stairs and my father's hands wrapped around her throat. Without thinking about the consequences, I pull Nonno's switchblade out of my pocket and push the gold button. The "click" is familiar to my father. He has heard a hundred switchblades open in his lifetime and immediately removes his hands from my mother's neck, causing her to drop to the floor. The look on his face is a mixture of shock and anger.

"Whatta ya think you're doing?"

My voice sounds strange and foreign. "Don't come any closer."

Amused, my father smiles a phony, patronizing smile. "You don't use one of them like a *toy*." and begins to pace back and forth like a circus elephant imprisoned by the chain. "You don't think I could take that switchblade away from you? Hah! —I've taken switchblades away from grown men! Men lots bigger than *you*."

My hand was weakening. "Don't come any closer. I mean it!"

My father laughs then slowly walks around me and out the door.

The next day things are back to normal. After that day, I felt a significant shift in power and no longer feared getting the belt. I held the switchblade as I slept and only in the morning light did I lay it down. I had beaten my father. Even if it was one small contest of will.

Sometimes we make the most horrific mistakes with the ones we love and cannot go back because the loved one has passed through an invisible door closed to the living.

All morning, I have been studying photographs of glamorous French twists worn by famous movie stars like Kim Novak and

Audrey Hepburn. My obsession began the day graduates of Fields Memorial School were invited back for a class supper. I dreamed of returning to school with a glamorous French twist and stunning everyone, and of never being called the class clown ever again. I made an appointment with Aunt Angie, believing she can help me achieve my dream. It is almost noon when my mother comes downstairs worried about Janice.

"Con...did you see Jan this morning? She started a new job today at *Teppers*. I hope it goes well."

I do not respond because I do not think my mother wants to know that my sister woke up late, poured a cup of coffee, and then spilled it all over her new uniform.

Instead I demand, "Ma, you have to take me to Aunt Angie's beauty salon. Today I get my French twist for the class supper tonight."

Stepping into Aunt Angie's salon is like stepping into the past. The assault on my nose and eyes from the ammonia and cigarette smoke is a familiar one. Unfortunately, the only air conditioner provides no relief, as it only sends warm air into the gaudy rooms. Through the haze I see Aunt Angie slowly making her way towards me. I am shocked, as her appearance has changed for the worse.

"Hey there, little Connie Mary, let's get you all washed up and underneath the dryer. I'll throw in some of them great big rollers because that's the way Kim Novak gets the glamorous French twist you want!"

Balancing a lit cigarette between pale cracked lips, Aunt Angie scrubs my head with surprising strength and energy. "Got to make sure you ain't got any of them damn lice. Goshdamn teenagers don't know they got the darn buggers sucking the blood out of their brains and stupid enough to share them with their friends." She cackles with laughter. "Lice are like men who like to jump from one head to another without getting caught."

After my hair is washed, she flings a towel over my head and pumps my chair into the air. When a customer comes over and whispers into her ear, Aunt Angie laughs so hard she has to go to the sink to spit out bloody phlegm. She makes the sign of the cross, murmuring, "Goshdamn cough is gonna be the death of me."

Another beautician scurries over with a worried look. "Ang'ch, you know how the mayor's wife wants #7 Blonde Temptress in her hair? Well, after I ran the product through her hair it turned out to be more orange than blonde. I'd say, a tad bit closer to #8 Orange Fling. What should I do, Ang'ch?"

My aunt stares at the ceiling for a minute and then smiles. "Tell her you read in *The Norwich Bulletin* that the mayor loves redheads. Tell her it'll drive her husband crazy with desire if she looks like Ann Margret!"

The beautician grins, clicking loose false teeth and disappears through the heavy smoke. Aunt Angie resumes working on my hair, asking the same old questions and answering them as well. "How's my little brother doing? — The poor bastard. You and me kid, Hell, we go way back don't we? Oh, Christ Almighty, remember the ponytail days?" She howls like a hyena. "If you were still wearing those tight ponytails, you'd be as bald as your old man is right now." I try loosening the rollers as she talks but she pulls my hand down every time.

"Let me tell you something, kid…now that you're old enough to hear the truth. More things go on in an Italian family than anybody likes to admit. And just because a house is painted nicey-dicey with a white picket fence and pretty window boxes to match—it don't mean shit! The day Bootsie turned seventeen, he forced Ma to sign his enlistment papers for the U.S. Navy. In my mother's heart, she knew Bootsie was safer in a war zone than living at home." She blows smoke in the air with disgust. "You'll see someday. Trust me when I say this, some Italian families are wonderful, but ours is bad for the health…just look at me." She reaches for a hairbrush and coughs loudly. Gasping for air, she starts talking to Jesus. "Lord Jesus, I'm coming soon, ain't I? Save a spot for me in Paradise Lord, 'cause I ain't got no worse sins than *The Thief on the Cross* and everybody knows you took him up to Heaven just like you promised."

When she plasters my head with Aqua Net and leads me to the hair dryer, I think I am almost done. The truth is I stay underneath the hair dryer for hours. At one point, I turn the hair dryer off and pretend it is still on. Whenever I ask my aunt how much longer she says, "Not now Con, can't you see I got an important client?"

Frustrated, I sat there all the way to 5 o'clock, one hour before the class supper begins! Frustrated and angry, I call my mother and leave—hair rollers and bobby pins intact. Once in the car, my mother cannot fathom how I was at the salon all afternoon and never got my French twist. "Aunt Angie never fixed your hair? What happened? Was she sick, did you fall asleep?"

"She was too busy to fix my hair! I'll hate Aunt Angie forever and never speak to her again!" Once we arrive home, I angrily yank the huge rollers out and weep at the sight of my wild bushy hair. Unexpectedly, this is when Janice peeks inside my room.

"What's the matter Con? Do you need some help with your hair? Did you know that I could make a French twist, too? Come into my room."

Desperate, I follow my sister and sit on a wobbly stool. I watch in astonishment as she elegantly swoops long sections of my hair into an upswing, giving me the French twist I desperately wanted! When finished, she looks down at me with love and admiration. "You look beautiful. Oh, how I wish I were you!"

I faithfully kept my vow and as the days turned into years—I never spoke to Aunt Angie again. I kept my hate alive, poisoning myself far more than I could ever imagine hurting my aunt. The day Aunt Angie died was the day I came to regret my stubbornness.

When my father learned of his sister's death, he threw himself on the bed sobbing.

"Ang'ch! Why'd you have to leave me all alone? Didn't you know, Angie? You were the only friend I had left in this world." My father knew he lost the only person who wanted everyone to know *his side of the story*. It is strange how someone's love can lift us higher to become the person they wish we could be.

"A Soldier in my Coffee"
A Tribute to WWI Soldier, Gustave O. Lorentz

I was sitting in the comfort of my sunny kitchen table when I looked
down and saw the face of a soldier in my coffee.
At times the face would change as the wars varied,
But every soldier during one battle or another had longed for a hot
cup of coffee.

In the trenches during WWI,
When rain filled the tunnels
And Hell and blood soaked the boots
A soul cried out—
For somewhere, a soldier was thinking of a hot cup of coffee.

As they walked over war torn battlefields where buildings were
annihilated to ashes
And fear raced madly around every corner...
Somewhere, a soldier was thinking of a hot cup of coffee.

As the battle raged over field and stream—
And eyes burned from poisonous gas,
A soldier lay dying.

In his last moment...
He walked into a dream
Where he returned to his wife
And together they sat at the kitchen table,
Drinking a hot cup of coffee.

As my life goes on and times change for the better...
I hope someday, I no longer see the face of a soldier in my coffee.

By Concetta Falcone-Codding

Part II

The Demise of Rose and Janice Falcone

12

Life Is Worth The Trip

"We love teenagers, we hate teenagers. The truth of the matter is, teenagers remind us of who we used to be and the pain left scattered across a lonely playground."

It was the summer before high school and everything was changing. While the Norwich Free Academy loomed above me, looking far more like a college campus than an ordinary high school, my mother returned to the Norwich State Hospital for a second time. That time she did not go kicking and screaming but ran quietly and willingly through ironclad doors. My mother's demise did not happen all at once. It began at the same time as Janice's insomnia, which had my sister wandering through the house like Marley's ghost.

I lay in bed listening, hoping the sleeping pills will keep my father from waking. Janice is preparing a midnight snack and the loud clatter of pots and pans makes me nervous. I do not know if my father is waiting in bed for the right opportunity to yell, "If I haven't told you once, I told you a million times—get back in bed!" or if he is actually sleeping, unaware of Janice's wandering.

Mere seconds after wondering if anyone else is awake, I hear my father get out of bed and head downstairs where an altercation and then a full-blown fistfight begin almost immediately. My sister stands no chance and my father knows this. After a few minutes of scuffling, an eerie silence penetrates the house. I cover my head with blankets and fall back to sleep.

Hours later, I wake to the sound of a struggle outside my sister's bedroom. When I investigate, I see my father in the hallway wearing his black striped pajamas and holding a nylon rope. The first time Aunt Grayce saw his pajamas she commented to my mother, "Your husband is wearing the perfect outfit for when he goes to prison."

My father is wrapping a frayed rope around my sister's doorknob and attaching it to the banister. He mumbles incoherently as he ties the knot.

"Goshdamn sister of yours won't sleep. This will keep her from opening the windows downstairs and making my oil bill go up," he laughs with devilish glee. "See, after tonight, she won't be able to do that anymore. I nailed the windows shut."

The next morning the rope was gone—disappeared, as if it never existed. That same day, my mother appeared at my bedroom door with a horrified look upon her face. She instructs me to be silent, placing one finger across her lips, and then waves for me to follow her, glancing nervously out the window at my father mowing the lawn.

We go into her bedroom and I observe the troubled look on her face.

"What's wrong, Ma?"

My mother is sitting on the edge of the bed nervously twisting her wedding band. She looks away and says in a strained voice, "I have to tell you what Janice told me. She said Dad threw her on the bed last night and put two fingers up her vagina. She says when I'm not around he calls her a *whore*. My daughter's not a bad girl. Why does that man call my daughter that bad name?" My mother has nothing else to say and begins opening the pill bottles on her nightstand.

I can barely breathe from the sense of hopelessness that suffocates the room. I feel that I am in a dream as I watch myself leave my mother's room, exit the front door, and walk down Fitchville road. Without a sense of purpose I walk for miles, not knowing where I am going or what I will do next.

I learned the hard way why algebra is the most dreaded subject in high school. It is not the math material, but the math teacher. With straight black hair and a cropped mustache his resemblance to a famous dictator is uncanny. We call him *Nazi* behind his back and, out of childhood ignorance, point our arms to salute him by laughing. I found out karma had been watching me when I was the only girl placed in his algebra class. For the first few weeks I manage to stay clear of his firing squad, but eventually the day comes when he points a yardstick in my direction.

"*Miss Falcone*, I want you to go to the blackboard and solve the equation."

I walk to the board and hesitate, pretending to solve the equation by scribbling random numbers. Nazi's reaction is to chuckle.

"Sit down, Miss Falcone. One of the *boys* will solve the problem for you."

After forty minutes of sheer torture the class is over. I dash out of the classroom and run all the way to the Commercial Building determined to drop algebra. I push my way into my guidance counselor's office, my speech well-rehearsed.

"Either I drop algebra or, I swear to God, I'll quit school today!" After twenty minutes, Mrs. Shrewsbury graciously ended my plight.

"All right Miss Falcone, do not fret. Starting Monday, your algebra class will be replaced with English 101. Hold on, let's see which English teacher has that section." As Mrs. Shrewsbury searches through the catalog, the sun peeks through the tall windows, illuminating the dreary room with golden light. When she sees the name of my new teacher, she beams with enthusiasm and points her cigarette at the ceiling.

"Oh my, somebody up *there* must be watching over you. Your new teacher is Alan K. Driscoll."

On Monday, I return to school, searching for the wide stone steps that will take me below the Slater Building. The bottom level looks like a dungeon with its cranky floorboards that squeak and fill the nose with dust. A wooden clock from a bygone era chimes and reprimands me for being late. With smug indifference, I strut brazenly into the classroom and hand my pass to the teacher slouching behind a desk sprinkled with worn and tattered books. The slumped posture and thick-rimmed glasses make him look more like a sleepy owl than an English teacher. His appearance does not match the voice that is confident and painfully sharp.

"You're late. Once is an exception. Otherwise, I shall hold this crime against you until death do us part. I would suggest not making this a habit. I am known to be quite the brute."

I look for an empty seat as contemptuous eyes follow my every move.

"Find a seat," beckons the voice of authority. "I have begun reading to the class."

I almost faint. Is this a joke? I stumble to a desk in the back row with the F-word carved over every square inch. Then I notice the boy sitting next to me: a hoodlum dressed in black who keeps kicking his dirty boots on the chair in front of him. I look around the room to see a group of misfits and detect the thick aroma of rejection hiding inside every person's lonely nest.

I look back at Mr. Driscoll, who looks as though he doesn't have a care in the world. He bites into a jelly donut, whose crumbs fall onto a newspaper as dozens of spitballs congregate underneath his desk. And just when I think this is going to be another boring class, Mr. Driscoll smiles, displaying an impressive number of teeth.

"Pray tell, what will you do with your allotted time on this good Earth? Will you dream big or will you settle for cutting fudge into perfectly measured squares at Grant's Department Store? Whichever path you chose, I hope you leave the world a better place than how you found it."

Hoodlum kicks the chair. "This guy's more nuts than me."

"Hell ya," says a girl, seemingly unaware of her enormous breasts in a tight sweater jiggling every time she laughs. "Hey, I know who this guy looks like...he's the fat friggin' Cheshire Cat! What a loser."

Despite the laughter, Mr. Driscoll holds up a dilapidated book with several pages hanging loose. "Ahem! Attention, please. The bell rings in less than one minute. For next class, I shall continue reading *The Catcher in the Rye* by J.D Salinger." He attempts to brush donut crumbs off his shirt, unaware that he is rubbing powdered sugar into his tie. "In order to read a novel of such complexity I must have no interruptions, no distractions, and no comments from the peanut gallery. Do not be fooled by the logistics of this class nor the manner in which I teach. Your participation and attitude will determine your final grade."

I leave that day not knowing that I have crossed paths with a kindred spirit nor how that path stretches miles long.

On Friday night I accompanied my father on a service call to the home of his childhood friend, Dr. Chooch. My father's clients respect him as a skilled plumber. My father knows as long as he keeps them happy and doesn't get caught stealing, he will stay in demand. My father also knows that, despite his popularity, his highly educated clients laugh behind his back, "The little wop is good, but he charges highway robbery."

My father has mixed feelings about Dr. Chooch. He loves him but is also jealous of him. This is because Dr. Chooch got to play football at NFA while my father never had the chance. Personally, I do not like Dr. Chooch. Especially after the day he called our house looking for my father to repair a refrigerator for a young nurse. When he asked me to write down his number, I politely asked him to repeat. This simple request enraged him and he began screaming like a privileged spoiled brat.

"Can't *you* people ever get anything right? Ugh! Ah, *dio lo aiuti*. What your poor father has to put up with. He not only has your hysterical mother—he's got *you* and *your crazy sister!*"

I am visibly shaken when I tell my father what Dr. Chooch said. My father's first reaction is anger before he recognizes he is powerless to do anything. Even if he had the power to do anything, what that power would cost. Either way, my father is guilty, knowing he opened his big, fat mouth one too many times to complain about his family.

"Ah, he meant nothin' by it. Don't take things so serious. If that's the worst thing that ever happens to you in life, you'll be lucky. Chooch is *one lucky bastard* all right, he's got a beautiful wife that works outside the home and gives fantastic dinner parties. Just look at Henry's wife Philomena, workin' day and night at the American Thermos Company. Christ, I wish your mother was more like them."

"What's so great about the American Thermos Company anyway, Dad? You're always talking about it like it's the greatest place on Earth." My father looks at me as if I said Frank Sinatra wasn't Italian.

"What are you talking about Missy? The American Thermos Bottle Company is known all over the world! Thermos built their factory in Norwich and within five years that baby doubled in size! You don't know anything about the history of where you was born. Christ, don't you know, when war broke out in Europe, thousands of Thermos bottles was riding high in our planes? Gus Lorentz always talked highly about the American Thermos Company." Having mentioned the name of Gus, my father pauses to reflect.

"Yup, if Gus was still alive, he'd tell you. And one thing we know for sure, Gus Lorenz never learned how to tell a lie."

My father steps into the past and softens.

"My whole family worked at The American Thermos. My father worked there for 25 years and ended up as a foreman in the glass factory. The old man, even with his broken English, worked himself up the ladder. Me, my two brothers and four sisters—we all worked there. At one time, the Laurel Hill Factory in Norwich employed over a thousand people! Connie Mary, *if you want to know which way to go in life, you have to follow the path that was started for you.*"

The following day my father signs my mother out for a home visit. It will be another disastrous weekend spent forcing my mother to return to a problem that has only grown worse in her absence. On the way home my mother brims with excitement.

"They gave me back my old job at the Canteen! I can't believe I didn't forget how to run a cash register!"

As soon as my mother arrives home and sees that Janice is not there to greet her but upstairs in her bedroom, she remembers why she left and wants to lie down. I resent my mother and do not think she wants anything to do with me. When she starts to walk up the stairs, I cannot hold my anger back any longer.

"Ma, don't you want me anymore?"

She stops and grasps the banister without looking at me.

"It must be the shock treatments I've been getting. Sometimes, they make me forget where I am. I'm so sorry Connie Mary."

When she shuts her bedroom door, I know she is gone for the weekend. I won't be like my sister who stays locked in her room; I will make my own fun. It just so happens that tonight, I have been invited to a party hosted by a wealthy teenager and have two friends who can drive me.

When the Cadillac Eldorado pulls into the driveway, I know Dennis is already high. Christopher is with Dennis and when he sees me approaching, he hops in the back, smiling through glazed eyes. I have known both of these boys since first grade. We have the same goal in life: *to avoid pain.*

Dennis is counting how many purple pills are in the palm of his hand when I interrupt.

"I see your Dad's working the night shift again."

Without answering he hands me a pill, slams his foot on the pedal—and away we squeal. Christopher whips his head around, admiring the long black tire marks while laughing with vindication.

"Hey Con, tell your old man we left him a calling card," he pauses before continuing, "But not when he's holding that friggin' shotgun."

It is dark when we turn up the elegant stone driveway lined with glowing lampposts and majestic trees. High above the grassy knoll stands a mansion as elaborate as the Taj Mahal. Dennis swerves erratically across the lawn, plowing down a row of cherubs guarding the entrance and parks the car looking concerned. He looks all of us in the eye before opening his door.

"No one better mess with my Dad's car. I'm gonna lock it up, just in case." He steps from the car and locks each door, forgetting the car is a convertible.

The house welcomes us with shrouds of incense floating by and posters of Jimi Hendrix, John Lennon, and Janis Joplin staring at us from the walls. Amongst the favored musicians and singers is a derogatory poster of Lyndon B. Johnson with the words *Hey, Hey, L Bee Jay, How Man-y Kids Did You Kill To-Day?* painted red to look like dripping blood. Eventually we come to an enormous bar with red leather stools and a perfectly curved countertop. A bartender wearing a white shirt and black bowtie hands me a Bloody Mary with a blue straw and we sit and drink to forget. Whatever is happening in the world right now is not our concern.

Several hours later, the atmosphere changes. Drunken teenagers topple tables over and throw empty beer bottles out the window, cheering at the sound of the breaking glass. Christopher and Dennis stand by a table known as *The Feast* and choose from platters that contain every drug imaginable. Needing to use the bathroom, I place my drink on the glass table and walk away. On the way back, I see a group of teenagers passing around a huge bong and playing Spin The Bottle. I try my best to avoid the bodies sleeping across the floor.

I finish my drink and close my eyes. After a few minutes, I look up and see two boys looking down at me like a specimen in a jar. A boy with long blonde hair is holding my glass close to his eye and making observations.

"Yep, it's empty all right—bummer." He looks at his redheaded friend. "Does this chick know she just drank my lysergic acid diethylamide?"

His friend replies, "I don't know, dude. Let's ask for sure! Hey Chick, did you know you drank Blondie's Bloody Mary mixed with LSD?"

My eyes dart to the glass table and my heart pounds. My drink with the blue straw remains there, untouched. The blonde looks concerned. "That's a drag, sunshine, but don't let it bring you down. Look on the bright side, tonight you'll liberate your body and mind!"

The redhead lights a joint and contemplates the situation as if he were John Lennon.

"Cool it, man, mellow out. You know, whatever you tell this chick becomes her new reality." They start to walk away when the blonde looks back.

"Don't get heavy sunshine. Think Flower Power and Strawberry Fields and you'll see parts of the world you never knew existed. Turn off your mind, relax, and float downstream."

I want to believe this is a bad joke, but my new reality is already taking form. In the room an ocean of water rises higher and higher, so I run to the bathroom and lock the door. I am floating on the crest of a wave when a familiar voice calls from far away.

"Open up…it's me, Christopher!"

When I open the door, Christopher's face melts like candle wax. This is my last memory of the party. As Dennis drives away, I sit in the back of the car and roam freely through the dimensions of past, present, and future without the restraints of time, space, or mass. I meet my soul and discover it is older than time and surprised that it is neither male nor female. I visit the sacred land I lived before I was sent to the womb and understand the language of every beast and human.

Not knowing what to do or where to go, Dennis pulls into Anna's driveway.

Anna's house is dark and forsaken until a bright light shines from above and I return to the past. Tiny and Tinkerbelle run alongside the moving car, barking with excitement and I can finally understand their language. "Remember Connie Mary, love lasts forever!" As the car heads towards Gus's Pond, the dogs vanish into the light.

Dennis parks by an overgrown bush and lights a joint. "I have a plan that will save us and it's simple: we'll walk Connie to her door." He passes the joint to Christopher and the atmosphere turns sinister. Something evil has entered the car. This is the hate that Christopher holds for his father. As Christopher helps me from the car his words fall to the ground and become a robin with a broken wing.

"My father used to punch my mother so hard, she'd hit the wall."

"Your father is a bastard all right," interrupts Dennis. "But what can you do about it? Hell, I think Fitchville is one big Peyton Place. Everybody knew what your old man did. But nobody ever did anything to stop him."

A large calendar floats through the dark sky and my eyes widen as its pages turn back to 1959. I soar above the treetops, traveling back to Christopher's childhood home. Christopher turns six years old today. His mother decorated the house with blue and white streamers and invited every classmate to celebrate. It is the kind of party every child dreams and she is the kind of mother who wears flowing dresses and pink pearl necklaces. These are the happy days for Christopher, a deceptive precursor to the future. The calendar flips ahead to 1978.

I am older now, standing by the side of the road with a group of men. We observe a Volkswagen that has been mangled and crushed. Even though we are unable to see inside the car, we know it contains the body of a young man. The men laugh, calling the mangled boy a fool for driving so fast and it makes me sad to think how little we understand about someone's life. Christopher's mom was not here to see her son die. After her death, Christopher could not reveal the secret that brought him to this moment. Even though decades have passed, many in Fitchville continue to blame his mom's death on a vague term called *domestic violence* instead of naming the abuser who shortened her life.

The three of us seem to walk for miles through the shifting planes of time. When we finally reach my house, Dennis peeks inside the window.

"Yup, the old man's here with his old lady. Time to let 'er go, Chris."

The boys grow wings and fly, disappearing behind wispy pink clouds. With blissful ignorance, I walk inside my house and casually sit on my father's lap.

"Hey Dad, guess what? I took LSD, I'm tripping." A horrified look appears on my mother's face. Events come and go rather quickly from this point. On the way to the hospital my mother holds me across her lap as my father explains the medical prognosis.

"She might never be normal. It all depends on how much LSD she took."

I stayed overnight at the hospital for observation. A nurse tucks me into a warm bed and I notice a little old lady sitting next to the bed, quietly knitting. The lady smells of lavender and has a sweet voice.

"I'm here to watch over you, sweetie. Relax and get some sleep."

As soon as I fall asleep…they come.

When the first visitor floats through the wall, applause is heard from a thousand WWI soldiers. I would know him anywhere, him in his green military uniform and battered helmet. His skin burnt umber from working long days in the hot summer sun. Somehow, Gustave O. Lorentz is standing above me. "I guess I didn't get the chance to dance on your wedding day, eh, Connie Mary? See, when the Lord calls, you gotta go. It's kinda like the Army."

I haven't seen Gus in years and have so much to ask. "Gus, is it beautiful up there in Heaven? Is it hard without Anna telling you what to do all day?" We both laugh, knowing no one ever told Gus what to do because Gus knew what was right and did it. The spirit of Gus shines brighter than a Christmas tree in Rockefeller Center.

"Anna's coming along very soon. Remember the things I told you 'bout Heaven Connie Mary? Well, I did you right. The Lord is filled with boundless love and forgiveness. You'll see someday. I'll wait for you and Janice at the gate." He drives away in his emerald green truck and disappears into the light.

Hours later, a strong scent awakens me. The smell is familiar, a combination of cigarette smoke and ammonia. It cannot be—oh yes it is! Floating above my bed, holding a lit cigarette, is Aunt Angie.

The cigarette is a surprise. "Aunt Angie, they let you smoke in Heaven?"

She laughs. "Oh ya… but trust me kid, they ain't like the cigarettes back on Earth. These ones are called Heavenly Lights and they don't have quite the same 'kick' as the cancer sticks, you know what I mean?"

"How is Heaven Aunt Angie? Do you like it up there?" She floats closer and shows me a sparkling new wedding band on her finger.

"Me and Rodney, we're back together. And things couldn't be better. Hey kid, I came to tell you somethin'…your old aunt is sorry about the last time you were in my beauty parlor. Remember? You asked for a French twist and never got it. Sorry kid, I made a lot of mistakes in life and that one was a whopper. I was too busy trying to make the old *denaro* and didn't bother to help my little niece who needed me."

The light grows dim when a frightful, gruesome image floats into the room and I recognize it immediately. It is Janice, restrained in a tiny bed. She is lifting her head and then slamming it down on the bed's metal rails. Blood flows down her face.

In fear, I cry out— "Aunt Angie! Is this what will become of my sister?" Aunt Angie is moving away, slowly becoming absorbed in the soft white light. In the distance is a familiar chuckle.

"Remember kid, life is worth the trip, even if none of us gets out alive."

The wind blows the curtains high and she is gone.

My last visitor is someone I would never have expected. A wooden boat sails above me, turning the room into the Sea of Galilee. Inside the boat sits a group of sun-drenched men looking anxiously across the sea, searching for someone. The one they seek is a vigorous young man with a smile that lights up the world. He wears a simple white tunic and red robe and motions for Peter to follow as He walks across the surface of the water. Peter steps upon the water but begins to sink and cries out— "Save me Lord! Save me!"

Christ patiently pulls Peter into His arms.

"Where is your faith, Peter?"

Christ is aware of my presence and smiles at me. In that moment, I realize He is the sun, the moon and the stars and everything good that has ever been or will be. When the vision fades, I am left alone listening to the nice old lady snore.

The next day, I go home.

Later that evening, as I recover from my experience, my father comes into my room and speaks words of wisdom that prevent me from seeing the horror hiding inside his lonely nest.

"See kid, now you know what it's like to burn your hand on the stove. You won't make that same mistake again." His voice starts to shake. "I've made some awful mistakes, Connie Mary. Bad ones. And I can't go back." He gazes out the window at Gus's house and looks about to cry. "No matter what happens in life, you have to put one foot in front of the other and keep on going."

I did not know my father was trying to confess his sins. Having made an attempt at redemption, he rests his head against the wall and sleeps until darkness devours the light.

13

Nonno's New Life

Janice's 1966 Norwich Free Academy yearbook photograph

"There are times in my life when I have loved and when I have hated. Love shows no remorse when it crushes your heart into a thousand pieces. On the other hand, Hate coils around your heart like a Mojave Rattlesnake never letting you forget who caused the pain. In the end, everyone knows Love is the answer...but Hate...Hate has a purpose."

The moment Bill comes into my sister's life, the sparrows sing a sweeter song.

Bill is a chicken farmer who lives on a small farm owned by his rich grandmother. My mother says Bill is not Cary Grant but he's sincere and stands to inherit the family farm once his grandmother passes away. My father believes otherwise.

"Hell will freeze over before the old bitch lets that happen."

Bill is tall and lanky and madly in love with Janice. He would be perfect if he did not have a mouth full of broken, rotten teeth. Janice tries hard to be what most men desire in a woman: all looks and no brains. She is beautiful, standing five feet six and having recently lost 50 pounds. She hopes to win approval from a society that holds a starving woman in high esteem. Having a witness on her side significantly changes my father's behavior and for a short time, my sister is safe. Bill helps Janice find a job as a secretary at one of the local chicken farms and, in return, my sister finds him a dentist and soon white dentures replace his black rotten teeth. My sister is incapable of hindsight and does not recognize the importance of Bill or how he could have been her North Star, leading the way to freedom.

In celebration of my sister's new job, Nonno invites our family to dinner at Club 41. Nonna is too sick to celebrate and stays in bed. She developed a cough last week that has grown worse with every passing day. Before leaving, Nonno makes the sign of the cross over Nonna's bed and promises, "Rose, we come straight-a home after we eat." True to his word, after dinner, everyone follows Nonno back to Talman Street.

My mother is the first one to see Nonna gasping for air. "Ma, you're very sick!"

My father becomes excitable when his mother does not respond. He stares at his dying mother and then looks at Nonno with rage. "Pa—why didn't you tell me Ma was THIS sick? This is all your fault.

You treated Ma like a dog. You murderer!"

Nonno looks relatively young for his age. This is partly due to his relationship with a younger woman named Ann. Nonno thinks Nonna does not know about this woman. When in fact, old Calabrian women see the evil hiding in the hearts of men. Nonno does not know it, but the life he took for granted is about to change.

"Don't you think I forgot what you did." says my father. "Tying Ma to a chair in the cellar when she wouldn't give you money for booze." My father wipes away his tears and spits on Nonna's polished floor. "And what you did to us kids. *Tu maiale italiano* (Italian pig)! You know what I'm talkin' about, don't you Pa?" My father leans toward his mother and strokes her wet hair.

"Ma, you didn't deserve to die like this."

In eerie silence, Nonno stumbles to a chair like an animal wounded by one of its own. When my mother looks at Nonno she bursts into tears. "Oh Pa, I'm so sorry!"

Nonno starts to beg, *"Bootsie, Non parlarmi in quel modo!* I good hus-a-band to Rose...I yam—I yam!"

No longer able to sit, my mother comes behind Nonno and rests her hand on his shoulder.

We sit in silence for a few moments and then my father lifts Nonna's body out of her bed and carries her down the stairs. We follow as if it were a funeral procession. When he goes out the door, everyone knows Nonna is never coming back.

Nonno keeps repeating: "Me no know! Me no know Rose so sick! Me no know." Overcome with grief, Nonno runs into the parlor and kneels by the statue of the Blessed Mother.

"Help me *Madre di Dio!* Please, Help Nunzio!"

At home the hours pass in surreal silence. At one o' clock in the morning, I hear footsteps coming up the stairs and angry words being shouted at my sleeping mother.

"Ma's gone. *My mother's gone.* That good for nothing Jew doctor! Ma had pneumonia and he knew it a week ago. That Bastard did nothing about it—he just let her die!" My parents climb into bed with my father still cursing.

About an hour later, my father wakes and wants to talk to my mother about what the *Italian Stallion* will do now that the latch on his cage has been lifted. "Ma's gone. I wonder what trouble the old man's going to get into now that he's all alone?" My mother responds with love.

"Albert, your father's going to be alone now. He is going to need us to be there for him. Try to get some rest."

My father has trouble sleeping and rises several times to argue with the darkness. "That *Figlio di puttana!* My mother scrubbed those floors on her hands and knees—'till they bled. If the old man knows what's good for him—he better hold onto that house."

It is almost morning when my father falls into a restless sleep. The faint sound of my sister's easy listening music manages to escape from behind her bedroom door. I have come to despise the never-ending melody that foreshadows the eternal emptiness dying inside my sister's lonely nest.

In the wake of Nonna's death, Nonno comes to our house for supper most evenings. Sometimes he arrives drunk and exchanges unpleasant words with my father. My mother worries about Nonno. She heard the old Calabrese women say that Nonno knew Ann long before his wife died and in retaliation for her death, they promised to send him a bad omen. My mother was shocked to learn that Ann was a hustler, a gold-digger and former prostitute. "Poor Nonno." she said and started to cry. As for the exact words to describe Ann, my father only has one: *Puttana.*

It's not long before Ann moves into the house where Nonno lived with Nonna for over fifty years. This enrages my father and siblings who helplessly watch Ann control Nonno. My father is hell-bent on revenge and drives by Nonno's house to see if Ann is in the yard. One day he sees her mowing the lawn on the hill and says with disdain, "I hope to God she falls off that friggin' bank and breaks her Goddamn neck."

Despite resistance from every one of Nonno's children, the situation goes from bad to worse when Nonno impulsively sells his five-bedroom Victorian house to Ann for $10,000. Like a lovesick fool, Nonno foolishly agrees to leave his home forged with the sweat and blood of Nonna's hands and move next door into his run-down, three-story apartment building. Nonno will tell my mother this arrangement was the only way Ann would stay with him.

On the same day Nonno loses the house, my father decides to take us to an Italian restaurant in New London. My mother is trying to find the right time to tell my father about the sale of the house, having already heard the news from Aunt Angie. I cannot imagine how she thought it would be safe to tell my father while driving on the highway with the four of us in the car. There is a reason my mother is known for her cooking and not decision-making skills when out of the blue, she blurts—"Pa sold his house to Ann for $10,000 and plans on moving into his apartment next door!"

My father's reaction is like a man falling off a cliff. He slams his foot on the gas pedal and accelerates. As his face glows red, he yanks the wheel to the right and we watch in silence as he veers off the highway and speeds along the grass. When the brakes screech to a stop, two long destructive ruts remain on the road behind to tell our story. Cars whip past us in blurs of colors as my father berates my mother.

"Why you miserable son of a bitch...why didn't you tell me this before? Huh? Why?"

My sister immediately defends my mother. "Stop calling Mommy bad names. Stop it! You have no right!"

An abuser is adept at detecting weakness and smells easy prey. Like a hunter estimating the approximate range and proximity to make the shot, my father turns around two times, tightening his grasp on the beer bottle resting between his legs. He emits a low growl before swinging his arm behind and smashing the bottle over my sister's head. As glass shatters and blood sprays into the air, specks of blood spatter across the back of my mother's head as my sister releases a horrible scream!

When my mother turns around and sees blood pouring out of Janice's nose, she looks at my father as if he is Lucifer in the flesh and cries, "Albert no! Dear Jesus, no, no!"

The hatred that held my father prisoner is released like a smoking gun after hitting the mark. He leans back and hands his handkerchief to Janice. The passing cars slow down to peer inside our car—*but no one stops*. At this time, society gives a husband complete control over his family and not even the police interfere. At the emergency room I am silent even though a volcano is erupting inside of me. In the next few months I will plot and plan and tell on my father. *Yes, so help me God...I will tell on my father!*

In my second year at NFA, I learned why they hide the unruly beasts below the Slater Building. They do not want to disturb the students with a real future. The lucky teacher in charge of the unruly beasts is sipping tea and trying to ignore the occasional spitball thrown across the room.

Hoodlum is back for a second season. He failed every freshman class with the exception of English, which means he is tossed back into Mr. Driscoll's lap. The equation is a simple one that even I can understand: *having the most difficult students is the reward for being a good teacher.* Due to his explosive nature, Hoodlum is assigned a seat in the back row. Having developed a fondness for Hoodlum, Mr. Driscoll calls him "McQueen" after the fast action hero in movies.

I walk into class five minutes late and laugh at Mr. Driscoll holding a handkerchief to his nose. "I never saw such a white handkerchief in all my life. I am guessing, Mr. Driscoll, that your wife washes your clothes?"

Mr. Driscoll barely catches his sneeze—*KER-phewww!* and looks at me with disdain.

"Now I understand why Helen Keller said, 'the highest result of education is tolerance.' Connie Falcone, once again—you're late!"

He is clearly agitated when he sees a spitball fly across the room.

"Please, everyone take a seat! Goodness gracious—settle down! We may dwell in this Godforsaken dungeon, but I have the highest expectations for how this class shall be conducted. Due to a deplorable cold that has left me in the clutches of despair, I will not read today. Instead, each of you will write a short essay pertaining to *The Catcher in the Rye.* This should be extremely effortless since I have been reviewing the importance of an essay having a beginning, middle and end since the beginning of the Ice Age."

After a long silence, Hoodlum snaps his pencil in half and the rest of the class starts to murmur.

Mr. Driscoll looks concerned. "Come, come, good people. This is a very small writing assignment and sneezes again. "Every student in class is more than capable of making a personal connection to the text." When nothing works to restore civility, Mr. Driscoll imitates game host Hal March from *The $64,000 Question* television show.

"Folks, here's the $64,000 question of the day: Holden is isolated during the most trying times in life. Have you ever experienced this kind of isolation and loneliness? If so, explain. This is an easy task…right?"

Silence.

"All right, how about you McQueen, what's your take on the question?"

Hoodlum gives the chair in front of him a swift kick and snarls, "This class is bullshit."

Whenever a student speaks disrespectfully to a teacher, no one cares. What everyone does care about is how that teacher responds. All eyes look toward Mr. Driscoll who is pretending to be busy sorting papers. Being ignored is not the response Hoodlum wants, so he strides up to the teacher's desk, his leather jacket crackling menacingly, and rips his paper in half. The students watch in awe thinking how wonderfully dramatic when Hoodlum does something even better. He takes his book and flings it across the room. Not impressed by this display of bravado, the portly, middle-aged teacher stands and faces a lean, muscular McQueen.

"William, I suggest if you have an issue with me or this class we take it outside."

Hoodlum shakes with anger. "Problem *I'm* having? What about the essay you sprang on us? And you know what else? I know why you read to us. You think we're stupid. You're a phony, Driscoll— just like all the people in that book and every teacher in this school."

The confession appears to have opened a wound. Hoodlum looks down and stares at the floor and as if transported by time, sees a young boy standing next to him. Hoodlum knows this boy well. He is the same boy who would wait for the school bus believing he would always succeed in school. He tries to stop his tears from flowing with the sleeve of his jacket but cannot wipe away the tears of a lifetime.

"I don't belong here. I don't belong anywhere. I'm sorry I couldn't be the person you wanted me to be." He walks out, slamming the door.

Mr. Driscoll hurries to the door and yells into the black corridor,

"Getting angry is a cop-out, William! When you come to your senses, I shall be in the dungeon! Damn this bleak, obsidian hole. The lights went out again. And to think Edgar Allen Poe would have been elated to teach here." Mr. Driscoll sneezes before he can reach the box of Kleenex —"AH-CHOO!"

In an effort to regain normalcy, he sits down and opens the Norwich Bulletin. His smile returns when he sees that the NFA Wildcats won again. Without further disruptions, we resume our work. My mind wanders as I try to figure out how innocent children become Hoodlums in the first place. On the first day of school every child is filled with hope. Why then, do so many children lose that hope by the time they reach high school?

One week passes and then another with Hoodlum still gone. When Mr. Driscoll calls Hoodlum's parents he discovers the phone is disconnected. He goes so far as to drive to Hoodlum's house, which is nothing more than a vacant lot. A week later Hoodlum casually strolls into class and takes a seat. Mr. Driscoll stops lecturing mid-sentence to observe Hoodlum's dirty clothes and sees that his leather jacket is gone. Mr. Driscoll is a master at looking oblivious. "Hence, enlighten me! Who completed last night's homework?" He would not have been so calm if he saw the words someone carved on the front of his desk: *We forge the chains we wear in life by Charles Dickhead.* After class, Hoodlum is the last to leave.

"May I speak with you after school tomorrow Mr. D?"

"Why, sure William. Pardon me for asking, but what happened to your leather jacket?"

McQueen shrugs his shoulders. "I lost it."

Mr. Driscoll's gaze never leaves Hoodlum's face. "Sure… sure thing William. You always know where to find me. Here in the dungeon, fighting the good fight."

In the following weeks, Mr. Driscoll placed a black top hat on his desk and asked students to sacrifice their cigarette or soda money for a good cause. All their change and spare dollars went into the hat. And when Hoodlum came to class for the last time, Mr. Driscoll handed him a new leather jacket he had bought with the collected money. Hoodlum stood in front of the class and bawled. A week later, he dropped out of school.

Mr. Driscoll eventually discovered that Hoodlum had not been living with his parents but inside an old abandoned car and never forgot the lesson he learned. Even though he did not save Hoodlum, he did something just as important: he eased his pain and gave him comfort. Before Hoodlum left, he knew how it felt to be loved by a good teacher. It does make you wonder though, why some children must go through life without a loving parent and the only kindness they will ever know comes from a stranger.

My father tries to keep the telephone he installed in the basement a secret but it only makes his lies come to the surface. I take advantage of the situation and sneak down one day when he's not home. With hands shaking, I call the police station and try to disguise my voice to sound older.

"Hello, may I please speak to an officer?"

A contemptuous male voice responds. "What's the problem?"

I want to slam the receiver down because my heart is beating so fast.

"*Oh, hel-lo* officer. I... I want to report a crime."

His voice quickens. "What kind of crime? What's your name?"

"I'm sorry, I can't give you my name. It's my father. He punched my sister and broke a bottle over her head. He wants to hurt her and maybe even kill her! And when no one is looking, I think he does worse!"

There, I did it. I saved my sister. The officer will probably need my address when he sends a patrol car over to take Janice away to a safe home. I can hide out at Anna's house until this blows over. Anna would hide me forever if I asked. I'll be safe because my father would never go against Anna. He wouldn't dare… and… and…

"Is your sister over the age of eighteen?"

That's a strange response. Didn't he hear what I just told him?

"She's over twenty-one, why?" The officer places a hand over the speaker to muffle the sound, but I clearly hear his words. "Tell 'em I want two creams and three sugars in mine."

"I'm sorry, Miss. Your sister is a *consenting adult*. We can't do anything about an adult who chooses to stay in a bad environment. If we did, we'd have to hire another police force to arrest the perpetrators. Why, if I had a dollar for every call from some concerned citizen ranting about some woman in a bad situation, I'd have my mortgage paid off and be living in Florida by now. Sorry Miss, I can't help you. Try a relative. Maybe they can help."

I stay in the basement inhaling the stench of mold and laundry soap while deciding what to do next. When I finally dial the number, I pray Uncle Henry will answer and by some miracle he does.

"Hello, Uncle Henry. This is Connie Mary."

My uncle's voice is as refreshing as biting into a ripe tomato on a warm summer day. "Hey, Connie Mary—How ya doing? Where's your mother and father? I bet your mother's out spending the old man's money while he sleeps on the couch after drinking too many beers." Typical of most Falcone men, his happy mood turns off like someone flipped a light switch. "No one's home. Phil went to work and left me some cold meatballs."

I know if I do not tell now, I never will. "Uncle Henry, I've got something to tell you… and it's bad. My father hits Janice! He slaps her around and it's getting worse."

I could not have stunned my uncle more than if I hit him on the head with a brick. Even so, I do not have to justify my story. My uncle knows from his own experience with my father that I am telling the truth and starts swearing about him in Italian.

"*Non ci assomigliamo per niente, bastardo, figlio di puttana!* Bootsie shouldn't be doing that to Janice. Janice doesn't deserve anything bad like that to happen to her 'cause your sister's good." He forces a weak laugh. "She's not a troublemaker like you, Connie Mary. No. Janice is an angel."

A painful silence follows.

"Listen, I want you to listen to what I have to say. Someday, you're going to get married and have a house. I want you to save one bedroom for your sister so she can get the hell away from that bastard brother of mine! Please, Connie Mary, in the name of Jesus, take your sister away!" My uncle is fearful. Snitching in an Italian family is serious and could result in the possibility of leaving his wife a widow and children orphans. No one is wiser to my father's ways than Uncle Henry. He knows all too well how it feels to be physically and mentally abused by my father.

When I hang up I know my uncle is unable to help me. I call Uncle Ettore.

Uncle Ettore is the complete opposite of Uncle Henry. He is a handsome, mild-mannered businessman who never resorts to violence as a means to settle problems. My father's relationship with Uncle Ettore is far different than with Uncle Henry. My father and Uncle Ettore are material equals; both went to college and both make good money. Uncle Ettore appears to be a wonderful person and would be, if not for the problem my sister and I had with him when we were younger: when visiting, he would come upstairs to 'use the bathroom' and then surprise us by pushing open our bedroom doors.

I thought Uncle Ettore was as smart as Mr. Driscoll but the longer I speak with him, the more I think he does not understand English.

Uncle Henry believed me without question while Uncle Ettore keeps asking me to repeat my story like one of those fancy lawyers trying to damage the credibility of the witness. Finally, he relents and gives me my way.

"All right Connie Mary. You win. I'll call your father tonight."

I pick up the receiver and listen when he calls. "Bootsie, is everything all right between you and Janice? I heard you might be having a rough time, losing your temper and resorting to violence with Janice. Is this true Boots?"

My father replies with the calmness of a man simply straightening his tie.

"Oh—no—Ettore, where the Hell did you ever hear that? I never laid a hand on my daughter, or anyone else for that matter. Just ask Rose, she's sittin' right here and she'll tell you."

My mother's response is silence.

Small talk ensues. The car needs new brakes, how hard it is for my father to pay for my mother's prescriptions and how draining it is for a man to come home every night to a sick wife and daughter. I hang up and search for the Dalmanes hidden underneath my bedroom rug and take a long nap.

On one of the last days in June I find my mother sobbing in the parlor.

"Janice broke up with Bill!"

I refuse to accept her words but then realize Bill is usually at our house around this time of day and feel the pit in my stomach expand. "What happened?"

My mother strokes Sam's head for comfort. "Bill said he couldn't tolerate what is happening to Janice. He wanted to marry her and get her out of this house. My daughter could have been a wife, a mother, have babies—my babies!" My mother starts to cry again. "Janice broke up with Bill!

I refuse to believe what I am hearing. My mother blows her nose and rises to her feet. "I need to take my pills now," and wobbles into the kitchen.

I run upstairs and knock on my sister's door. "Jan, it's me. Can I come in?'

She responds too cheerfully. "Sure, Con. Come on in."

My sister is sitting on the bed drawing black lines on her face where her eyebrows once flourished.

"Jan, what happened? Why don't you want to marry Bill?"

My sister responds by laughing as if she did not have a problem in the world.

"Oh Con, don't be silly. I like Bill a lot. But I do not love him." Both our heads turn to the window as we hear the sound of wings flapping. A chickadee attaches its talons to the window screen and stares at Janice. My sister's eyes open wide with excitement. "Look! I love chickadees!" The chickadee shakes its head up and down and sings to Janice.

"Little chickadee, do you know that I love you?" says Janice. The bird flitters back and forth in a rapid motion and chirps, "chick-a-dee-dee-dee," before taking flight. My sister stares at the empty screen and I feel her loneliness.

"Janice, please! Think of what you're doing. Won't you miss Bill? Didn't you like having him protect you?"

She says nothing.

After a long silence I lose my calm and plead— "Oh, Jan! What will happen to you?"

My sister changes position exposing ugly black and blue marks over her arms and legs. She chuckles at the absurdity of marrying Bill. "I can't marry someone I don't love, can I Con? That would be unfair to Bill."

I have no more to say and walk away.

If only I could have seen the future. What atrocities were waiting for my sister and then I would have screamed—*Oh yes you can marry someone you don't love! What about you Jan? How come life is not fair to you? Oh please God, make Janice marry Bill!*

14

A Child Of God

Janice and her parents, courtesy of Michael and Phylis Falcone

"We are born a child of God and will die a child of God. We can turn away from the face of God, but He will never turn away from us."

Mrs. Donna Elsensohn

My junior year begins with sadness when I discover I do not have any classes with Mr. Driscoll. Often, I find myself walking below the Slater Building just to sit in the hallway and listen to him teach. One day he spots me before I have time to leave.

"Well, hello stranger. Or as Shakespeare would say, 'Welcome to Rome.' About time you came to visit." He points to my shoes. "I saw you walking around campus with your head hung low and thought without a doubt she is making sure no one steps on her Bass Weejuns."

When I force a smile, he sees what many teachers do not.

"I know how tough it is for students to come to school. I compare it to having to come in every morning and teach English to the masses that detest writing. By the way, how's life treating you?'

I say what every teacher expects to hear. "Good, you?"

"Fighting the good fight as usual. As you can see, I still reside in the dungeon that permits me to tend directly to all the prisoners. Oh, I almost forgot, I have a tidbit of information you may find useful: next year, my schedule changes and I'll have seniors. Yes. They always give Driscoll the best schedule." He rolls his eyes. "Nevertheless, there is a high probability that you could attend. I would sign up quickly since students find the dungeon an easy bolthole to illicitly kiss in the dark." He glances at his watch. "Oh darn! I want a meatball grinder before the football team tramples the cafeteria. God knows those boys devour everything in sight with nary a crumb left for a mouse. Anyway, it's late and I'm hungry, so I shall bid you adieu!"

I watch him run toward the cafeteria like a fast moving penguin.

A few weeks later, late at night, the phone rings. My father isn't home. He's at Club 41 fixing the ice machine. Or, at least, this is what he told my mother. I tiptoe into my mother's bedroom and pick up the receiver to listen to Aunt Grayce speaking in hushed tones.

"Is he home honey—where are the kids?"

After my mother confirms my father's absence Aunt Grayce delivers an urgent plea.

"Honey, tell me—how is Jan?"

My mother starts to cry. "Grayce, I need help! He is so mean to my daughter! Oh Gray, I don't know what I'm going to do."

There is a short silence before my aunt explodes.

"Honey, what do you mean…'I don't know what I'm going to do?' You help your daughter—that's what you do!" She pauses. "I'm going to tell you something and I want you to listen real good. If any husband of mine ever hit my kids, swore at my kids, or looked the wrong way at my kids—it would be the last thing they ever did."

My mother seeks to appease her sister and agrees wholeheartedly. "Oh yes, Gray, oh yes!"

Aunt Grayce does not respond. She knows my mother says one thing and does another and has no plans to do anything about my father. Still, she intervenes for the sake of Janice.

"I'll tell you what Honey, you send Janice to me in New Jersey and I'll help that girl. Okay? You send my niece to me and I'll deliver her back with the strength of David!"

Within days, my sister packs a suitcase and flies away on a small plane to Camden, New Jersey. In the next few weeks my sister will have a reprieve. My godmother, however, will not. She will hear an appalling and painful story that is both enraging and heartbreaking. The pain will be so severe that it will feel as though someone hammered and nailed her feet to a cross.

With Janice gone, a false sense of calm falls over the house. My mother hums a soft tune to herself as she pours a can of Italian tomatoes into a cast iron pot. My father enjoys a cup of coffee while reading the *Norwich Bulletin* and has nothing to complain about. We have all been given a glimpse of life without Janice, and it is a very peaceful one.

After several weeks, my sister is scheduled to return home. My father gives orders for me to pick up Janice at the Groton Airport. My mother comes along for the ride with a face etched in stone. Once we arrive, I park the car and the two of us make small talk watching the planes unload passengers.

"I forgot to lower my spaghetti sauce," says my mother flatly.

I grow restless and start to whine. "Ma, when are you getting more money from Dad? I need new clothes. Everyone has new clothes at school except for me."

Our conversation is interrupted when Janice steps out of the plane and into the bright sunlight. Her face is unrecognizable from a distance. She reminds me of Lazarus returning from the dead, although her welcome home would not be the same. She looks different than the woman who left home a week ago. My mother is surprised to see her wearing a green gauzy scarf and an elegant pantsuit with her eyes made up to look like Elizabeth Taylor.

Janice opens the car door and apprehensively steps into the back seat. My mother is overmedicated and unaware that her words add salt to an open wound.

"Aren't you glad to be home Jan? I bet you missed your father."

Janice flies into a rage. "I'm not taking any more crap from dad, I can't! I won't! I won't be treated badly anymore!" She begins condemning my mother with sheer disgust. "You could have stopped him. But you didn't. I hate you too!"

The rage I feel is directed at the wrong person. I have lived with an abuser all my life and seen so much violence, that, out of fear, it is easier to blame the victim and remain loyal to the abuser. Though I have started the car and it is rolling, I suddenly lunge at Janice in the backseat and slap her several times on the head. As a final insult, I pull off her wig and throw it to the floor. She is completely bald except for the short pieces of hair scattered across her head; tender, delicate wisps trying to grow back. But they will not grow back, because as soon as they start to grow, she takes a pair of scissors and chops them off.

Not knowing what else to do, I drive around in circles in the parking lot. My actions have left me in a state of disbelief and shock. Janice says nothing as she picks up her wig and puts it back on her head.

My mother, who has witnessed this debacle, cries out— "Oh God, please…I need to go home and lie down!"

The minute we arrive home, my sister trips inside the house, spilling her bags of clothes across the floor. There is no welcome. No kind words for the prodigal daughter only, "Gosh damn it. She's home," grumbles my father.

I buried this memory inside my lonely nest for over twenty years. It was 1992 when Aunt Rosalie forced me to remember. I owned my own home when Aunt Rosalie and Uncle Joe came to visit. Still trying to impress my mother's wealthy sister, my father offered to drive them to my house. At this time I had forgotten Janice. I could not remember the month and day she died. The word *forgotten* carries a tone of choosing not to remember the past. I believe what happened to me was something called "dissociative amnesia." Dissociative disorder is an emergency defense mechanism that shields the mind against overwhelming trauma.

When my guests arrived, I gathered everyone into the parlor. I went into the kitchen to make coffee and found it strange that Aunt Rosalie followed me. From the kitchen I saw my father and mother laughing with Uncle Joe. Aunt Rosalie was also looking at them, but with sheer disgust.

"*Did you know Connie Mary?* Did you know that when your sister went to New Jersey she told Aunt Grayce that your father forced her to give him *oral sex?* And did you know that your mother caught your father in bed with your sister?"

I was standing a few feet away trying to balance a tray of coffee cups and immediately rationalized that Aunt Rosalie was telling lies. *Aunt Rosalie is only making this up to make trouble for my mother. Were not my mother and her oldest sister always at odds?*

I answered my aunt as if I always knew the truth. "Yes, I knew," I uttered before walking back into the parlor. When I saw my father I could barely stand and felt as though I would faint.

"Sit down, Connie Mary," said my Uncle Joe, smiling. "I hear you're a schoolteacher now. That must be rewarding."

Before I could answer, my father interjected, "Yep. She's got her master's degree and she'll be getting another degree soon. What's it called, kid?"

"A sixth year," I croaked.

"Yep, she'll be gettin' a sixth year from *The University of Connecticut.* I always told my daughters, no matter what happens in life, no one can ever take that sheepskin away from you."

My father playfully pointed to his brain and looked at me. "I tried to explain this to Janice, but she never wanted to listen. Thank God I got one daughter who graduated from college."

Aunt Rosalie's smile was a thin line of revulsion watching my mother stuff a whole cookie into her mouth. Slowly lifting her cup of coffee, Aunt Rosalie burned a hole through my lonely nest, sneering, "Oh Joe, you must be so *proud* of Connie Mary. Yes, so proud."

I did not bother to confirm Aunt Rosalie's story and continued to deny the abuse that happened to Janice. It was not until 2009 when I became desperate to know the truth. I knew Aunt Grayce was the best person to ask but she had passed away in 1987. I decided to contact her oldest son, Steven Lerro. He confirmed Aunt Rosalie's story without hesitation.

"The week Janice stayed at our home, apparently she felt safe enough to tell my mother the truth. I'm not sure my mom was prepared to hear what she said. How could anyone prepare for something like this? My mother was livid, enraged and grieved beyond belief, as she repeated Jan's words to me: *'Aunt Grayce, my father is making me give him oral sex—and it's disgusting!'* Janice also told my mother how she felt about your parents. *'I hate them both. So much so, I'd like to kill them!'* More horrific was the fact that days after Janice's homecoming, my mother called your mother and told her everything. But your mother did nothing to save Janice from further abuse."

Still in denial, I asked a foolish question. "Are you sure your mother told my mother?"

Steven's voice was livid. "You must remember your godmother Connie Mary? How could someone like my mother, Grayce Lerro, defender of the underdog, hold onto something like that? My mother would never keep silent—never! NOT MY MOTHER! She'd die first! I'm afraid there's more. After your mother learned Janice was forced to give her husband oral sex, she said to my mother, 'Grayce, you can always get another daughter, but you can't get another husband.' I'm sorry Connie Mary. But these are your mother's *own* words."

The dysfunction in my family continues with little hope of change as I delve deeper into the world of alcohol and drugs. After a night of drinking and dropping pills, I fall into bed with the room spinning in circles. I feel queasy and am about to vomit when I hear my sister's headboard banging against her wall.

I followed the glow of the red nightlight and found Janice underneath a blanket. I assumed she was playing a joke and yanked her blankets to the floor. I stood in horror at what I saw. Her body was twisting and shaking and her eyes were rolled back. I could hear a strange clicking sound and discovered she was chomping her teeth together and screamed—

"Dad! Janice is having a fit!"

My father rushed her to the hospital, and so began what others would see as his heroic crusade to save my sister. One must never underestimate an abuser. Intuitively, they know when their victim is close to telling and move swiftly to squash the truth. This evolved into a farce and a tragedy as my father arranged for Janice to be evaluated by the best hospitals in the east where a team of qualified doctors developed theories.

"Could be the late onset of epilepsy, possible brain tumor, or chronic nutritional deficiencies," said a prominent member of the group.

"On the other hand," said a young intern, "It could be a hidden immune disorder, or a liver or kidney failure, which may account as a side effect of the numerous drugs prescribed."

Out of all the outrageous speculations, possibilities and observations, the home environment was never questioned. Abuse seemed out of the question given the obvious care and concern of the father. There is, however, one fact to which every doctor agreed: *all medical tests performed on Janice Lynn Falcone revealed no physical disease or cognitive disorders. The seizures, the self-mutilation, the loss of fine motor skills, and the falling and banging of the head, all stemmed from something else.*

The Lonely Nest of Michael Falcone is breaking into pieces. Nonno has not been doing well since he sold his house to Ann. One night I go to his apartment and find him hiding behind the curtains, spying on his old house. When I asked him why, he answered with resignation.

"She want me no-a more." I try my best to console him,

comparing Ann to a cunning hen who went and took advantage of a vulnerable old rooster, but his remorse is far greater than anything I could say.

He laughs cynically with tears in his eyes. "I should-a given house to Bootsie. In old country, no one gets away with crime like-a this. Ann no live long."

Everyday that passes seems to magnify how thin and weak Nonno has become. His only companions are the empty bottles of Johnny Walker Red poking out of the trash can. I try to change the subject.

"Sit down Nonno. Tell me about your childhood in Calabria, when you were a runner for the mafia." Begrudgingly, he turns away from the window to sit in one of the few chairs he has left and blankly stares at the worn rug.

"Bootsie, right. Me no good for Rose. Me no good for bambinos. Look at my little Bootsie. Who is this man? Where did *Mio figlio* go? He picks up a spoon and dips it into a container of ricotta cheese. "Nipote, sometimes change comes late. Nipote, before I die, I hope Bootsie finds peace."

I stay with Nonno and watch him eat his ricotta cheese until the container is empty. When it is time to leave, I give him a gentle hug. The sweet musky odor of pipe tobacco is painfully familiar and I almost cry when he whispers, *"Ti amo nipotina."*

I take one last look at Nonno alone in the dark, not knowing this is the last time I will see him alive. Weeks later on a dark and rainy night, he gets drunk and demands to see Ann at his old house. When she does not answer the door, he becomes enraged. After banging on the door and yelling her name, he tries to find his way back to his apartment in the dark. He loses his footing and tumbles down the steep bank in his front yard that Nonna always warned him about.

He managed to stand on Talman Street and continue walking, but it was foggy and in his drunken state Nonno could not see clearly.

He walked right through the opening of a chain-link fence that was built to keep cars from plunging down the steep banking. His body came to rest near the Shetucket River where his children played in happier days. He survived a few days in the hospital in a semi-comatose state and then died.

God, it was hard to lose Nonno. I loved him despite all the bad things he did and begged God to answer one question: *God, tell me…how can the Falcone men be so bad and yet so good?"*

Nonno remained loyal to my father by signing the apartment building in his name. I imagine Nonno hoped this would repair the damage and violence he committed against my father as a boy. Nonno died wishing my father would find peace.

He never got his wish.

After years of receiving impunity for the violent crimes he committed against his daughter, my father grows bolder and chooses a different population to torment. He has always found the Elsensohn family to be a constant source of contempt. He cannot stand how high they allow their grass to grow nor how happy they appear despite having little material wealth. However, the biggest reason why my father hates the Elsensohn family is because every time they park their van next to our yard, they must step on our grass to reach their house. It drives my father insane!

One day my father forces himself to be polite and asks Mrs. Elsensohn to move her van.

Mrs. Elsensohn looks him in the eye and says, "Oh sure, Mr. Falcone. If I have time."

A day passes and the van is not moved. That night I see him dressed in black and walking out the door with his shotgun! I run to my mother who is frying eggplant in the kitchen.

"Ma, come quick! Dad went outside with his shotgun! I'm sure it's about Mrs. Elsensohn and her van!"

Before my mother can reply we hear an ear shattering—"BOOM! BOOM!"

With an eerie calmness, my mother lowers the setting on the stove and slowly walks outside. I follow behind with my hands shaking and ears tingling from the gunshots. My mother stands by the Elsensohn's driveway and studies the dark house. Two more shots explode into the air, causing sleeping birds to scatter into the night.

"Ma, what are we gonna do?"

My mother says nothing. I follow her back into the house where she gently flips the golden eggplant in the pan.

"My goodness, Connie Mary, don't worry. The Elsensohn's are not home. Their house is dark. Sit down and have some of my eggplant. It's my mother's Sicilian recipe."

An hour later my father comes back inside, looking more agitated than ever.

"That *bitch* insists on parkin' her car near my grass? I'll fix her. I'll get my ice pick."

I follow him outside, blending in with the shadows of the trees. The Elsensohn house is no longer dark. The rooms are brightly lit, illuminating several people inside. This does not stop my father from walking up to their van and driving his ice pick through the front tires.

As time marches on, my father's dysfunction becomes worse. It was not enough to just hurt Janice or my mother. He becomes obsessed with how to hurt the neighbors without getting caught. All of the neighbors he wants to hurt are already vulnerable, frail, and elderly with Mrs. Elsensohn being the prime target.

I recall a conversation I had with Mrs. Elsensohn in 2009, six months after my father died. I was outside cleaning the yard when I looked at the house next door. The Elsensohn family had lived next door to my parents since I was a little girl. I was still ashamed that I had stayed silent for so long. Mrs. Elsensohn emerged that morning, the portrait of a lovely, elderly woman who had been widowed for a number of years. She began to rake the same grass that had enraged my father and when she walked on it, I knew I must tell her the truth.

"Hello, Mrs. Elsensohn. I'd like to talk to you. Do you remember me? I'm Connie Falcone, I used to live here."

Immediately she smiled. "Of course I remember you." and walked over to give me a hug.

After a few minutes she appeared to sense what I was about to ask. "Did you know Mrs. Elsensohn, that it was my father who slashed your tires?"

The elderly woman answered with unwavering strength. "I held out hope it was not Mr. Falcone, but my family believed it was him." With wise grey eyes she looked back at her worn peeling house and recalled the painful memories. "Your father punctured the tires on our van several times. Other times he removed the tire valves so the air would slowly seep out."

She pointed to her bedroom window. "See that upstairs window? It was punctured by a bullet and still has a big round circle around the glass. Your father did this to the Nolans and Louise Meyer as well. He would slash their tires too."

I strolled with her through the yard until she stopped and took my hand.

"You know Connie, your father did some good things for me too. One day I was mowing the lawn and the back wheel fell off. Your father was outside and apparently saw what had happened. Later that day he came over with an old lawn mower. 'Here,' he said gruffly, 'you can have this one. I just bought a new lawn mower.' There's more. Another time, it was Christmas Eve. My husband was alive and my children were very small. My husband was preaching at church when a fuse blew in the house. It was the dead of winter and I had no lights to see the tree or anything. I called your Dad and he came right over. He rigged something up with extension cords. Anyway, it worked. The children had their Christmas tree and I had my sanity. Oh, your mother was good to me as well. One day she came over with a huge stuffed bull and said your father won it at a fair. She said she wanted to give it to my children."

We continued to walk, stepping over garbage and rusty hammers hiding in the tall grass. We gazed fondly at Beebe's Fields, knowing that Farmer Beebe and his cows belonged to the past. We eventually returned to where we began.

With renewed gratitude I whispered, "Thank you, Mrs. Elsensohn."

She looked at me with eyes that knew love was stronger than hate.

"Remember Connie Mary, we are born a child of God and will die a child of God. We can turn away from the face of God, but He will never turn away from us."

As I watched Mrs. Elsensohn go back to raking her yard, I vowed to expose the complexity and dimensions of a narcissist abuser, the same abuser who had helped people during the most trying times in their lives. Now I know the answer to the question so many people ask those who live with their abusers: *Why don't you just leave?* What many do not understand is there is often still enough good left in the abuser for the victim to want to stay with them.

As for Mrs. Elsensohn, she threw me a life preserver that day. Some people spend their lives in darkness, inflicting senseless pain onto those around them, while others spread the good news by proclaiming the ineffable love and forgiveness of Christ.

15

Chains Are Made To Be broken

Janice restrained in bed at The Norwich State Hospital with my mother by her side.

I woke up in the middle of the night to the pouring rain. I heard screaming and saw my sister being dragged from the house by men in white uniforms. I followed them outside and saw my mother, her tears somehow distinct from the rain. My father was standing there, too. He kept his distance, but I could see the fear in his eyes.

Before the doors closed, my sister pointed at my father and yelled, *"YOU BASTARD! I hope you rot in Hell!"*

At the time I was confused at how deeply my sister seemed to hate my father. I could never have imagined the truth and what my father had been forcing her to do.

We followed the ambulance to the Norwich State Hospital through the gloomy fog, losing sight of the ambulance several times. The office staff at the administration building knew the routine. They said my sister was taken to another building for surveillance as the doctors feared she would hurt herself. In the waiting room my mother talked about Janice as if she were a stranger.

"She is getting worse. Honestly, I don't know what's going to become of that girl."

Afterward, we drove to the Kettle Building and found my sister sedated and restrained in a tiny bed. The nurses greeted us with care and offered to give us a tour, not knowing we had already taken the tour. The day room had not changed since my mother's stay. It smelled of cigarettes and bleached-scrubbed floors; a despair only confirmed by a never-ending line of patients walking around in circles searching for an elusive feeling called *hope*.

I followed my parents into the psychiatrist's office where the walls were painted dull-brown with a lingering scent of pee and bleach. My father, the smoothest operator on the face of the earth, paints a portrait of his own shock and confusion, as if he has no idea why Janice is deteriorating so quickly.

"It's the damnedest thing Coric. First, she ain't eating at all, and then she's eating me out of house and home. Tell me, why does my daughter fall down all the time? And did you see *that* hair? Jesus Christ, she's balder than me underneath that wig!"

My father thinks he has fooled the doctor and lets his guard down. "That kid always did have something wrong with her." He gives my mother a dirty look just in case she dares speak. "She tripped over my toolbox when she was a kid and snapped her arm in half," he chuckles. "Hell, anyone could see *that* body was too big for her age."

My mother is also a patient of Dr. Coric and has been seeing him at his Ledyard office for over a year. She admires how he risked his life to escape communist Yugoslavia and was detained in a refugee camp for years before coming to America. She voices her true feelings when we leave to use the restroom.

"I wonder what the doctor thinks now," and laughs bitterly. "I bet the bright young man who came to America would never have imagined the disturbed mind of someone like your father. I wonder if he has discovered yet that the people who love his patients the most are the ones most likely to be causing their suffering."

We return to see Dr. Coric closing my sister's file. The doctor studies my father with a keen awareness that he is in the presence of a skilled liar and makes an attempt to pacify him.

"Your daughter will stay here for a short time. You say she has bad eating habits? No worry, we regulate food. You say she falls down? No problem. We will restrain her with a plastic belt. From our observations, we can see your daughter is losing control of her arm and leg movements. We are concerned she may have other serious problems. Has she ever been tested for Tardive Dyskinesia, Huntington's disease or Parkinson's disease?"

Shocked, my mother looks at my father to say something. At his silence she turns back to the doctor. "Now what does this poor girl have? My poor Janice, she never stood a chance from the minute she was born. She looks at the floor and tries to hide her rage.

"You know Doctor, *he* wanted a boy, not a girl. He wanted Connie Mary though."

My father's face turns bright red with anger. "What are you talking about Rose? That's a bunch of bullshit."

The doctor quickly intervenes.

"Mr. and Mrs. Falcone, we must focus on the present. We will take good care of your daughter. We will give Janice tests to see why she is losing control of her body. To be safe at night, she will be restrained in bed with a safety net. When socializing in the day room, she must sit in a chair wearing a restraint. When walking, she will have an escort. Mr. and Mrs. Falcone, we will keep your daughter safe. Let me know if you have further questions. You may call the hospital and have me paged if needed. Have a good day."

One week later I returned to a familiar world. A world that was keeping my sister safe as it did my mother. I stood in her tiny bedroom looking at the white nylon net that prevented Janice from leaving her bed. The net hung from the ceiling and was attached to the floor, enveloping the bed like a net hunters use to capture an animal in the jungle. The nurses referred to this as a 'Posey bed' and said there was no chance of escape as not even a knife could penetrate the strong nylon. Curious, I asked her what she did when she had to use the bathroom.

Clearly embarrassed, she whispered, "I wear a diaper."

After several months the hospital releases my sister with no formal diagnosis and labels her mentally ill. On the day she leaves to return home my parents and I come to help her pack.

Despite the outcome, my sister explains to my mother why she still has hope.

"Ma, I met this patient named Marlena and she gave me the number of a full-blooded Italian looking for a wife. His name is

Rocky! Isn't that a cute name? He's Sicilian like you. Oh Ma, he might be the one!"

My father is fixing the snap on my sister's suitcase when he rudely interrupts the conversation.

"He sounds like a *Rocky* all right. I bet he's got a few rocks in his head."

On the drive home, my father blasts the Yankees' game on the radio without any concern for others. Whenever we pass a house with flower boxes my mother laments, "Albert, why can't we put some flower boxes on our house? Our house would look so pretty with flowers!"

My father never answers. He hates flowers.

My sister huddles next to the door holding a pencil and pad. I sneak a peek and see she is making a list of future goals: *Get a new wig, buy diet pills at Cooper's Drugstore, call Rocky, ask Rocky to dinner, get engaged, get married, have children and leave this monster!*

One month later, Rocky comes into my sister's life and her seizures mysteriously stop. Rocky is short and cute with black curly hair and has a good job laying concrete with a bunch of other Italians he playfully calls "jackasses." This turn of events thrills my mother, who is already planning her grandchildren.

"Connie Mary, Rocky reminds me of your father when he was young; the coal-black hair, beautiful body, and he's one hundred percent Italian. Janice and Rocky will have beautiful children. I can just picture my little Joseph and Janice now!"

I roll my eyes in contempt.

When my mother removes her rose-colored glasses she has different thoughts.

"Well, maybe, he's not that good-looking. He sort of reminds me of poor Uncle Henry with one glass eye. Well, Rocky loves Janice and that's all that matters!"

Yes, it seems too good to be true. Rocky really does love Janice! He opens her door and gives her diamond jewelry. Of course my father disagrees.

"That jewelry is *hot* and when the mafia gets wise, they're going to snuff his lights out. Then again, they probably know it's a waste of time because he's too stupid to kill."

The best part about Rocky is he thinks of me! He calls me *Sorellina* and buys me Italian candy from Westerly, Rhode Island. As far as I'm concerned, Rocky can stay forever.

After six months of relative bliss, the big day finally arrives. Rocky gives my sister a diamond ring and my father finds fault. "Shit, you need a magnifying glass to see it."

Rocky is serious. Tonight, he is bringing Janice home to meet his sister Griselda. Rocky jokes that Griselda is as stubborn as a mule and controls every major decision in his life because she owns the house they live in.

Before the big date, I watch Janice combing her wig in her bedroom. It usually doesn't bother me, but tonight it makes me nervous.

"Jan, does Rocky know you wear a wig?"

She giggles with the naivety of a child. "Con, Rocky doesn't care. He loves me for who I am!"

All week long my mother has been cleaning the house like a madwoman. My father has been so happy he has been drinking out of a bottle of Lambrusco. But tonight he gives me strict orders. "As for you Connie Mary—keep your big mouth shut and stay out of everyone's way. Your sister's gettin' married. After that I don't give a shit what you say to that asshole with rocks in his head." He shakes his head in disgust. "What the hell kind of name is Rocky anyways?"

He winks with a sly grin. "See, tonight, if we play our cards right, tomorrow you'll be moving into your sister's bedroom."

After my sister is gone, my father offers to go to Club 41 and get us a pizza. He thinks we don't know what he really wants to do is to drink and socialize. My mother and I stay huddled in the parlor, watching television and trying to ignore the nagging feeling that something is wrong. Squirming restlessly in her chair, my mother looks out the window at the long row of maple trees lining Fitchville Road.

"Look!" she says as if witnessing a miracle. "The maple trees look like bouquets of flowers blooming underneath the streetlights." She lifts a curtain covered with black fingerprints that tell the story of a husband who likes to watch his neighbors. She changes position and stares at the dark shadow enshrouding Anna's house and sighs.

"Connie Mary, where did the old days go? Remember the picnics we used to have with Anna and Gus? We had good times when Gus was alive. Now everyone is disappearing and I am all alone. When you grow up, Connie Mary, don't be alone. *It's very dangerous for a woman to be alone.*"

Hours later with an empty pizza box lying on the floor, the news anchorman asks a familiar question. "It's 11 o' Clock. Do you know where your children are?"

And just when I think nothing bad could ever happen again, the front door bursts open, causing my mother's ceramic statue of an old man and woman holding hands to drop and shatter across the floor. A terrible look is in my sister's eyes. Her face is stained with long black streaks from mascara-filled tears. My father can hardly speak because he knows his dreams are disappearing before his very eyes.

"What...the...what the hell happened?"

Janice drops into her chair and painfully stutters, "It's Rocky. He...he...called everything off!"

Within seconds, my mother and sister are huddled at the kitchen table holding hands. My father sits motionless as he stares into the bleak future. What was supposed to have been a joyous occasion has turned into a nightmare. I walk quietly to the kitchen and listen by the wall.

Janice is telling my mother what happened when she went to use the bathroom and overheard Rocky talking to his sister. My sister uses the perfect Italian accent as she imitates Griselda's voice and it would be amusing if it were not so tragic.

"Rocky! says Janice. "You no bring-a this girl home no more! She *demenziale*. You see the way she slam-a my cabinets and spill-a my coffee over Nonna's table cloth? You no bring-a home this girl no more. And if-a you marry—you out *mi casa*."

After a long silence, my sister covers her face and sobs.

Apparently, Rocky had been living with Griselda for decades and finding it quite lucrative, especially in the off-season when construction jobs are few and far between. To make a long story short, when forced to choose between true love or having a roof over his head, Rocky chose the roof.

When I walk back into the parlor I see three empty beer bottles that were not there before and know my father's sadness is about to turn to rage.

"Goddamn it! I thought we were going to have a new life around here. Nope, just the same old bullshit."

To ease the pain he drinks two more beers and then lies back down. After an hour or so, it is getting late and my sister and mother want to go to bed. In order to reach the steps they must walk past my father. Moving stealthily, they tiptoe by the couch. Both are surprised when my father opens his eyes and sarcastically remarks to Janice, "You know why Rocky didn't marry you? Men don't marry whores."

The next day and for the rest of the week my sister does not leave her bedroom. I am angry that Janice lost Rocky. The truth is Rocky treated me like a little sister and big brothers protect little sisters from bad men.

Knowing this is my last year in school, I use my pen to painstakingly carve my only legacy, my name, among the other ageless graffiti which covers my desk. At the same time I try my best to listen to Mr. Driscoll complain about his unmotivated seniors.

"All right, all right, let's get cracking! Seniors have less than two months of wandering the desert before finding the Promised Land. Everyone has been less than thrilled about reading *A Christmas Carol* in April, and I offer my sincere condolences. Nevertheless, I specifically requested everyone to focus on the words of Marley's ghost in order to perform the final exam:

'I wear the chain I forged in life. I made it link by link, and yard by yard; I girded it on of my own free will, and of my own free will I wore it.' Personally, I believe chains are made to be broken and we can change our destiny by rendering the past powerless. My question is— do you?"

Mr. Driscoll looks across the room at the unresponsive faces and washes his muffin down with cold coffee. "Having said my piece, shall we discuss the senior activities? Senior class trip permission slips to New York are due on the 5th of June. Anyone wishing to miss the trip please return your permission slips on June 6th —do I make myself clear? Without further ado, we shall embark on a new beginning as I happily watch another senior class fade into the sunset."

At the sound of the bell, everyone rushes for the door. Mr. Driscoll's response is to scowl. "Seniors. Take one more step and you may find yourself in detention. I hear detainees have graduated from making birdhouses to cleaning toilets. I would advise you to have your toothbrush ready."

After dismissal, Mr. Driscoll stops me at the door.

"Connie Mary, please take a seat. I thought we should continue our discussion as to where you should apply to college. My first choice is Mohegan Community College as it would provide the needed time for you to become acclimated to a college setting."

My response is shock. "You *really* think Mr. Driscoll, I can go to college and actually pass?"

He laughs. "Yes, I believe you can go to college and actually pass. I believe you have the potential to do anything you make up your mind to do." He raises one eyebrow and gives me a sly look. "Judging by the carvings on your desk, you may have a future career in art."

"You knew I did that?"

"Connie Mary, as a teacher, I must use my better judgment and decide which battles are worth the fight and which are worth looking the other way."

After our discussion he closes his briefcase and walks out the door not seeing the surprised look on my face.

After school, I stopped at Grant's department store to finalize the sale of a gaudy green tie that I planned on delivering to Mr. Driscoll on the day of graduation.

I arrive home to find my sister and mother listening to the radio in the parlor. Both look peaceful; my sister is knitting while my mother reads *Movie Star* magazine. But the sudden squeal of my father's tires causes Janice to yank her housecoat below her knee and soon my father is at the door fumbling with his keys and cursing. He stumbles into the house, stinking of beer and cigarettes. His first response is to look at Janice with disgust and growl at my mother.

"Where's dinner?"

The recent development of strip clubs has given my father a new hobby. As my mother prepares lasagna in the kitchen, my father sits at the table and giggles like a mischievous boy.

"The Titty Bar closed tonight. The cops found one of the *whores* doing illegal acts in the back room." He laughs, "Shit. Joe Sludge was making an extra-grand a week on those whores.

Pump 'em up with drugs and those whores will do anything."

After two more beers my father complains about a sick stomach and goes upstairs to use the bathroom. Soon we hear the unsettling sound of an object being dragged across the floor. Each minute that passes is torment as we do not know what will happen next.

Soon we hear steel-toed boots come stomping down the stairs and Janice gasps for air. My father stops halfway and raises a machete into the air. The machete is sharp. I know because I heard him sharpening it in the basement when everyone else was sleeping. My sister's arms begin thrashing in all directions like an octopus fighting a predator in the sea.

My mother shouts—"Albert put that thing away!"

My father grins.

"I could cut off your friggin' heads and there ain't nothing you could do about it and nobody would care either! Nobody gives two shits about you or your daughter."

With gleeful eyes he looks specifically at my sister's legs peeking out of her housecoat. I know, just like me, my mother saw him do it. Our secret stays quiet because it is too horrible to believe: *the man we call father lusts after his own daughter.*

Suddenly he explodes with anger, sputtering, "You lazy bitch, when are you going to pay your bills?" as he rushes down the steps to Janice. My father glares at her with murderous eyes and yells, "I should throw you out the door!" He acts on his words and begins to drag Janice to the door. My sister is frail and with one strong push, he heaves her out the door where she falls across the hard cement. My sister is not able to hurt the monster that did this and goes into a self-mutilating rage against the only person she can hurt. With a wild, crazed look she slams both arms on the cement and my mother screams! Janice takes one more look at the grinning beast before leaning her head back and crashing it down on the cement. Blood and confusion is everywhere and I cannot remember where I was when the ambulance took her away.

Even in the midst of my sister's abuse, my life outside of home appeared normal. I was living in two different worlds. It was only when I stepped outside the world of my family that I could lead the life I thought I deserved.

The day of the New York class trip is finally here. This is the last time seniors will have to listen to threats made by Mr. Driscoll, the head chaperone. "I went through a tremendous amount of time and energy to plan this trip and there is no way on God's green earth will I tolerate anyone's shenanigans. Understood?"

After two hours on the bus, during which we finished off the mixed pints of vodka and orange juice we had hidden in our backpacks, we arrived in New York. Mr. Driscoll stands outside and reads us our rights.

"You may sightsee and attain souvenirs, however, all of you *better* be back on this bus within three hours. If you are late, we will leave without you. We have a tight schedule and an unbending agenda. If you plan on being late, I suggest you put your pennies together to pay for a taxi back to Connecticut."

Jodi and I venture cautiously from the bus. We are surprised to see people sleeping on the sidewalk and lying across benches using dirty newspapers for a blanket. We were more amazed to discover the legal drinking age in New York is considerably lower than Connecticut.

I turn to Jodi. "Think we can pass for eighteen?"

After ordering one drink, we soon lose count of the rest. By some miracle we make it back on the bus on time and travel to Broadway to see a play. The theater is large and dark with a long stairway that drops precipitously to a bottom level. As Jodi is walking in front of Mr. Driscoll, he loses his footing. Immediately, I see Jodi's silhouette tumble down the stairs. No one seems to find it funny that he reached the bottom level long before we did. I try not to look at the fury written across Mr. Driscoll's face as he listens to Jodi joking with the crowd.

"Don't worry folks, I got a metal plate stuck in my head." He taps the top of his head. "See? Hard as wood."

Jodi and I missed most of the play because we were sleeping. Back on the bus, the mood grows solemn. The sad truth sets in: our senior trip is over. Luckily, when the bus gets stuck in the middle of traffic, there comes an opportunity for mischief. The nervous little driver watches his passengers with suspicion and every so often grabs his loudspeaker to yell: "DO NOT—I REPEAT—DO NOT OPEN THOSE WINDOWS!"

Jodi begins to feel woozy and despite the driver's staunch warning, opens the window and vomits on top of a passing police cruiser. Everyone goes wild, raucously laughing and pointing at Jodi's colorful vomit dripping down the back window of the cruiser.

The driver is clearly flustered and states indignantly to Mr. Driscoll, "Sir. I believe your students are inebriated."

Three hours later with the stars twinkling across the black velvet sky, we approached NFA. I am one of the first students to step off the bus, and though I try my best to avoid Mr. Driscoll, it is impossible. He is waiting for me with a beet red face and smoldering eyes.

"*You* and your fine feathered friends ruined my class trip!" Seething with anger he tries to control a trembling voice. "I want you to remember this day, Connie Falcone. Every choice we make in life has a consequence that either helps us stand or fall by the wayside. And when we fall, everyone we care about falls with us!"

I am suspended for the last week of school and miss every senior activity due to my self-indulgent behavior. Restless and bored, I watch the last precious days of high school float away like white filaments of dandelion seeds on a summer day.

On the day of graduation, I leave Mr. Driscoll's gift on his desk, wishing I could change the past. After the ceremony, I pass by the Slater Building and notice him standing out in front. Upon a closer look, I see that he is smiling and waving my gaudy green tie into the air! Alan K. Driscoll has given me one last gift: the gift of forgiveness.

It is said a loved one must die in order to let the ones left behind to learn their lessons. Several weeks after I graduate an ambulance comes and takes Anna away. We find out she was taken to the *Uncas on Thames* in Norwich where many go to die. We did not know that Anna had terminal cancer. But someone did. A week later, a niece and her husband come to Anna's house and take all her valuables away. My mother looked horrified watching from the parlor window.

"Anna's not even dead yet and they're taking her valuables away. Where were *these people* when Anna needed help?" I cry silently, watching the last remnants of Anna and Gus get packed away in a pickup truck and disappear down Fitchville Road.

The next day we visited Anna at the hospital. It is hard watching my strong and brave Anna beg my mother for help. "Rose, I just want to go home. Please, Rose. Ask Albert to come take me home!"

"I'll ask him Anna," says my mother with a look on her face that tells me something different.

After all the years of living next door to Anna, I never saw anyone visit other than Shirley and the grandchildren. It is different at the hospital. Anna has been receiving frequent visits from estranged relatives. With every passing week her ability to reason remains clear even when she realizes the future is grim.

"Gus and me wanted our grandchildren to have what we got left in life. People don't think I do, but I know what's happening to me here. And it's not good, Connie Mary. People are trying to get me to sign papers to get my house and property. They say if I don't, my son Pinky is going to drink up all that my Gus worked for."

I do not know what to say. Actually, I am not sure if Anna was ever coming home. I am seventeen years old and foolishly self-absorbed in my world.

During Anna's short hospice, the three short months she stayed at Uncas on Thames, *a small group of people* convinced her to sign her entire estate into their hands. This consisted of the house and property on Fitchville Road, Gus's Sand and Gravel business, and the massive trucks and equipment on their property. Gus also had stocks, bonds and a second house and property on Gardner's Lake. The transactions were privately settled between Anna, a lawyer and the few who benefitted.

In 2012, I had the opportunity to speak to Anna's granddaughter, Debby A. Charette, at the funeral of her brother, Christopher Lorentz. During this conversation I discovered Debby and Christopher received only a miniscule settlement from the estate. As an adult, Christopher Lorentz knew the truth and fought all his life to have the grandchildren's inheritance restored. He never received justice and died fighting. Even though the surviving grandchildren were legally first in line as direct descendants to Anna and Gus's son Pinky, these children received very little given the enormity of material wealth Gustave O. Lorentz accumulated in his lifetime. The people who benefited most were not direct heirs—but collateral heirs that took what rightfully belonged to Pinky and his children.

The last time I saw Anna she was sweating profusely while gathering the strength to talk.

"Connie Mary, will you promise me something? Will you promise to tell my grandchildren what happened to me here and that I loved and wanted to help them very much?"

I smiled weakly and made a promise I was afraid I could not keep. "Yes, I promise Anna."

Gus finally called Anna home. Gus's Pond was quickly sold and the path blocked with fallen trees, brush and anything else that would stop people from entering. When I saw the roadblock I imagined what Gus would say looking down from Heaven.

"Dang fools. The Good Lord lent you that land in the hope you would share it. No one could ever own Gus's Pond. Not even me."

16

The Greatest Teacher Of All

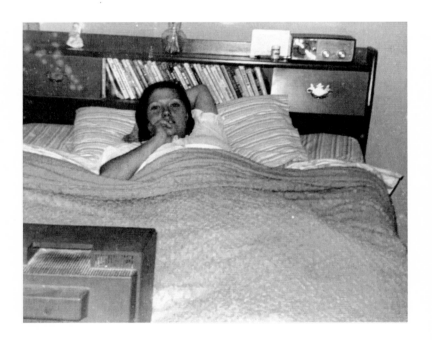

"My mother took this photograph of Janice in 1973 to document the truth, as we had no witnesses except the camera."

I began my days at Mohegan Community College as it first came to exist: in a run-down, dilapidated building in Norwich. I was surprised when my sister applied for the one-year Child Development program and was accepted. Another door of opportunity opened for her.

My father was thrilled and promptly paid tuition for the two of us, his voice ecstatic.

"My God, I have two daughters in college! I never thought I'd see the day."

During that time I drove my sister to college and we became closer, telling each other our hopes and dreams during the commute. Along the way we would point out the glorious colors of the changing fall leaves as Janice recalled her days of pressing leaves into books and storing them in a deep drawer, always planning to put them into scrapbooks, but of course, never getting around to it. "Con, I love the fall leaves best. The colors are so beautiful. I always thought it was such an unfitting finale to see them fall to earth, crumble and die."

My sister looks beautiful today, dressed in a white safari jacket, black slacks and flats. If not for the chopped and lopsided wig covering her head, no one would believe she had a problem in the world. Thinking of the scrapbooks hidden in a drawer reminded my sister of the dreams she buried alongside them. "I hope someday I can work in a daycare. Wouldn't that be grand? I could find a job caring for children and maybe get my own apartment. Think I could do that Con? Think I could get my own apartment?"

I smile weakly. Through my peripheral vision I can see her tugging impatiently at her wig until a chunk of synthetic hair falls upon her lap.

"There," she said, looking in the mirror. "Now I look better."

As the months pass, my sister's dreams begin to shatter after failing several classes. I do not understand how someone so smart can fail so easily. One evening I go into her bedroom and desperately ask—"Jan, why don't you study? Have you even started the project for Child Development?" I cannot contain my frustration any longer. "Don't you care Jan? Don't you care about anything?"

My sister does not answer and stares at the wall.

It does not take long for every student and professor to recognize who Janice Falcone is and this presents a problem for me. There is one morning in particular that stays with me. I was in the cafeteria discussing Vonnegut and Capote when Janice came careening through the door like a train veering off its track. I feared our relationship to each other being discovered and held my breath as she walked unsteadily toward the vending machine. The cafeteria grew still as she tripped over a backpack and fell to the floor. I slid my body down my chair as she attempted to stand. She searched through the crowd and I am sure she saw me, but made no effort to acknowledge. When someone in the crowd giggled, she tried to ignore them by fumbling in her purse for loose change. After finding two quarters, she looked relieved and placed them in the palm of her trembling hand. She seemed surprised when the coins dropped and rolled beneath the vending machine. Then I remembered the two pennies we lost so long ago at Yale New Haven Hospital, and even now wondered if the pennies were still there, waiting for two lost little girls to come back and claim them.

A studious-looking young man disturbed my thoughts by snickering with disgust.

"That girl is a mental case."

Sensing my uneasiness, he looked at me suspiciously. "Do you know her?"

I lie easily. "No, of course not."

The girl sitting across from me laughed with disbelief and shook her head. "That woman should be locked up, never mind allowed to go to college, you think?" She looked at me for confirmation.

"Yes," I whispered.

I watched my sister struggle. No one came forward to help, not even me. When she started tugging at her wig I got up and looked for the nearest exit. Before I left, I made the mistake of looking back and bumped into an old professor who knew that Janice was my sister. He smiled coyly at my guilty face and intentionally blocked the exit.

"*Poor girl*," he said. "Isn't peer pressure an interesting phenomena as to what lengths people will go to be accepted?"

I pushed past and lied, "I don't know what you're talking about."

I disappeared down the hallway and ran outside to my car, locked all the doors and hid in the back seat trying to stop hearing the crowd's laughter in my mind.

At that moment I knew how Peter felt after he denied Christ three times.

In June, we receive our final grades and Janice fails every class. I, however, make grades that will allow me to go on to Eastern Connecticut State University in September and leave my sister behind in a house of horrors. My mother knows the only witness left is leaving and pleads, "Please Con, come home when you can."

Time travels just the way you intend when you train the mind to become indifferent to the suffering around you. But sometimes the suffering finds a way to grasp your attention. The summer before I left for college I witnessed a strange incident that bordered on the supernatural. Prior to that summer, I had witnessed paranormal activity in my home, such as shadowy figures walking in the middle of the night or voices calling from the cellar. But out of all the unexplained experiences I encountered, this was the strangest one of all.

It began on a hot August morning when I awoke to the feeling that someone was watching my every move. I ignored the feeling and concentrated on going shopping later that afternoon. I picked out a shirt to wear and then noticed it needed ironing. I dreaded the task, knowing the ironing board was in the cellar amongst the mice and slimy creatures that hid between the cracks in the wall.

I entered my sister's bedroom with no particular interest and stared at the blankets and pillows tangled in a pile on the floor. Unconcerned, I looked out the window at the bright morning light and noticed my father's truck was gone.

I walked downstairs, passing empty beer cans in the parlor, and paused at the screen door in the kitchen to listen to someone mowing the lawn. The scent of fresh cut grass made me happy. It smelled of youth and cows and childhood days of picking dandelions.

My thoughts were disturbed when I saw a brilliant flash of light shoot across the yard. The light turned into a shimmering white ball that hovered above the ground. It was transparent and luminous and I stood mesmerized in disbelief. Then, as quickly as the light appeared, it vanished into thin air!

I remained behind the screen door looking and waiting for the light to reappear. In the exact spot where the light had vanished, my sister suddenly appeared, wearing a black wig and white safari jacket tied around the waist. This was a familiar encounter so I had no reason to doubt this was Janice.

Janice continued walking with a look of joy, fascination and wonderment upon her face. She would pause and make little dips and turns and then come back as if seeing the yard for the first time. When she crossed into Anna and Gus's yard, she stopped at the kitchen window where Anna would often call our names. And even though the house was empty, it looked as though she was talking to someone at the window.

I did not see her walk back home, but apparently she did, because she was standing by the pool and facing me. All this time I did not know that she was aware of my presence, until her eyes met mine with a look of revulsion and disgust. I was so stunned that I took a step backward and thought *this can't be my sister!*

Hours later, on a pitch-black moonless night, I found myself driving alone on Fitchville Road. I began to panic, as I had no memory of what happened after my sister had given me such a gruesome look. Breathing hard, I manage to drive home and haphazardly park my car on my father's lawn. Leaving the motor running, I ran inside the house and found my father in the parlor eating pizza with Sam by his feet.

Immediately I attacked him with a barrage of questions.

"Dad, where were you today? Where was Janice? Was she here today? Something strange happened to me today."

If looks could kill, I'd already be dead. My father does not like being disturbed while watching television and didn't hold back his disgust.

"Are you crazy or something, parking your car on top of my lawn? What's the matter with you anyways? Don't you know I just fertilized that lawn?" He studied my face with distrust.

"Are you drunk or something? Today, Janice and your mother were helping me clean out all the shit in my apartment building that Harry and his *puttana* left behind when they moved out."

"No Dad, it was Janice. I saw her."

"Ah, you probably saw the neighbor's relative and she looked like Janice."

I looked at my father with determination. "No Dad. It was Janice. I saw Janice."

My father attempts to humor me.

"Christ, then why didn't you tell her to come in and clean the house while she was here? Now, get that car off my grass Connie Mary—*now.*"

I ran upstairs and without knocking, pushed open my sister's door. The room was engulfed in darkness with one small light emitting an omniscient glow over the lone silhouette sitting on the bed. My sister faced the dark window. A warm breeze was lifting her hair. Still looking out into the darkness, she whispered to me.

"I heard what you said downstairs, Con. And I want you to know that I believe you." Then she said something I did not understand at the time. "*Somehow, I found a way to tell you.*"

For many years I searched for an explanation as to what I saw that day and why. My extensive research and investigation into paranormal experiences paired with the writing of this book led me to a valuable conclusion. Various studies on sexual abuse discuss a coping strategy called *dissociation.* This is a way of disconnecting from one's feelings, memories, or sense of identity. Dissociation is frequently used with victims of abuse who need to mentally leave their body to alleviate the pain. Day after day of being forced into sexual abuse, I believe my sister was able to break through a painful physical barrier and enter some sort of parallel world that was safe and familiar to her. I believe the vision I saw was intended to teach me that people like my sister, who are forced to keep secrets, will find a way to tell, even if the truth is revealed four decades later.

The weekends I do not come home from college become the most violent years of my sister's life. With the only witness gone, my father grows bolder.

One night, I came home late unannounced. When I turn on the light, I see the coffee table flipped upside down and broken in half.

The next day I asked my mother what happened.

"Your father picked a fight with Janice. He wants her out! That man is so cruel to that girl. Last week when she tried to run up the stairs—he ran ahead and tried to push her down! I tell you, Connie Mary, he is trying to *kill* my daughter! He wants her gone."

"Ma, did you tell anyone? How did the table get broken?"

My mother looks at the table and begins to sob.

"I told Henry's wife Philomena and she said to call the police. But where am I going to go? Your father will put me away and take the house and I won't have anywhere to live!" My mother closes her eyes as if someone is jabbing her with a knife. "Yesterday, he picked Janice up and threw her across the table. She fell so hard it broke the table in half." I watch her bottom lip tremble and feel nothing. I am no different than my father who wants to be free. I can't stand to look at her and turn away.

"Where is Janice now?"

If I could describe the look on my mother's face it would be *sheer hopelessness.* She lingers by the sink full of dirty dishes and listens to the rain beat against the roof.

"Janice cannot live here anymore. My beautiful daughter cannot live in her own home. Go upstairs and see the broken bed! While you're at college this is how we live. Oh dear God! What goes on in the middle of the night? I don't know because I take my sleeping pills. The next day I see things that are beyond belief! Whenever I ask your father what happened, he always says, '*She wakes me up because she never sleeps and runs through the house breaking things.*' Connie Mary, this is how we live."

Within a week, my sister is placed a mile down the road at the Bozrah Convalescent Home where the old and feebleminded live and die. My gentle and beautiful sister is far safer living in the midst of strangers with dementia than at home. I can only imagine how she felt there. The two months my sister lived at the convalescent home I never visited nor inquired about her status.

Her next housing placement is *Gateway*, a facility connected and operated by the *Norwich State Hospital*. It is a better placement than the convalescent home, as it has a reputation for giving clients the opportunity to experience community-based-living, different from the endless confinement of past hospitals. My sister is assigned to jobs on the hospital grounds and will have the opportunity to graduate to community living. Even though Janice is not living at home, my parents continue to sign her out for home visits. According to my mother, these visits turn out to be as violent as when she lived at home. When I ask Janice why she continues to go home, she responds with tears in her eyes.

"I don't know why, Con...I just miss home. The fields and pond, the birds...I miss Sam most of all."

After a month at *Gateway*, my sister stays in bed and refuses to participate in group therapy and job training and my parents receive several warnings from the head therapist.

"I have already informed Janice of the consequences of her behavior. If she does not improve she will be terminated. I hope Janice realizes there is a long line of people waiting to take her place."

Janice did not understand.

"Why don't people like me, Con? Why? What's wrong with me? How come I always have to leave everywhere I go?"

Several weeks later, my mother reads my sister's final report: *Despite various interventions tried over a period of several months, Janice Lynn Falcone has failed to make sufficient progress in the Gateway Outreach Program, and at this time, termination is recommended. Until appropriate placement is established, she will continue to reside at 93 Fitchville Road.*

By the time I was meant to graduate college, I had not only failed student teaching but had been berated by my supervising teacher who said I was unable to understand basic math skills and my spelling was worse than a third grader. I did not walk across the stage with my graduating class that spring. Luckily, I got a second chance by agreeing to be tutored over the summer.

I recalled the days of my childhood spent at Fields Memorial when Mr. Pavy would glare at me with disapproval, every one of his words hitting the mark. "Miss Falcone, do you actually think you are fooling anyone by pretending to be able to read? Those who think they fool others are only fooling themselves."

How funny that I then ended up in Mr. Pavy's small apartment, observing a massive bookcase full of hundreds of books, so many years later. Once again, I had the opportunity to hear Mr. Pavy's wisdom and this time I listened. The summer passed quickly. During the last session in August, I noticed Mr. Pavy walking slower than usual and inquired about his health.

"Are you feeling okay, Mr. Pavy?"

"Please excuse me Connie Mary," he responded. "I have a slight case of leukemia that has a tendency of making me weak. Now, let's speak about you. Congratulations are in order for successfully completing your allotted time of study." He glanced across the room at the antique typewriter proudly displayed in the corner. "I shall have your report typed and mailed to your professors by tomorrow."

He began to cough and was soon gasping for air. I brought him a drink of water and he regained composure by speaking to the characters in his books that he called friends.

"No need to worry, David Copperfield, Ulysses, and Huckleberry Finn. Even though I walk through the valley of the shadow of death, I will fear no evil; for thou art with me; thy rod and thy staff they comfort me." He paused as if trying to find the right words to say to me and forced a smile.

"Connie Mary…if you would give me a penny for my thoughts,

I will say what is on my mind without intending to offend. It is about your sister, *Janice Lynn.*"

At the mention of my sister's name, I suddenly felt shame and guilt.

"Actually, I thought Janice Lynn would be the one going to college. She was devoted to all genres of literature and highly proficient in written expression." His face grew weary as he began to recall her memory. "I often wonder what could have made such a gifted, caring student stray from her path. I believed she would have become a Master of English and someday teach college."

He studied my face as if asking permission to continue. I could not look into his eyes.

"Janice Lynn was artistic as well, illustrating the many brilliant stories she wrote." He laughed softly. "I remember how she would press wildflowers on colored paper to illustrate a particular poem or narrative." He furrowed his brow, quietly tormented in his quest to learn the truth.

"Come to recollect, I never had another student as brilliant as Janice Lynn Falcone."

He sighed. "I am convinced Janice Falcone battled unspeakable demons and these demons destroyed her spirit. Old teachers know these things."

An uncomfortable silence built an imaginary wall between Mr. Pavy's loving memory and my inability to reveal the truth. The afternoon sun began to lower in the sky, producing a radiance that shone through the immaculate polished windows. The tone in the room changed.

"Well now, how is Janice Lynn doing? I heard she was ill."

Nervous butterflies fluttered wildly in my thoughts before retreating to the pit of my stomach. "Um… well, ah, my sister has problems. She goes to the hospital a lot."

This was all I could pry loose from my hidden nest of secrets.

Mr. Pavy nodded, clearly understanding more than he was willing to reveal.

"Ah, yes of course, of course. Please tell Janice Lynn I said hello."

Before I left, I gave him the modest check he requested and felt as though I would cry.

"Thank you, Mr. Pavy, I appreciate all you have done for me and my sister."

He rose with the help of a cane.

"There is no better gift a teacher can receive than to hear a student say *thank you*. And yes...someday, you, too, will have the privilege of being called: "Teacher." I hope you will always remember the Greatest Teacher of all is Christ the Lord. Only then will you be given the wisdom and grace to change a student's life. It was very good to see you again. Goodbye, Connie Mary."

Weeks later, I walk past the Otis Library to return some books when I see a familiar figure smiling at me through the window. It is a younger version of Mr. Pavy, wearing a brand new pair of spectacles, a polished gray suit, and a bowtie as bright and blue as the summer sky. The image lasts for a minute or so and then disappears. When I tell my mother about the vision she looks up at the ceiling and smiles. "Connie Mary, Mr. Pavy died a week ago. Rest in peace, good teacher."

For a short time the memory of Mr. Pavy gave me courage. After graduating from college, I witnessed a particularly brutal episode with my father and Janice. In a moment of rare strength, I packed my things and left—taking Janice with me to live in the rat-infested apartment my father inherited from Nonno. I discovered I was too nervous to teach children and instead took a job packing eggs at Colchester Egg Farm in North Franklin. My sister was unable to hold a job, and I was foolish enough to believe my assembly line position was enough to support the two of us. After one month of living with Janice, problems began to develop. The toilet was constantly clogged with hair. My sister was still cutting her wigs and hair and flushing it down the toilet in the hope I would not discover.

Every day before I left for work, I would give Janice strict instructions about letting the children belonging to the other tenants stay in our apartment all day. "Don't let any children into this apartment. They make a mess and eat all our food, and I don't have money to buy more. And make sure you have supper ready when I get home."

I replaced my father as a tyrant by setting unrealistic expectations and making intimidating threats at Janice. "If you don't start doing what I ask, you're going home!"

Nothing changed. She continued to let the children stay in our apartment with the same explanation.

"Con, don't be mad. These children have no place to go. Their mothers send them out when strange men visit and lock the door behind. And they're hungry."

One evening I came home from work to discover fire and policemen gathered in the street. After I parked my car, a policeman walked up to me.

"Is that your apartment there? Are you living with a woman named Janice Falcone?"

"Yes," I nervously replied. "She's my sister. Why?"

"You need to tell your sister, if she's not going to be home, it's best not to leave the stove on. She almost burned the whole building down!" I take a closer look and see the gaping doors and windows flung open with thick black smoke streaming out into the air. And then I see the angriest person of all: my father.

"My apartment building!' he yells. "I'm gonna break her goddamn neck!"

I told my parents I could not live with Janice anymore and the next day she moved back home. Relieved, I stayed in my father's apartment a few more months and planned my escape.

I was determined to find a new life no matter what it cost.

17

The Escape

"I wanted to tell them to never be afraid of the truth. It is the evil that hides behind silence that we should fear the most."

I ran from my sister's pain believing my father was too strong to fight and looked for a way out. After moving back home I received a phone call from someone who would change my life forever. I met Robert C. Codding, a married thirty-nine-year-old plant manager from Colchester Egg Farm, who had seven children. Within a year I knew this is the man I would marry without ever having met his children. This man was safe and kind. However, without realizing it, I had stepped into a new kind of Hell. In the old Hell, I was free to come and go as I pleased because I was not the one being tortured. In this new Hell, I could not escape the body of pain that I would create for me and every person connected to my life.

My parents begged me to reconsider. My relatives told my mother I should be locked away for wanting to marry someone fifteen years older with children. I did not listen. I wanted something secure. My mother could not bear to witness my self-destruction and a few days before the wedding, she left for Boston to have surgery to correct an eye condition called Graves Disease.

My father begrudgingly attended, wearing the same grim face as every other relative in attendance. The wedding reception was at the Moose Club in Bozrah, a half-mile from my home. I had not seen Kathy Grabowy Bosworth and her husband in a few years. They were both unaware of the depressing circumstances until my father sat down at their table to complain.

"Kathy, my daughter is marrying an old man today with seven children. How can I be happy about that? I wanted a son I could go fishing with."

I might have been the guest of honor sitting at the bride's table, but instead of well wishes, hateful words were passed all around me like a dish of poison-coated almonds. The atmosphere was more suggestive of a funeral than a wedding. Sitting in back of the wedding party were two of my Italian aunts gossiping loudly for everyone to hear.

"Bootsie says Connie Mary left him to fend for himself with a sick daughter and wife in the hospital. Did you see Rose Falcone with them two ugly eyes?" The other aunt blew smoke and guzzled a shot of expensive scotch. "I never liked Bootsie's younger daughter anyway. She's nothing but a *puttana;* imagine that young girl sleeping around with that old man and him with those seven children— humph! *Maronna Mia!* I bet the ex-wife is giving them the *Malocchio* as we speak."

At the end of the night my sister caught the bouquet and what followed was a horrible argument between my father and husband. My father originally said he would pay $500 for Frankie Delgado's band but decided to claim the opposite when it was time to pay. The conflict escalated as the three of us huddled in a dark corner, yelling and fighting, unseen by the partying crowd. Janice stood next to me wearing our mother's evening gown that she had been, not as secretly as she thought, ripping on purpose all evening. Oblivious to what dangerous space she was in, she continued giggling and swaying to the music. My father suddenly noticed her and with a look of disgust slapped her hard across the face.

My sister was shocked. I could not move or breathe. My husband was still standing next to me but I could not see him anymore, all I could see was my sister's painful expression. An eternity seemed to pass before she touched her blistering cheek and then ran out the door into the chilly November night. If Sam had run into the night, I would have searched for hours until he returned. With Janice I stood like a pillar of salt. My father walked back into the crowd of admiring relatives. Soon, I would leave for Nantucket Island and leave the innocent doe alone with the inhumane hunter, and yet, it did not stop me.

As I studied the noisy crowd I wondered why Janice did not ask for help. They were all there—aunts, uncles, nieces, nephews, cousins, all of whom loved my sister dearly. It would take me decades to realize that Janice understood something more than anyone else did: our relatives would not protect her anymore than her mother and sister.

By the time we left it was late. No one waved goodbye or wished us good luck. As Bob picked up speed on the highway, for a brief moment, I considered going back. When we were miles away, I heard a minister speaking on the radio. *"Indifference is a disease far more hideous than hatred and anger. It is the invisible mask we wear which allows us to hide behind every sin known to mankind."*

Our first home is in an affluent neighborhood on Sycamore Road in Norwich. My father continues to beg me to come home. "While you still got your looks, come home! I'll give you money if you need it. He's an old man, shame on you, Connie Mary!"

My father's reasoning does not surprise me. It comes from someone who, against all attempts to appear structurally sound, still stands upon a crumbling foundation. In my absence my father has grown bolder with his need to debase Janice, continually subjecting her to violence in his quest for power. Then it finally happens.

My mother wakes in the middle of the night sensing an ungodly presence and stares at the clock with trepidation. "3:26 a.m. Those numbers mean something." My mother does not go back to sleep. Instead, she tiptoes toward my sister's bedroom and stares in horror at the incestuous scene that no amount of drugs will ever let her forget. There are unfathomable sights and sounds. My father's heavy breathing, my sister lying on her back staring blankly at the ceiling making gurgling, choking sounds. My father does not see his daughter. What he sees is the twisted fantasy involving some stranger. Mesmerized by the scene, my mother cannot stop staring at my father's belly jiggling on top of Janice's nightgown tangled around her waist. Once a happy little girl, my sister is depleted like an animal, gutted and dying. My mother lets out a scream and chaos ensues.

More screaming and cursing fills the air as my father begs forgiveness. When it is clear that my mother will not stop screaming, my father silences the rage by slapping her into submission. Violence has served my father well. It has been a prelude to the incest and a weapon against those standing in his way. Everyone has forgotten about poor Janice, who is crying tears of shame. Despite all that is seen, documented, and witnessed, nothing changes.

My husband gives Janice a part-time job packing eggs at Colchester Egg Farm. When she ends up performing well, my father interferes. "Jesus Christ, Bob, can't you give my daughter a full-time job? This part-time shit is no good."

To appease my father, Bob assigns my sister to work eight-hour days instead of four-hour shifts. My sister becomes overwhelmed and begins to steal the worker's lunches. Finally, she walks off the job leaving dozens of eggs falling off a moving ramp and is quietly dismissed.

My sister is physically deteriorating with each passing day with a mind that remains as sharp as ever. My silence torments me. I know I should yell— "My father is killing Janice!" But I remain silent. Even though I am emotionally unstable and prone to fits, I decide to take my sister over to my house every Saturday to spend the day with me. At first these visits happen frequently and then slowly diminish over time. My sister is excited and happy to be here.

"I'm finally in my sister's luxurious house! Did you rent the movie A *Christmas Carol* for us to watch Con? Oh Con, it will be like old times!"

During the movie Janice is intensely focused. As soon as it ends she immediately loses control and dashes through the house tripping and crashing into objects. I am exhausted from trying to prevent my sister from slamming her head on the hardest surface she can find. With one swipe, she can wipe a tabletop clean destroying everything in sight. I purposely made a plan to watch two movies in order to avoid trouble.

As soon as the second movie ends my sister studies a ceramic pitcher and bowl I made on the coffee table. Before I can stop her destruction, she slams her head on the coffee table causing the bowl and pitcher to fall and smash on the tile floor! Blood is everywhere and as painful as it looks, Janice shows no emotion. I lose control and start slapping her on the back and arms until she helplessly falls to the floor. Once I realize what I have done, I stop. Surprisingly, my sister is calm and slightly indignant. *"You're exactly like that maniac I live with. You're just like him."*

After silently watching years of violence committed against a loved one, it only required a little pressure for me to become my father.

One month later, Janice is accepted into a newly built high-rise in Norwich called Hamilton Park Apartments. My mother buys everything that is required so Janice can leave behind a tormented life with a bundle of hope in her arms.

My father receives good news as well when he learns televisions have become capable of bringing pornography into his own living room. I would never have imagined the old Sylvania we watched with three channels would be replaced by cable television with over a hundred channels. It seemed very few of us envisioned how technologically advanced American life would become, or how filthy for that matter. With one phone call, my father can watch the Playboy Channel while the rest of us try to ignore or sometimes even participate in this debauchery.

Soon after the television upgrade, Bob and I visited, and found my father in the parlor watching pornography. Knowing we could do nothing to change the situation, we acquiesced, and sat down to watch it with him. After a few minutes I grew bored and strolled into the kitchen to talk with my mother about meatballs and where to buy the least expensive brand of *Pastene* tomatoes—all the time hearing the moans and groans of women having sex in the background. Luckily, the Playboy Channel did not last long. After my father received the first bill he cancelled the subscription and decided to look for ways to obtain the channel illegally.

The reprieve from dysfunction does not last long. Within a month, the Director of Hamilton Park Apartments calls my mother. "Mrs. Falcone, your daughter forgot to turn the stove off after cooking. Heavy black smoke filled the first floor and all the residents had to be temporarily evacuated. Mrs. Falcone, I would advise you to speak to your daughter concerning this dangerous matter. We cannot have this happening in our building. Do you understand?"

My mother hangs up, believing Janice can always come home and how this time could be different. My mother's irrational thinking causes further suffering when her loneliness and isolation become so strong that she believes Janice must come home. One visit turned into a violent rampage: Janice slammed her head on the edge of my father's desk, causing Nonno's lamp to fall on the floor and break. At about 2 o'clock in the morning, my father drove my sister back to Hamilton Park Apartments in a rage. The next day, several residents reported they saw my father squeal into the parking lot, stop, and throw Janice from the car. I asked them why they did not call the police or tell a staff member, and they said they were too afraid to tell. I wanted to tell them to never be afraid of the truth. It is the evil that hides behind silence that we should fear the most.

Later that day, I fought with my father and he denied everything. There was nothing else I could do. Calling the police was not an option, as that proved useless in the past. There were no Falcone relatives to tell; either they were too afraid to help or loved my father too much. I had not seen my mother's relatives in years and knew I was forgotten. The war with my father had begun as thoughts of hatred and madness and even murder ravaged my mind.

The worst pain of all is when my father tells his relatives, "My daughter is the most selfish woman on the face of the earth. She doesn't help her sister or mother at all!" It is painful because it borders on the truth. My relatives stop talking to me. My father tells everyone he is unable to cope with my sister not realizing he *created* Janice as if she were steel honed from his own soldering iron. As menacing as my father already was, another equally frightening paradigm began to shift inside his deranged mind as the possibility of a life with a younger, more attractive woman consumed his imagination. This thought loomed large and strong, giving my father a sick kind of hope to escape the life he despised.

Two more times Janice sends residents running for their lives and each time the fire is worse. Numerous times she has failed to follow the safety codes and is asked to leave.

One week passes.

Carrying two boxes, I find the door to room 102 open and see Janice sitting in the semi-darkness surrounded by an array of packed and sealed boxes. I try to sound sincere but my words come out empty and hollow as I sit by her side.

"Oh, Jan, I'm sorry you have to leave this beautiful apartment!"

My sister covers her face and cries as she says goodbye to the only home she will ever live independently. "Goodbye, beautiful apartment, goodbye room 102! I will miss you. Thank you for letting me stay here. I wish that someday, I can find a way to come back to you."

What role did my sister's injustice and suffering play in God's divine providence in granting her wish? In 2012, over twenty years after she passed, Janice's wish did come true. It happened when my cousin Bobby Meyer applied for an apartment at Hamilton Park Apartments. Bobby previously had a stroke that resulted in a traumatic brain injury and required handicapped assistance. He was immediately accepted and even though Hamilton Park is a six-story building, he quickly moved into apartment 102. I entered the apartment as if time stood still. Everything looked the same. I walked into the small kitchen where Janice had caused the fires and her thoughts and movements filled my mind. I walked back into the living room and stared through the picture window imagining the sound of my father's tires squealing through the parking lot with the residents watching behind their curtains, horrified at my father's actions, yet too afraid to tell. No longer able to contain my disbelief, I cried out—"Why Bobby? Why did you get the same apartment as Janice?"

Even with a traumatic brain injury and permanently confined to a wheelchair, my cousin comprehended my question with scathing accuracy. "Connie Mary…it's simple. She came back because she knew you needed to remember her story for the book."

"Janice Lynn Falcone is a danger to herself and others," declared the medical staff. "She must be placed in an environment conducive to personal safety."

After a week of living at home, my sister is transferred by ambulance to a convalescent home in Waterford. But it does not matter where my sister lives; she will never be free of the menacing monster nipping at her heels in an obsession to destroy her mind, body and spirit.

The convalescent home reeks of hopelessness. From every pair of soiled diapers to plates of over-boiled food rises the smell of despair. After the first week, visitors grow a shell of indifference that allows them to look away at the slow deterioration of their loved ones. My sister's temporary stay turns into months. Many days she is left alone in the hallway, restrained in a chair. Other days, she is tied into bed with sores slowly bleeding through clean white sheets. Her motor control continues to worsen as the convalescent home is understaffed and cannot give Janice the time to exercise independently. My sister remains an enigma. Some days she is able to walk without assistance, other days she loses her balance and falls. It has come to the point where I can observe my sister in her room searching for the hardest objects to slam her head so she can do the most collateral damage to her body. During this time Janice speaks a new mantra.

"*I hate myself. I wish I were dead!*"

"Why Janice?" I plead. "Why do you hate yourself so much? You did nothing to deserve this life." She stares into space and does not answer.

Whenever I call my mother to discuss Janice, my father starts yelling in the background.

"We only got one daughter Rose, because this one is dead!" I can hear him swearing at me in Italian cursing the day I was born. My mother calls me back when my father is at work and whispers dire warnings, "Connie Mary, you better stop calling me. Your father wants you dead! He might try to kill you!"

I continue to call. Sometimes he picks up the phone and we fight, just to see who can hurt the other the most.

"*I swear to God Dad, someday, I'm going to get back at you for all the rotten things you did—you rapist!*" The names my father calls me feel like acid thrown in my face. My words do not upset my father at all. In fact, he laughs.

"You're no good. You never did anything for your mother and sister. And that husband of yours, all he cares about is his own blood." My father knowingly places a wedge between my mother and me whenever we talk on the phone. If my mother does not curtail our conversation fast enough, he explodes.

Rose, I told you to *get off that phone now!*"

My mother pleads nervously, "Con, I have to get off this phone," and hangs up without saying goodbye.

I have learned something about abusers since then. I didn't recognize the signs when I was trapped in the maelstrom because I did not know that most abusers have a plan to isolate their victims as my father did to my mother. As my sister's life neared the end, my father was getting away with murder and devising a plan to destroy the last obstacle.

My sister's days at the convalescent home come to pass when a placement at the Worcester Rehabilitation Center in Massachusetts becomes available. This appears to be a more appropriate placement due to the younger age of its clients. It is during this time that Sam begins to have problems. It is important to document the last days of Sam's life in order to understand the multiple personalities of an abuser and why so many victims hesitate to leave.

At nineteen years old, Sam is severely disabled and must be euthanized. This is an especially sad day for my mother as Sam is the only living creature my father ever loved unconditionally. When Sam died, the last bit of compassion my father possessed died as well.

I was married, but lived through this experience by listening to my mother's words…

"The day we all dreaded came when Sam could not lift his body anymore. It had to be done." My mother starts to cry. "When your father called the doctor, Sam already knew, and did not leave my side that night. The next morning with tears in his eyes, your father looked at Sam and said, *"Sam, it's time."*

My mother is unable to go on because she is crying too hard. "Sam knew! Oh, we call these animals dumb—oh, what we could learn from them! That morning, Sam walked with dignity and stood at the bottom of the steps. He remembered the bedrooms were upstairs and began to bark."

Again she begins to weep.

"*Oh, sweet Jesus—he wanted to go up those stairs and say goodbye to you and Jan!* He knew he could not make it, so he barked to say goodbye. After we arrived at Dr. Graves' office we were taken into a white sterile room. Before Sam was given the shot, we bent down and hugged him. I swear on Jesus that dog raised his head and looked at me with so much love and gratitude...I had to turn away. After we left the office, your father cried for a good five minutes and then we drove away in silence."

I never realized something when my mother first told me this story. In fact, it would take me decades to realize what I had missed. My father had cried for Sam, yet had never shed a tear for all the pain and suffering he had caused his own daughter. He was never sorry, he never apologized, and all his life had denied his part in the hideous crimes that shortened my sister's life and eventually led to her death. Worst of all, my mother and I had never made the connection and this is why this story needs to be told.

307

18

Goodbye My Beautiful Sister

It is 1989. Janice is with my mother sitting in a padded chair that protects her from hitting her head. These next four years at The Worcester Rehabilitation Center in Massachusetts will be my sister's last days.

Janice has a new placement and my mother could not be happier.

"There are young people at The Worcester Rehabilitation Center and some are your sister's age! And guess what else Con? Janice has a roommate named Katelyn! The nurses say Katelyn is the same age as Janice and doesn't get any visitors. I bet this will be a good situation for both of them." I noticed a sudden change in my mother's tone.

"Well, there is one more little thing. Katelyn had a terrible motorcycle accident and is paralyzed from the waist down. The man she loved never came back. She's very angry."

"Oh—no," I gasp, feeling a sense of doom, not for Katelyn, but for Janice! Before I can say anything else I hear my father yelling in the background.

"Rose, are you talking to that damn daughter of yours again? Get off the phone—now! My pants and shirt are wet. Go get me another change of clothes."

"I… I must get off the phone, Con." My mother nervously hangs up without saying goodbye and I feel helpless. My sister's decline is ripping me apart and I can no longer pretend to be hopeful. Over the years Janice has been subjected to countless tests to find the so-called "disease" that is destroying her balance and causing her self-mutilating behavior. It is only a matter of time before the Worcester Rehabilitation Center discovers the real disease and the tests suddenly stop.

From a distance, the hospital shines like a new preacher making promises on Sunday morning. My parents visit every Sunday—rather, my mother visits and my father begrudgingly follows. My mother knows the routine and brings Katelyn jewelry, money, or anything else she requests. In exchange, my mother hopes she will treat Janice well.

From the beginning, I sensed Katelyn is a tormented soul incapable of feeling compassion. In time we learn that Katelyn is only nice to Janice when others are present. Without witnesses, Katelyn has fits of rage and viciously hurls food trays across the room at Janice who is restrained in bed. We start to notice bruising on my sister's face, unable to fathom that Katelyn is the culprit. Janice loves Katelyn very much and does not want to tell.

One day the staff questions Janice about a bleeding nose and the truth is uncovered. I am present the day my mother is told. Rightfully, she demanded the staff take action to protect her daughter from further harm. How swiftly the necessary affection towards Katelyn quickly died. My mother demanded the staff move Janice to another room and for the next four years my sister lived out the rest of her days, alone and without witnesses.

The day after Janice was gone, Katelyn saw my mother passing through the hall and from her bed cried—"*Rose, Rose, please forgive me Rose, I love you!*" My mother, having seen too much pain, coldly turned away. Katelyn existed no more. I never learned what happened to her. I do know that Janice forgave Katelyn and wished nothing but good things to come her way because that is the kind of sister I have.

In time, Janice's bed was padded with thick blue foam as was her table, chair, and toilet. Even still, Janice was determined to slam her head into whatever hard objects she could find. During a visit, I came up with an idea: I suggested she wear a motorcycle helmet to protect her head. In time, my mother bought her a smaller bicycle helmet instead. But no matter how many gains Janice made, the path she walked was sabotaged the day she agreed to home visitations with my parents. I lived less than thirty minutes away and had asked my mother to bring Janice to my house. My father despised me and would not honor my request, preferring to randomly drive around with my mother in the back seat holding Janice in her arms. Sometimes my parents would take my sister all the way back to

Bozrah, where abuse would immediately occur. When Janice returned to the hospital, the nurses began to notice black and blue marks on her face and arms. They grew suspicious of my father and started to document his behavior more closely.

During the years my sister stayed at the hospital, she had no visitors with the exception of my friend Judy Chapman and Grayce Lerro. Judy visited Janice at every placement she stayed since the day she left home. Aunt Grayce drove all alone from Pennsauken, New Jersey determined to see her niece one last time. Aunt Grayce knew things before they happened and trusted her instincts. My mother had not seen her sister in some time and was alarmed at her appearance.

"Con, my sister's skin was the color of cigarette ash and she smoked and coughed the whole time she was here!" My mother knew things too. "I think this will be the last time I see my beautiful sister alive."

My mother was right. A few weeks later, Aunt Grayce died. It was sad to think of my godmother gone. She helped every niece and nephew in our family and left the world a better place. I cried bitterly knowing I would never find another Grayce Lerro in my lifetime.

Several weeks after her passing, I was surprised to pick up the phone and listen to my mother's strange announcement. "We can't visit Janice anymore." She begins to cry. "I can't bear to see what's going to happen to that girl." I knew my mother was not telling me everything. This is when she randomly disclosed a serious incident involving Janice.

"I wanted to tell you what happened several weeks ago to Janice. An orderly sexually abused her in the middle of the night." I responded to my mother's words with silence. No questions, no urgency for details, nothing. If someone had taken a knife and cut open my heart, there was nothing I could have done but sit and watch the blood flow.

A week later I promised my sister I would visit. By the time I arrived it was late and Janice had been waiting all day to see me. I hated coming this late because I would be expected to feed her, as Janice could not hold a utensil without dropping or hurling it across the room. Lately, she has been eating soft foods like applesauce or Ensure. At 105 pounds she was slowly disappearing. Still, my sister never complained of being restrained in bed. She patiently spent her days watching *Bewitched* or *I Dream of Jeannie* on a small television or listening to music without words. Never once did she beg me to visit or ask the staff to call me. Janice expected very little from me and this is what she received back: very little. I visited less and less, not knowing this was my sister's last year on earth.

One month later, one of the nurses calls to ask if I can visit Janice more frequently. Her concerned and desperate voice fills my ear.

"Please Mrs. Codding, could you please visit Janice? She is such a sweet young woman. Day after day she has no visitors. Now that your father cannot visit without supervision this means your mother does not come either."

I feel my stomach tighten and churn as though it is filled with crushed glass.

My voice trembles. "Why-y does my father need supervision?"

The nurse pauses before stating incredulously, "Didn't you know, Mrs. Codding? You must have known. Your father was caught abusing your sister in her own bed!" She speaks of my father as if he were the rat caught underneath the baby's crib.

"Your father is not allowed to see Janice anymore without a staff present. To show we have every intention of following through, we posted a guard at your sister's door." Her words seize me as if I were suddenly trapped between the jaws of a lion and carried away through a dark jungle. Again she asks me, "Didn't you know, Mrs. Codding? You must have known. *Your mother knew.*"

I cough nervously. "I'm sorry. I cannot visit my sister. She makes me too nervous."

For a moment I visualize Janice strapped to a chair and anxiously cry out— "My God, I'm sorry, so very, sorry. I just can't come! My God, what does my poor sister do all day?"

The nurse sighs patiently having heard every excuse in the book. "Well, we did find a book for Janice. One donated to our library called *A Christmas Carol*. She truly loves it. Janice told us she used to watch that movie over your house quite often. Mrs. Codding, your sister loves you very much and speaks highly of you. We try to make her feel as comfortable as possible. We read aloud to her and she loves that. Maybe, someday, you can come and read to your sister too."

When the nurse hears no response she sighs. "Well, thank you Mrs. Codding. I appreciate you speaking with me."

After the nurse is gone, I sit immobile. Not moving, not breathing, feeling as though I am sealed inside a tomb and begin to think of ways to die. It is then I visualize Alan K. Driscoll talking about the chains that hold us bound. *"Personally, I believe chains are made to be broken. The chains that held us captive yesterday lose their power through the choices we make today. We can change our destiny and render the past powerless."*

One last time, my sister dreams of being normal.

The staff scheduled an appointment at a hospital in Massachusetts for Janice to hear the results of genetic testing that my family and I participated in several weeks ago. My sister was anxious to learn what her testing would reveal and hoped for a new start in life. Together my sister and I will travel thirty minutes away in an ambulance to hear whether or not she has a degenerative disease.

Janice is thrilled at the possibility of receiving help and despite everything that has happened, she continues to be positive. As I push her wheelchair toward the ambulance, she pulls me toward her with a thin, bony arm and kisses me with dry cracked lips. She looks up at me, not knowing that her smile reveals a row of chipped broken teeth, and speaks with so much hope it breaks my heart to hear.

"Con! I'm finally going to get help! They are going to find out what's wrong with me! Just think Con, maybe I can have a normal life!"

I find it strange that my mother and father did not come with us today. I thought they would be curious, or maybe, they already knew the outcome without hearing the results.

The hospital looms before us, holding my sister's life in her hands. After a short intake, a friendly nurse brings us into a stainless steel room where we meet a young doctor. I can tell by the look in his eyes he has been down this road before and it hurts him to meet another patient looking for a miracle. He looks at my sister with sympathy because he knows she is unprepared to hear the truth. And so am I.

"Miss Falcone, we have analyzed the chromosomes of your family. What we have learned is that your sister, mother, and father's chromosomes are what we consider to be of 'regular-shape.' However, your chromosomes are 'irregular-shaped' and what we consider to be abnormal unlike your other family members. What we have determined from your blood work and genetic makeup, *excluding the mystery of the irregular-shaped chromosomes,* is that you do not suffer from any form of degenerative disease. In fact, a complete analysis of your chemistry appears to be functioning within the normal range, free from disease."

My sister slumps in the chair and weeps softly. The doctor looks at my sister with sadness. "I know you were looking for a disease that could be treated. At this time I can say with confidence, Miss Falcone—*that you have no disease.* Most people would rejoice at this news."

After a few minutes a nurse enters and begins wheeling my devastated sister away.

But I stayed.

"Excuse me, but could my sister's irregular-shaped chromosomes have been caused by abuse?" My words rush out of my mouth as if someone will come and snatch them away.

"Doctor, I want you to know something. For over four decades my father abused my sister in every possible way: physically, mentally and sexually. Do you think the abuse my sister endured may have caused her chromosomes to look different than the rest of us?"

The doctor does not flinch at my suggestion. I sense he has answered this question before. "If that were the case, Mrs. Codding, every person who happens to be walking around with irregular-shaped chromosomes would have a history of abuse, perhaps banging their head or falling to the ground. No. There is no scientific evidence to date that states that abuse has a factor in any of this. No, not even abuse can change the DNA structure." He smiles at the thought.

Even after hearing the knowledge imparted by a brilliant physician, I still refuse to accept and recklessly begin questioning the doctor. "Doctor, is there *even* a small possibility the abusive environment my sister endured from the time she was born until the present moment could somehow have played a part in her chromosomes looking different? I mean, I understand DNA remains unchanged, but somehow, is there any possibility at all that my sister's chromosomes were somehow affected by the suffering she endured? I mean…do we really understand all there is to know the effect abuse has on our bodies in the long term?"

The doctor closes my sister's file, signaling the conversation is over and responds casually. "You prepared quite a challenging argument, Mrs. Codding, yet I can assure you, there is no conclusive evidence to date which points to specific environmental factors causing chromosome abnormalities. And with no current data to prove or even hypothesize your theory—it ceases to exist. Yet…anything's possible unless proven otherwise, I suppose."

Janice and I ride back in silence with nary a glimmer of hope existing between the two of us. When we arrive back at the hospital, I help tie her into bed and feed her a supper of thick chocolate pudding and a can of Ensure. I gaze out the window and into the darkness to admire the soft flicker of streetlights. They shine like the beloved faces of children yearning for love and comfort and I wonder how many other children will never have the opportunity to grow and lead normal lives due to the abuse hiding so eloquently behind their bright shining faces?

My sister is ready for sleep and resigned to her fate.

"I didn't have much luck, did I Con? I'll never have a normal life, will I?"

My sister can never be solemn for very long and laughs fondly. "Remember when you were a little girl and you asked me why I read books all the time? And I said it helps me with the *loneliness* and you thought I said the lonely nest?" Content, my sister lays her head back and closes her eyes. "After that we spoke of how each one of us has a lonely nest and a Mama Robin that helps us tell the difference between right and wrong."

With sad acceptance my sister looks above and makes the sign of the cross. Unknown to me, her last words were a summation of a life lived in a war-torn battlefield where visions of buttercups and violets continue to flourish. She spoke softly, "Con, I know where the first lonely nest came from. It was born into existence when Mama Robin discovered the tree her babies nest upon had been chosen for the Cross of Christ."

I can hardly drive home because I am crying so hard. It is one of the few times in my life I felt a gut-wrenching ache for my sister. Even so, I did not realize this was the last time I would see her alive.

My spirit never fully accepted what the hospital physician said. It was decades later when I came across several studies that stated a correlation between abuse and shortened telomeres. Telomere length is critical to protecting cells. When telomeres shorten too much the cell stops replicating. The cell may die or there may be genetic abnormalities that result within the cell. Shorter telomeres have been linked to a higher risk of developing chronic diseases, such as type 2 diabetes, cancers, and cardiovascular diseases in adults. One study discovered patients who reported childhood abuse had the shortest telomeres, suggesting a link between early stressors and accelerated cellular aging.

According to one study, "Chronic psychological stress may accelerate aging at the cellular level. Women exposed to intimate partner violence (IPV) experience chronic stress and report worse health. The World Health Organization noted that 20% to 50% of women who experienced IPV reported that it resulted in physical injury and deleterious health effects (e.g., broken bones, problems walking, memory loss, suicidal ideation) lasting long after the violence ended and that IPV interferes with even simple activities of daily life (*Telomere Shortening in Formerly Abused and Never Abused Women, 2013 Apr 1*).

I will never know for sure if this information has anything to do with what happened to Janice and the results we received in the doctor's office. I do know that childhood abuse and neglect have long-range effects on an individual all the way down to the cellular level and the biological implications of such abuse is life-altering.

On Easter Sunday, March 26, 1989, Janice Lynn Falcone left this world to join the countless other nameless angels who die alone. Or did she really die alone?

After Bob and I arrived home from church, I listened to the dreaded words on the answering machine. "*Connie, Connie Mary! This is your father! Your sister, she died today!*"

I fell to the floor screaming— "How did Janice die, Dad? HOW?

You better tell me how my sister died!"

When I call my father back his voice is one of calm acceptance.

"The hospital said Janice choked on her food in the middle of the night."

Even though my reaction is hidden underneath layers of grueling guilt, I sensed injustice. *Janice could not feed herself. She had no food in her room. Who was there when Janice died? Someone is lying.*

Having lived my entire life acquiescing wrongdoing, I never bothered to call the hospital to confirm my father's statement, preferring to blindly accept it. Decades after her death, while researching my sister's life, I received her death certificate in the mail from the state of Massachusetts. I was shocked to read the primary cause of her death was *Huntington's chorea* with *Seizure Syndrome* as the significant underlying condition. I knew this was a lie. My sister had no formal diagnosis of a degenerative disease, as she was tested at every stage of her life. The death certificate stated the case was not referred to the medical examiner nor was an autopsy performed, as both were denied by a certain party named Albert J. Falcone, whose name on the death certificate read as: *"Informant."* I remember my mother being upset that my father had not requested an autopsy, as she too had found my sister's death suspicious.

In 2012, Sister Connie Charette of *The Daughters of the Holy Spirit* in Putnam, Connecticut tried to help me obtain Janice's medical records by going to the Worcester Rehabilitation Center to request them. She was told that records are destroyed after seven years. I contacted several major hospitals in Massachusetts but had no success and concluded that a needle in a haystack would be easier to find than my sister's records. The problem was that I could not remember the name of the hospital where Janice and I were given the results of our DNA testing. Living precariously, protected behind a husband, a house and a lie—*I kept no records.* I am hoping that someday, someone with the proper credentials will read this story and help trace my sister's records. Perhaps her life could help others. Janice would have been happy to help people, and through this book, I believe she will.

19

The Murder of Rose Falcone

Rose Falcone
May 1998

"Some might say I was too damaged to know any better having lived with an abuser so long. There is some truth to this. The real truth is harder to accept and far more egregious when I say we learn to sacrifice the ones we love in order to survive."

One year after my sister died, I gave birth to my first daughter named Concetta Rose. This was followed by a second daughter named Cathleen. It secretly pains me that my daughters will never know there was someone special in my life that could have taught them how to make wildflower scrapbooks or identify every species of leaf and tree. Having sealed her memory inside my lonely nest, I will not speak of Aunt Janice for decades. For the first few years, my children have a wonderful relationship with their grandparents; it is a brief period in Camelot where rose-colored glasses cover the horrors of the past. I return fully loaded to my parent's home with precious ammunition called *Nipoti* (grandchildren) which is powerful enough to collapse the walls that once separated my father from me. I am the prodigal daughter who visits every Saturday, driving my children to 93 Fitchville Road. My mother adores my children as if every breath they take is her own. Never was there a more loving Nanny than my mother, who surprises my children with special treats and gifts. It is not long before history repeats itself, and like my mother, I begin taking photographs to document images too horrific for words.

My father *appears* to love my children. But the Mama Robin in my lonely nest reminds me that my father's love is narcissistically askew and that I must never forget how my sister dwells inside of me, guiding me, breaking through my denial, especially when my father questions with all the innocence of a grandfather seeking atonement, "Why can't we take the grandchildren overnight?"

I see my sister's worried face and calmly reply. "No. My children will never be out of my sight—never." This offends the master manipulator who turns to his relatives for sympathy.

"My daughta' won't let us take our own grandchildren. She don't trust us." Despite the depth of my dysfunction, I know my mother loves my children with all her heart. *I also know my mother cannot protect them.* My father is a situational abuser. He is smart enough to know when it is safe to sexually abuse and when it is not. During my childhood there were children who came to our house but to my knowledge, he only abused Janice. Janice was a safe gamble, weakened from a young age by the verbal, physical and sexual abuse that incapacitated her ability to live a normal life. My father holds his family captive with intimidation and violence, punishing both mother and daughter when necessary. In less than a year, I experience a lull of bliss, oblivious to the return of evil. A lack of knowledge prevents me from knowing an abuser will not stop abusing until rendered by authority. I misunderstood the magnitude and skill of the beast rearing its head in the direction of my mother. And thus begins the murder of Rose Falcone.

The first time I heard the familiar sound of the ugly slap, my mind refused to comprehend it, rather than confront my father and ruin another idyllic Saturday in Bozrah. My children were watching *Sesame Street* in tiny yellow chairs like two precious flowers, never imagining evil was near. Suddenly, without warning, my mother abruptly left the loving scene and followed my father upstairs. Within minutes there was a sound indistinguishable from anything else— "SLAP, SLAP, SLAP!" followed by angry words: "*I told you not to do that! Now look at what **you** made me do,*" accompanied by two more slaps and my heart plunges into darkness.

Innocently absorbed, my children were unaware of the violence taking place because I did not run upstairs and righteously demand— "*How dare you hit mom!*" After several minutes my mother descended the staircase and entered the television room looking older than I remembered. She walked gingerly, placing two feet on each step before proceeding to the next. As my mother's arthritic body approached, I began to put the puzzle together and the realization was as clear as the stars lining the sky above. All this time my mother had been making excuses for the black and blue marks and back operation that never healed. By the time my mother reached the bottom step I knew the truth. My mother was being murdered... one slap at a time. My sister's premeditated murder required decades of uninterrupted violence. My mother's would not.

When she sat down, I fell to the floor and gripped her leg.

"*Ma—did Daddy slap you?*" My mother studied the rug where Sam once laid his head and whispered so my children would not hear.

"The first time he did it, I was so surprised. I couldn't believe he was actually slapping me."

Terror hid behind my mother's legs. My voice was a low, hysterical whisper. "No Ma! No, no, no!" My mother looked lovingly at my children as if accepting the part she played in creating her reality and said in a sickening, appeasing voice, "Kids, guess what Nan's got for you?"

My children giggle and run to their Nanny, eyes twinkling with memories of sunny days, popsicles, and *Cabbage Patch Dolls.* In the midst of this happy and chaotic scene my father moodily walked through the room, smelling like a fresh shaven king and looking as though he was about to step out with a girlfriend instead of going on a job. He walked by us with his head held high and slipped out the door without saying a word.

D r. Chauvin was my mother's last doctor and was, by far, the most indifferent to her suffering. The doctor communicated as though I was a nuisance uselessly questioning his authority. "*Your mother has an enlarged liver. I told you this before. What's not to understand?*"

His indifference was not from a lack of education but an unfamiliarity with who or who does not fit the profile of a violent abuser. In all fairness, my father was a master at portraying the doting husband. I knew then that my mother would die so covertly that no one—*not even my mother*—would recognize it as murder. Repeating the same modus operandi that erased Janice, the premeditated murder was happening logically, systematically, a slow extermination that ran as smoothly as a German cyanide machine.

At this point in time someone within the circle of my mother's contacts witnessed the abuse and anonymously reported my father to Social Services in Norwich. After a few weeks, my mother began receiving social services with home health aides and a social worker that specializes in elder abuse. Acting flagrantly, my father changes the rules about his social security check. In the past my mother had access to withdrawing money that she rightfully earned as a housewife working over fifty years. Now she was told by my father not to touch it, along with her social security check that was deposited into a joint savings account. This came in handy since my father preferred to spend my mother's money gambling and drinking lavishly with young prostitutes at Foxwoods Casino.

With every day that passed the abuse became more visible. I was haunted by the sprained wrists, arms in slings, and bruises that made it look like my mother was falling as frequently as Janice. I begged my mother for the truth.

"Ma, I want to know! Is Dad hitting you? Please, tell me the truth!"

My mother would stare into space and with staunch determination quietly utter "No." A word that resounded louder than a sonic boom. I called Social Services and pleaded with the social worker. "Please, you've got to help my mother. My father killed my sister! And now he is physically and mentally killing my mother! The social worker followed up with a visit and returned my call with a voice far too amicable to believe.

"Connie Mary, I wish I could help with your mother. I cannot tell you how many of these 'so-called-cases' I see on a daily basis. Elderly men and women who are being abused by spouses, siblings and *so-called* relatives, and still, they choose not to leave. I see it every day."

I ranted in disbelief. "You must get my mother out of that house—you must! I see what is happening here—my mother is getting sicker and sicker!" Her response was motherly yet resigned.

"Connie Mary… your mother is an adult. We cannot force her to do what she chooses not to do. Your mother wants to stay. She loves your father and home. This is the saddest part of my job—elderly clients who refuse to leave and die at the hands of a caregiver."

I refused to take no for an answer and called the police, only to receive the same answer as years before. "Mrs. Codding, how do you suppose we go about removing your mother from the premises? We have never received a single report of abuse from your mother," and snidely added, "And not from anyone else for that matter."

I begged my mother to come live with me. My mother's response came from years of sorrow and resentment, whose thinking she shared with my father concerning my husband. "I would rather *die* than live in your house."

My mother has made a choice. How was I supposed to accept and turn a blind eye, knowing so many elderly people choose to stay with murderous caregivers rather than leave? What ethical duty do we as a society have knowing so many elders are trapped and dying in their own homes?

The steady deterioration progressed with each passing day. My mother suffered from osteoporosis so severe she had to wear a brace. The two back operations she endured months prior rendered her disabled, and because my mother was diabetic, her health demanded the twice daily insulin injections she needed to maintain her blood sugar level. Her blood needed to be drawn so frequently that eventually a central venous access catheter was lodged in her chest. But even if you had combined every one of my mother's illnesses, the results would not have been as fatal as the daily mental and physical abuse from my father. I was in a constant state of helplessness, begging my mother to stay at my house when she occasionally slept over in our spare room. In the midnight hour I laid by her feet, begging her to leave my father.

"I don't belong here," she answered with resignation. "My life is in Bozrah with your father." There was another reason my mother would not stay with me. My mother knew when she was away from home my father brought women to the house.

"Ma, don't you see? Daddy doesn't love you anymore! You can go ahead and deny it—but I know that bastard has been hitting you! Ma this is the truth—Daddy wants you dead! With all your diseases, he knows that no one would ever guess that he is slowly murdering you—one day at a time!"

My mother did not believe me.

"Connie Mary, I don't care what you say. I know there is *love* between us… it's there. Your father loves me. It is strange though. Some things have happened. Odd things. Like Viola, the lovely woman who was my home health worker…she never came back. I thought it was strange and looked for her number. I was shocked when she told me she had to quit because your father would not leave her alone! He even called her house. She cried when she said, 'Rose, I'm sorry. But I don't feel comfortable coming to your house anymore… Goodbye Rose.' And then there is the telephone in the basement. One day I was resting in bed when I heard the phone ring and answered. It was the voice of a young woman. She said, 'Hi ya, Al Baby, it's me, Sapphira!' Your father is in the basement and knows I'm listening and yells, 'Rose hang up this Goddamn phone and mind yer' own business!'"

Disgusted, I stood up. "Oh, Ma, he's got a girlfriend! — I can't believe it! Who would want that fat old man?" My mother laughed cynically.

"I told you Connie Mary—your father has money and can get any woman he wants. And the kind he wants is no good. Albert always did like the bums. They make him feel better about himself. Imagine my own husband telling me to mind my own business? If he's not my business who is? —I'm his wife!"

Months pass.

One cold winter night, the phone rings, waking my husband and I from a sound sleep. It is my mother who is sobbing hysterically. *"Your father... he's NO good Connie Mary—he killed your sister AND I told him so."* My mother pauses momentarily, causing my brain to implode with dread and doom. She hesitates as if suddenly encountering the Grim Reaper. "Oh no! He's coming! —NO! NO, ALBERT STOP! N-O-O-O-O!"

My mother drops the receiver and screams as I listen to the sound of massive fists pounding her elderly body. My father is punching her in a back-and-forth manner like a boxer in a ring. "WHOMP! BOP— BOP—BOP—BOP—WHOMP, WHOMP!" There is crashing and fumbling as my father brazenly and shamelessly hits my mother, all the while knowing I am listening. That is how entitled he has become. My father is over 180 pounds with the muscle mass of a man decades younger. He is pummeling my mother with the same force and speed as if she were his equal. My mother's voice pitifully wails—"No, ALBERT! NO!"

By some miracle, my mother returns to the phone with a clear and resilient voice—how she found the strength I will never know. "He's been beating me, punching my face, my stomach, even my back where I had my operation." My father is in the background, coy and taunting, sounding like he was caught by the truant officer for cutting classes.

"Ahhh, I wasn't hittin' your motha,' I was-ent."

My father laughs. This enrages my mother. The scene is reminiscent of a Mama Lion who trusted the papa to protect the babies, but he callously ate instead. "YOU HIT ME ALBERT—YOU LIAR! YOU HIT ME BECAUSE I SAID YOU MURDERED MY BEAUTIFUL DAUGHTER JANICE!"

I scream back, "Ma—Hang up! I'm calling the police and coming right now!" I slam the phone down and call the police telling my sleepy husband, "My father's beating my mother—I have to go!" My husband begs me not to go until he knows there is no power on God's earth that could stop me. I speed 90 miles an hour southward on highway 395 to Bozrah. A couple of times I think I will crash but cannot slow down…I cannot slow down.

Twenty minutes later I arrive to find my mother in bed. I immediately call the police demanding to know what is taking them so long to get here. The officer who answered is composed and unemotional. "We came to the house. Your mother said your father did not hit her. We had no case, no prior record of assault or complaints, so we left." Trembling, I slowly place the receiver down. I walk upstairs and look at my mother's war-torn face and she tells me not to worry. "It is quiet now. Your father went out. Everything is going to be all right."

As unbelievable as this may sound—I left and did not call my mother back for fear my father would answer. It would be sometime after my mother's death when the steel encasement sealing my lonely nest cracked. Some might say I was too damaged to know any better, having lived with an abuser so long. There is some truth to this. But the real truth is harder to accept and far more egregious when I say we learn to sacrifice the ones we love in order to survive.

I coped with my inability to fight by sleeping long days in bed leaving my children in front of the television for hours. Within weeks, all was forgotten and everything reverted back to normal, as though the beating never happened. When you live and breathe violence, one day melts into the next without thought or awareness.

I returned to 93 Fitchville Road on a Saturday. The routine felt so comforting, although I knew deep down nothing was real. My daughters settled into the parlor with coloring books while my mother and I made sauce in the kitchen. The scene was surreal. My mother crushed garlic as she normalized what has become her way of life. "When your father holds Nonno's shotgun to my head he thinks it scares me. Ha, if he shoots me my problems will be over."

"Yes," I replied, "If he shoots you. Dad is too smart to shoot you. He knows he will go to jail. Why should he shoot you Mom when he can kill you a little bit each day and no one would guess he is murdering you?"

Again, I called Doctor Chauvin to ask about my mother's condition. He answers with a stinging tone. "I already explained this to *you* several times. Your mother's liver is enlarged because she does not take care of herself. She is a diabetic and has been abusing prescription medicines all her life. These are the reasons your mother's liver is not functioning. That being said, I am keeping her a few extra days in the hospital—*to give your father a break*." The doctor was not saying that in less than six months my mother would be dead and buried next to Janice. My mother was dying and should have been under the loving care of hospice, not the callous hands of a criminal. But how could I speak up for my mother when I could not find my own voice?

It is a beautiful summer day when my mother calls to tell me about the little swimming pool she has for my children. "Con—just wait until my Concetta Rosie and little Cathleeny see the beautiful pool I bought! And guess what else? I bought them each a basket of toys— ha! Now they can pretend they are at the beach on 93 Fitchville Road."

"Thanks Ma, we'll be there tomorrow afternoon."

The next day I pull into my parents' driveway and step slowly from the car as the girls run into the house happily chanting, "Nan, Nan!"

Upon entering the kitchen I encounter a deadly silence. This is when I see that the glass in the door is cracked in half with a long strip of black duct tape holding it together. Through the glass I see my mother sitting outside in a folding chair holding a can of diet soda with her back facing me. My children hover around Nanny like bees to honey, giving hugs and kisses before combing through the bright colored baskets by my mother's feet. I reassure myself. See? Everything is normal. Everything is fine. I walk outside and pull up a chair next to my mother— and then I see her face. It shines grotesquely in the summer light, displaying sinister black-and-purple bruises and angry indentions all across her cheeks and forehead.

My voice is far too calm. "Ma—what happened?" I glance fearfully at my children who are jumping joyfully from the grass and into the pool. My mother is slow to respond and shifts mechanically like a robot whose batteries are dying. She attempts to drink her Diet Pepsi, unaware of the straw being broken.

I demand indignantly — "Ma! What happened to your face?" My mother has become proficient at protecting her abuser.

"I fell off a chair."

How often have women said these five simple words that absolve an abuser? I repeat the ludicrous statement: "You fell off a chair? What do you mean you FELL off a chair?"

In the distance I hear the low rumble of my father's lawnmower dying and then silence. Within minutes he is standing above us, looking down at my children without seeing them. My father stares through my children as if they were nothing more than a fading dream forgotten by tomorrow. Without looking at my mother he addresses her in a rough, crude voice.

"When you want me to put the steaks on—huh?" My mother's response is pitiful.

"Oh, anytime." My father walks away looking strange and sullen like the rattler lying low in the bush until hungry again. Without much thought or reason, I silently reach for the camera and take my mother's picture.

After we eat, my children and I stroll through the neighborhood and run into an old neighbor that I knew since childhood. Mr. Nolan faces my parent's yard from a folding chair as his wife quietly hangs laundry. At first the talk is casual.

"My, your kids are getting big," laughs Mr. Nolan. After a few minutes I cannot hold back and awkwardly declare—"Mr. Nolan, my mother's face is horribly black and blue today!"

Without missing a beat, Mr. Nolan boldly responds, "THE OLD MAN PROBABLY BEAT 'ER UP! Did you know your mother doesn't come outside anymore? Nope! She's given up!" I shake my head back and forth, pretending I am learning something new. At this point Mrs. Nolan turns and utters with disgust, "Your father's no good! The man's no good."

Mr. Nolan nods in agreement. "Did you know there are days when I walk by his house and find him in the garage grinning and pointing a gun at me? Other days he stays close to the front porch hidden from sight and yells, 'Nolan, you Polak bastard' or "Mother F-u-c-k-e-r.' The worst days are when he comes outside, creeps behind me, and tries to step on my heels whispering dirty, filthy things. Things I wouldn't repeat here, out of respect for you and your children. That man is clearly disturbed. Can you imagine hiding inside your garage laughing like a monkey and pointing a rifle at someone? We all know he put the bullet hole in Donna Elsensohn's window screen, flattened her tires more than once, and slashed old

lady Meyer's tires. Your old man doesn't think we know it's him—
but we know!"

Mrs. Nolan shakes her head as she looks in the direction of my
father's house and spits, *"That man's no good."*

With quiet desperation I ask, "Why doesn't anyone call the police?"
Mr. and Mrs. Nolan look at each other and burst out laughing.
"Your father's got guns, Connie Mary. We're old folks here.
Someday you'll understand. Besides—we're moving anyway.
Leaving, saying goodbye and good riddance to your father." Mr.
Nolan lowers his voice and bows in reverence as if recalling someone
who died. "Your poor mother; she never stood a chance—*and neither
did your sister."*

After we returned home I sent my camera film to be processed in
the mail. Within a week or so, my mother's black and blue
photograph arrived and I hid it inside a box with hundreds of other
photographs. The picture stayed hidden until one night in 2009,
when my mother appeared in a dream. In the dream my mother was
frantically pointing to the box in the closet. She was visibly upset.

"Get up Connie Mary! Get my picture out of that box—the one
with the black and blue face!" I was dreaming, but it seemed so real.
I knew I was half-awake because I could feel myself trying to open
my eyes.

"Oh Ma," I answered despondently, "I can't find your picture. I
threw it in a box with hundreds of other photographs. I'll never find
it."

My mother's face grew stolid, her voice relentless. "Get up!
Connie Mary, don't you know? *You're going to need it for the book
because people will not believe you!"* I was shaking when I rushed
downstairs to take the box out of the closet. I took a deep breath and
reached my hand deep into the hundreds of photographs. The first
one I pulled out was the picture of my mother with the black and

blue face. I took my mother's picture and laid it across my heart. I knew that one day everyone would know what the face of domestic violence looks like.

A new delusion seeps into the mind of my mother whenever the violence pauses for a day. She is thankful for a day without violence and irrationally justifies the lack of abuse for kindness, sympathizing with my father whenever I call. "Con, your father wants me off this phone. He says you don't care about us."

"Ma, that bastard is trying to kill you! Get him on this phone—now!"

I can tell my mother wants to lie down and avoid conflict. "Please Con, that will make him mad."

I scream—"Get that bastard on this phone now!"

My poor mother timidly hands the phone over to my father and he chuckles.

"You're no good, you ain't never been any good. You never visited your sister in that Godforsaken hospital because you was enjoying yourself in Danielson with *his* family. You're no good."

I explode with rage—"Who do you think you are telling my mother to get off the phone? Why, you're nothing but a rapist and a murderer! You monster! I know you have a girlfriend and she's a pig like you. You murdered my sister and now you're murdering my mother!" An abuser is adept at targeting the Achilles heel in their opponent, thus provoking name-calling sessions between the two of us. Hate consumes my body and soul and, in a strange way, saves me.

"You're going to be sorry, dad… you just wait!" I slam the phone so hard it jars loose from the wall and crashes to the floor.

"What were you thinking?" asks my husband, who is using a screwdriver to repair the damaged phone. And that is it. I say nothing, for where can I turn? With despair I look at my children and know…I must let my mother go.

Christmas comes and goes without seeing my mother. Not a minute passes or day goes by when I am not tormented by my choice knowing my father is frolicking without a care in the world. Some told me I should have killed my father rather than let my mother go. I admit there were times I imagined him dead and my sister and mother alive! Still, I closed my eyes, rather than fight a monster called domestic violence.

January 1999 arrives, bringing a New Year and hope to others. I miss my mother so much that one afternoon I drove to Bozrah. I glide through the front door like a ghost from the past shocked to see the living, breathing corpse sitting in the parlor. My mother is vaguely aware that someone has entered and tilts slowly in my direction. I hesitantly ask, "Where's dad?"

My mother replies unpretentiously, "He's at the casino with his girlfriend."

My mother does not wonder where I have been or why I did not come home for Christmas. Instead she says, "Sit down. I want to talk to you."

With apprehension I stare at the dirty clothes piled in heaps and soiled paper plates that surround her. I sit like a guest, somehow knowing I am seeing things for the last time. My mother looks up at the ceiling where Janice once slept and retreats into a private exodus exclaiming with euphoria, *"Con, I'm going to see my Janice again!* I'm going to see that girl again." She abruptly changes when the light in her eyes fades.

"Con, I want you to go upstairs to see the blue dress hanging on my closet door. Yesterday your father told me, *'That's the dress you're going be buried in.'"*

At first my brain cannot comprehend such horror. *"What?* What did he mean, 'that's the dress you're gonna be buried in?" My mother repeats the sentence slower.

"Your father told me...'*That's the dress... you're going...to be buried in.*'" In disbelief, I go and look and sure enough there is a blue lacy dress hanging on the closet door. I come downstairs and sit by her feet. "Ma this is murder... you've got to leave now!"

Without any sense of emotion my mother stares at her music boxes. "There is not much time left. Bring the music boxes home before your father comes back. I don't want his girlfriend to get them." Dysfunction breeds dysfunction as I run through the house gathering as much as I can carry. After the music boxes are safely packed away I plead one last time, "Please Ma, leave with me. There is nothing here but death."

My mother answers firmly: "*No.*"

When I am about to leave my mother points to a statue of Christ and says, "*If you don't believe in Him, you don't believe in anything. He is my beginning, and He is my end.*"

The winter sun begins to lower as I drive away. The clouds glow orange-pink against the purple sky, reflecting a blood-red sheen over the earth. As the sun leaves the sky I decide to visit Fields Memorial School. As I drive up to the school building I am dismayed to see how much it has changed since I was a little girl and makes me realize how everyone is given one childhood and one chance to be a child as the path traveled is no longer recognizable and no one finds the way back. I sit on a lonely swing when the lone figure of a man approaches in the distance. As he comes closer the familiar blue-gray eyes meet mine and once again I know where the sun hides on a rainy day.

"Hey Connie Mary, why I'd recognize you anywhere." He laughs. "Did you recognize me with my baldhead? It's me, Gregory McGillis. I guess we couldn't stay away from Fields Memorial School could we? I come here just to think. Mind if I sit down?"

Before I can say anything, a clumsy six-year-old with a crooked tie and dirty shirt plops down on the swing next to me. There is no hugging, no emotional reunion, it is as if we entered the same dream and levitated back to our beloved playground where we performed supernatural feats like flying airplanes or me winning all of Gregory's marbles.

"I'm not going to be here much longer Connie Mary. My mom lost the house after my dad died." Gregory hesitates before shyly admitting, "I heard you was married. I looked for you a long time and the years sort of went by." He laughs softly, "I did not have Tom Terrific's thinking cap to find you. I sure am glad I met you Connie Mary. You'll always be my best friend. Wish we could have had more time though. Maybe in the next life huh?"

When the last ray of light fades, the stars strike the sky with sharp edges cutting willfully into the night. Gregory observes the darkness. "Well, I best be going if I want to catch my ride," and it looks as though we will never meet again. "Goodbye Connie Mary."

We hug like two lost children and I wish we could go back and play airplanes if only for one hour in a safer world that all children deserve. The little boy with the runny nose and ripped pants stands and a middle-aged man with hunched shoulders walks away. After a short distance the dark silhouette looks back and waves before blending into the shadows.

January 19th, 1999, 4:30 P.M.

When the phone rings I glance at the caller I.D. and hold my breath when I see it is the Backus Hospital. When I answer, a man projects a sense of urgency.

"It is crucial that you come to the Backus Hospital *right now*. It is your mother. There is not much time." It is a message that should have come from the doctor—not an unidentified stranger who hangs up when I ask his name. Due to this phone call I am able to reach my mother before she falls into a coma. Weeks later when I call the hospital to thank the person who called I discover no one has any idea who called me.

I sprint through the emergency room running from room to room finding my mother sleeping between crisp white sheets moist with perspiration. When I say, "Ma," to my surprise she opens her eyes and with uncanny determination strains to come closer. For a brief moment my mother looks into my eyes and whispers, *"Connie Mary."* Silently pleading, she fights to keep her eyes on mine trying to make me understand how much *she loves me.* This is the last time I will speak to my mother.

I wish I could say my mother died peacefully. The fact is by the time my father, *the wandering tumbleweed* blows into the hospital a few hours later my mother's liver and major organs have shut down despite a heart that continues to beat strong. Injected every hour with morphine my mother continues to die and in the process starts choking bringing the nurse every hour to suction her throat.

Two o'clock. I cannot stand anymore and ring the nurses' station once more demanding, "Nurse, my mother won't stop choking!"

Four o'clock. The sound of my mother suffocating is too much for my father and he jumps to his feet. "I won't stand another minute of this! *I'm going to take that pillow and cover her face!"* I say nothing silently knowing a true narcissist would never risk his life to end my mother's suffering. I watch his words disappear like stars sucked into a black hole.

Seven o'clock. The choking subsides and with several long gasps my mother desperately fights for life. A decade will pass before I see the death certificate and discover my mother died at 7:05—the exact time my daughter Concetta Rose was born. My mother found a way to deliver a message of hope that she is with Janice. Exhausted, I stare at the gruesome face of my dead mother. It is as horrific as the face of Lon Chaney's *Phantom of the Opera* when the mask is ripped from his face. My mother left this world mouth gaping and eyes fixated on some unseen horror, an appropriate exodus to a life of suffering. More bizarre is watching my father throw himself on top of my mother crying —"Rose! Rose!"

I wish I could say my father changed after my mother died. That he regretted his actions and became the father I wanted and the grandfather my children needed. My father does not know, but he is about to meet his match *and I do not mean me.* I leave the Backus Hospital greeted by cheerful nurses and smiling doctors and realize that everyone is on the same journey traveling through the most beautiful part of Hell. On the drive home I pull over to vomit. Kneeling on the ground I lift my eyes to Heaven and beg, "O' God Jesus transform the blood that runs through my veins into cold calculated steel because this is not over!"

Nineteen years after the death of my mother a woman named Kerry Butler contacted me explaining she had worked for my mother as a home health aide in Bozrah. I wish to thank Kerry Butler, a complete stranger, who was brave enough to come forward decades later to document my mother's story in a letter for this book.

June 20, 2018

Hello,

I believe your name is Connie.

I saw your name on my Facebook page.

In 1988, I briefly worked as a home health aide for your mother in Bozrah, Connecticut.

I believe her name was Rose. I glanced at your page because I remember your mom saying your name and it stuck with me. I want you to know Mr. Falcone was the reason I quit and I'm so sorry. He was a plumber I believe. It has always bothered me how vicious and demeaning he was to his wife and inappropriate towards me. I won't rehash it...it just broke my heart to see she passed while still in that prison. I cared for her. And I knew in my heart your dad did something foul to his daughters. I'm a survivor as well so I can see it a mile away.

Maybe I'm saying more than you should know...

But anytime I drive by that house I feel the filth like it was me who suffered there.

I grew up in Bozrah and graduated from Fields Memorial in 1985. I'm so sorry. Your mother was so fragile and afraid. And he was such a demon.

This incident has always bothered me. One day Mr. Falcone took my car down to Fitchville Auto and paid for repairs. That's where he started soliciting me. I took your mom out to Caldor in the mall. When we got home, your father had a fit that she spent her own money!

I'd find disgusting notes in the upstairs bathroom asking me for sex.

He knew I'd find them. I was so grossed out I had my agency replace me. But I do remember your mom being terrified of him and telling me she was so humiliated that I found animal porn in the VCR in the living room...Your mother cried at times. But more than that, she just seemed utterly broken. Defeated.

The one time I got her out your father was so nasty when we came back...she was scared. At the store I pushed her in her wheelchair and she wanted to buy my child something.

I'm a survivor of abuse myself. And I just knew he did something evil to his daughters.

I just knew something wasn't right in how he treated her and talked about his daughters.

When your mom told me how you stayed away and kept your children away, I knew. Because I've lived that way with my father since I was 3 years old. I escaped at 15 and never allowed him near me again. My hell happened close to you in Bozrah in the 1980s and looking back, my teachers failed me. My family, friends and neighbors...how could they not have seen what was happening to me? But because my father was so well loved and a businessman I was the lying whore.

I'm not going to go into a lot of detail but when I worked for your mother, your dad started leaving me weird little notes in the upstairs garbage can.

Then it was letters with money. One day it was a big steak in butcher paper. Those notes were disgusting. Asking me to do things that were absolutely offensive. Your mother was so mortified. It was odd to me because even at that time in 1998 he was old to me to be so perverted about sex. Your mother was in a lot of pain taking Oxycontin medication.

The great thing your mom did for me was telling my supervisor she thought I wasn't a good fit and I was moved. After I quit...Mr. Falcone would call me breathing heavily on the phone. I think he was touching himself. I felt violated. I had given your mom my number praying she would call so I could get her out of there! She never did. As soon as I saw your name on Facebook I knew it was you.

And I remembered...

By Kerry Butler, Norwich Connecticut

Part III

My Father's New Life

My Father

My father would tell me his dreams...
  "One day, people will respect me and won't treat me like dirt anymore."
  He would take me on jobs servicing the richest doctors in Norwich
  An awkward little girl happily tagging along
  I would hand him wrenches and copper pipes and screwdrivers with fancy names
  And the doctor's wives would smile and say, "I wish I had such a helper!"
  Eventually my father lost the business
  And stayed in bed for months trying to understand why
  His shrink would tell him in order to get better
  He must think of wonderful things, happy things, like flying airplanes through clouds or fishing in clear blue streams and then his business would come back
  But it never did
  I remember crying when he told me I was no longer needed
  And years later I would cry again when I learned
  At night—
  My father had been visiting my sister when convenient
  Slaughtering a childhood and ruining the chance of normalcy for an adult
  How does one remember the good in a father who committed such acts of horror?
  The nights I listened to my sister cry in the dark
  Unable to fathom why
  How could I have ever loved such a despicable dishonorable Dad?
  The fault is in how
  We are born and bred
  To love thy mother and father

No matter what sins they commit

I wish I could erase that part of my soul that honors the father

Who taught his little daughter to memorize the name of every tool

And never forget that evil lives in the hearts of men who sexually abuse children

I must make sure my love for this monster remains

Hidden from the world

Where the battle between love and hate

Fight to be heard

Concetta Falcone-Codding

20

Be Careful What You Wish

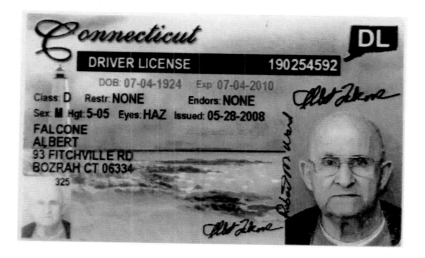

The last photograph of my father is one of grim resignation and lingering despair that he alone created honed by the choices he made in life.

The tears my father shed for my mother soon evaporate.

I returned to my father's house the next day to discuss the funeral arrangements. Overwhelmed by the memory of my mother, I go upstairs to lie down in my old bedroom. As I am about to fall asleep I hear my father making phone calls and ruffling through paperwork, no doubt looking through my mother's insurance policies to see how he will spend the money, when I realize I am not alone. Nonno suddenly appears. He is leading Nonna by the hand through a hazy fog. He turns and smiles at me, his gold tooth shimmering in the light before passing through the wall. Seeping through Janice's bedroom door I hear the familiar sound of easy listening music, which prompts me to call, "Jan, is that you? Are you here Jan?"

The music stops when I am jolted awake by the loud ringing of the telephone. Energized by some guiding force, I suddenly recall how my mother was forced to listen to my father planning his new life and having to swallow that rage. I listen to the grieving husband as he seeks sympathy from his girlfriend and my blood boils with hatred.

"Yes. Rose died yesterday. Yes. Thank you, Sapphira. Yes, yes, it was for the best." The Narcissist blows his nose and ends the conversation in a low, inviting voice, *"I'll see you later."*

What saved me from running downstairs and committing murder was my father's mantra: *Never forget, Connie Mary. Our Calabrese blood runs one and the same.*

Soon, my father will learn the true meaning of those words.

My father's new goal in life was the pursuit of pleasure. Sapphira, a prostitute in her 30's, and her daughter Salome (who would have been a high school senior if circumstances had been different) took dominion over my mother's house, each bringing an addiction to heroin. Sapphira also brings an extensive police record with a history of prostitution, drug dealing, drug pandering, larceny-theft, and aggravated assault. Before taking residence with my father, Sapphira lived with an elderly widower for years. When he died, his family was surprised to discover his life insurance policy was in her name. Women like Sapphire are not born hustlers and swindlers. They become victims of dysfunctional families and from a society that does not take kindly to poor, uneducated women on welfare.

The first time I met Salome, I saw a child whose heart had been broken too many times. Like my father, Sapphira was a narcissist who used her daughter the same way my father used Janice. In the coming months, she would persuade Salome to perform reprehensible sex acts for my father in exchange for money to buy drugs.

Salome and Janice had much in common. The adults they loved do not protect them and both their lives come to a tragic end. As Sapphira settled comfortably into my mother's chair, my father avoided a scandal in the small town of Bozrah by claiming she was a niece who had come to help him cope with the loss of his loving wife of fifty years.

Soon after Sapphira and Salome move in, my father makes two significant mistakes. The first mistake stems from a series of restless dreams he has where my mother demands that he sign the house over to me. The dreams influence him deeply. No longer willing to bear the guilt, he transfers the house into my name, adding a special clause that allows for his continued residence in the house, provided he pays for the taxes, insurance, and general bills. For the next nine years he will come to regret this decision and attempt every dirty trick in the book to steal the house back from me. The second mistake is a rather costly one. One day, he hands me a paper bag filled with $25,000 cash and asks that I hold the money for safekeeping, given his girlfriend's greed for cash. I still believe my father wants to have a relationship with my children and me and so I foolishly agree. I go home and hide the bag in my closet with every intention of keeping it safe, despite the suffering my mother and sister endured.

Within a month, Sapphira turns my mother's house into a haven where drugs are delivered, shipped, or sold, attracting every drug addict and dealer to Fitchville Road. I learned this information the night my father called my husband to complain that Sapphira was using his truck to transfer drugs to Willimantic.

Despite their differences, my husband still tries to help my father.

"Mr. Falcone, get rid of that truck now!" he warned. "If Sapphira is caught, you will be indicted on drug charges as well. Remember, that truck is in your name!" My father immediately sells his truck, thus ruining Sapphira's highly profitable business.

A few days later, while Sapphira is out on one of her three-day escapades, my father calls me with a specific purpose in mind: to confess his lurid adventures. He tells me about the night he paid Sapphira money in exchange for sex with Salome. He also gave Salome money for heroin and she overdosed in his presence. Being the Good Samaritan he is, known for bringing my sister to the emergency room after a beating by his own hand, he rushed Salome to the hospital and was surprised when he was treated like a hero.

"They let me go," he says in childlike awe. *"They said I saved her life by bringing her to the ER as fast as I did!"* Delusional liars often omit information that is unfavorable to their position. What my father failed to tell the hospital staff was that he paid for sex with the young girl and gave her the heroin as well. I listened intensely, as if my life depended on every word he said. I wanted to remember all the ways the man I once called "father" had become an utter monster.

Suddenly Sapphira interrupts our conversation by yelling in the background.

"I need to use your car tomorrow night!"

Like a cat suddenly hit with a bucket of scalding water my father screams—"You're not using my Goddamn car! I had to sell my truck because of a bitch like you! Get that idea right outta your head, you *pazzo puttana!*"

The screaming and fighting ensue in such a vicious manner that I hang up.

That same week, my father calls me and says he accidentally slapped Sapphira across the face and *Miss-Don't-Take-Any-Shit* walloped him back, packed her bags, and left. For the next nine years my father would not lift another finger against Sapphira. God had sent my father a rare gift: a woman that fights back. It is too bad my mother had not been that woman.

The next time I go to my father's house, we fight. I demand that he admit he sexually abused my sister. I am upset because my fantasy of having a father and grandfather has fallen apart and I am beginning to question my judgment—how could I have ever wanted this devil back in my life? But I did. I wanted him back as badly as any neglected child longs to return to the only parents they have ever known. Even though Nonno often struggled to clearly articulate the English language, he captured this concept perfectly when he said, "No matter how bad parent is to child, child always long for *famiglia.*"

My father sits on the couch and tries to avoid me while I stand above him. His fingers nervously twitch. I am no longer afraid of what he can do to me.

"I know you did it, Dad. Admit it! Did you have sex with Janice?"

His hands stop twitching. "I never laid a hand on my daughter."

My wrath looms into a tidal wave, destroying everything in sight.

"YOU LIAR! Get off that couch—you're going to jail!"

No matter how many times I demand he tell me the truth he still denies everything. What is most infuriating is his manipulation; with his denial he also denies my mother and sister's existence.

"YOU MURDERER! You raped my sister!"

He remains steadfast and calm, a soldier fixating on the enemy at hand. Even though I know he is thinking of how to kill me, I am no longer afraid and call his bluff.

"Try it Dad, just try it," I hiss. "Let's find out if we're *both* capable of murder. After all, our Calabrese blood runs one and the same." Even with no weapon to defend myself I bolster my confidence.

"I should have killed you a long time ago! You beat and raped my sister and threw her out the front door. But you weren't done were you Dad? You turned around and beat my mother black and blue! You picked out her funeral dress while she was still alive—and told her to wear it! *Spregevole bastardo marcio!*"

He sits frozen with rage. I look down at him and imagine the words "murderous mayhem" written across his fingers. This is the first time in my life I truly understand that my father wants me dead and if the opportunity arose, he would kill me. And once more, he would get away with it. *Don't you see?* To every doctor, he is the good appliance man. To every one of his relatives he is the grieving widow. Accidents happen. How can he help it if he has a crazy daughter who pulls a knife on her elderly father? To my father, I am just another woman who *needs* silencing. To society, I am just another woman who is lying.

I look at my mother's vase on the table and wonder if I can reach it. My father watches with clenched fists. If this were a few years ago, I would already be dead. The onset of years has turned the odds against him and placed them in my favor. I am younger, stronger, and more importantly—I am filled with a lifetime of hate strong enough to rip him apart using my bare hands. His words come out as weak as a deflated balloon.

"Get out of my house, you never was no good."

My father looks old. His face is dark and drawn with lines and furrows set deep inside his brow. This is the last time I will have to listen to his lies.

"I never touched my daughter, now get outta my house now!"

My mind snaps. Half crazy, I turn around and begin taking my mother's favorite knickknacks off the shelves. I shove them in my pockets, down my shirt and even in my pants shouting at the walls, "THIS is mine—AND THIS IS MINE—your girlfriend won't get them. *She won't get them!*"

He watches me strut around the house as I grab what is rightfully mine. When I can hold no more I begin walking out the door but stop and turn around. I see my father looking terribly sad. For a split second I almost feel sorry for him until I look at the floor where my sister once sat and stare at the circle of dried blood: her blood. When I turn the door handle I do not look back when I say, "*I promise, Dad. You're going to be sorry.*"

I cry all the way home but not for my mother and sister. I cry for the father I will always love and hate for the rest of my life. For weeks on end I stew like a pot boiling over the stove and then it finally occurs to me what I must do. Another week passes before I call my father and give him the great news.

"Congratulations Dad! I used your $25,000 to buy Concetta Rose a $8,000 baby *Kawai* grand piano! And then I used the rest of the money to put a swimming pool in our backyard. Just think, Dad— *you got off cheap!* $25,000 is not much to pay for the silence of two murders."

He starts screaming so loud I must pull away from the telephone. "I WANT MY MONEY! I WANT MY MONEY BACK!"

I force myself to laugh. "Sure, Dad. I'll give you back your money—when you give me back my mother and sister," and slam the phone down. One would think I would have been elated by this small victory. But it did not bring comfort, as revenge is not all that it is glorified to be! At first revenge tastes sweet and soothes the soul until you realize you just drank your own poison.

Gus Lorentz had a saying that still holds true today. "Oh, what a tangled web we weave when first we learn to deceive." To get back at me for stealing his money, my father stops paying the taxes and insurance on the Bozrah house.

For a few years my husband and I foolishly continue paying but then I stop caring about whether or not the house goes into foreclosure. I tell my father, "I don't give a damn anymore—let them take that *good-for-nothing-house* filled with the blood of my mother and sister. I'm not paying anymore of your stinking bills. You and Sapphira can park your butts outside on the curb on Fitchville Road and be picked up by the garbage man for all I care! I'm serious, Dad, and I'll tell you something else. If you don't pay those bills, when you and Sapphira are not home, I'm coming with a can of gasoline and with one strike of the match— I'LL BURN THAT HOUSE OF PAIN TO THE GROUND!"

Needless to say, the very next day my father goes to the Bozrah Town Hall and works out a plan to pay his taxes. Whatever good intentions he had in mind did not last long. Smelling opportunity, Sapphira agrees to bring the money to the town hall and then blows it all on drugs. As this is all going on, my father develops colon cancer and begins the last years of his life with a plastic bag holding his feces attached to his body.

As the end nears my father senses doom. One day out of the blue, he calls me up mournfully regretting his actions. "Connie Mary, you gotta help me. I can't live with Sapphira anymore—she's no good! You gotta help me get out of here! You can have the house, my money, anything! — Just let me live at your house! Please let me come live with you. *You gotta help me Connie Mary, I'm your father!*"

I feel shocked and confused when I notice a little girl sitting next to me. She is about eight-years old with a ponytail tied in her brown hair. She has big blue eyes and reminds me of the days Sam and I would wait outside for my father to come home from work and surprise him. At this point, my father begins to give me a little of the truth reminiscent of how Satan whispers in our ear to deceive us into making the wrong choices.

"I admit it. I was a son of a bitch. I did bad things. The blood of your sister and mother is spread all over this house. And you know what? — I'm still doing bad things. See, I fell in love with that *whore.*"

I hold back my disgust. "Why do you call Sapphira a whore?"

He chuckles. "I picked up *that* whore hitchhiking right next to your house and loved it. She was a whore before we met and she'll be a whore long after I'm gone. She introduced me to other whores, too. I visited them when I needed some tail but that's just what *men* do."

My father's final swan song is to laugh like a high school jock bragging in the locker room.

"Hey-y-y what can I say? I wanted to get laid, you know? Men are natural born hunters. It's too bad women are the ones being hunted, but that's just the way it is. It's human nature."

The receiver feels cold and hard in my hand. I know what I am going to tell my father as soon as I can shoo away the little girl sitting beside me.

"You can admit yourself to the convalescent home in my town. You can stay there until you can get yourself into senior housing. I will help you do this... but you cannot come here."

I show my father more mercy than he ever showed my mother or sister. He takes my advice but stays one day in the convalescent home before calling Sapphira to pick him up. A week later he called me again.

"Connie Mary, *you gotta help me, I'm your father.* I can't stay with this woman no more. She's no good— please, you gotta help me."

"Dad," I say, with no more care than if I were throwing out the evening garbage, "You cannot come here. You can never come here. *Never.* I'm sorry dad," and hang up the phone. For weeks on end I must listen to the little girl crying beside me repeating my father's words. Even after decades come to pass, and to this very day, I can still hear my father's words—

"*Connie Mary, you gotta help me—I'm your father!*"

My father and I speak no more. A year or so passes when he goes into the hospital for a knee replacement and ends up developing an infection in his lungs. Unlike my mother and sister, the cause of death written across his death certificate is the truth.

I am with my daughter Concetta Rose when the nurse from the Backus Hospital calls me. "*I am sorry Mrs. Codding, your father died an hour ago.* We didn't know Mr. Falcone had a daughter or we would have contacted you sooner."

I have to tell you my first reaction was unrelenting sorrow and to bitterly weep and then questions for the nurse. "Did my father die alone—*Where was his girlfriend?* Did my father have visitors? —I didn't know he was dying!"

"I'm so sorry Mrs. Codding, but as long as your father stayed here—he had no visitors. Then, of course it was so sudden. Your father was admitted to a convalescent home first to help him recuperate from knee replacement surgery. At that point he developed an infection. Your father had been at the Backus for a little over a month. I'm sorry he died alone."

I hung up and cried in my daughter's arms. "*Grandpa died alone.*

He died alone. He did not call us. He couldn't. He died alone." Now, you might think I would have rejoiced in how Karma comes at the end. But the pull of my own blood—*my Italian blood*—was stronger than all the forces in the Universe.

After my father died, Sapphira received the insurance money and used $800 to pay for his funeral. I continued to allow her to live in my house along with a male friend under the stipulation they pay rent. Out of the six months they stayed, they paid rent once. I wanted to help Sapphira but was naïve to the ways of an alley cat clawing her way through life. She never paid her bills and would constantly lie, "Don't worry Connie, I'm going to pay my bills!" Soon thousands and thousands of dollars were owed on the lights, cable, oil, taxes, phone, etc., in addition to my father's charge cards she secretly loaned to friends.

Sapphira received thousands of dollars of my father's insurance money. What she did with the money I never knew. However, there was one insurance policy she knew nothing about: a $10,000 policy from the United States Navy. My father had told me about the policy over ten years ago. He even gave me the information with a letter attached adding nonchalantly, "I served in the U.S. Navy fighting in WWII. After I die, if you ever need money, use this. It's worth $10,000."

It is still a mystery to me as to why he never told Sapphira about the policy. If my father hated me that much, why didn't he leave the policy to Sapphira instead of me?

After I learned that Sapphira was bringing men into the house, getting them drunk and rolling them for money, I asked her to leave. I saw her one last time when she came back to collect some items she had forgotten and noticed her physical demeanor had changed. She wore a thin, revealing shirt with tight pants and I knew she had returned to the streets in search of another benefactor.

Three years later, I felt the need to call Sapphira. I wanted to ask if she thought my father was mentally ill. She laughed hysterically, "Oh Connie! Your father helped me so much. I don't know where I'd be without his help. I know he was bad, but he was good too! Do I think your father was mentally ill? Hell no! Not at all! Al was smart and could handle anything that came his way."

Sapphira's last words only compounded the secret nature and many dimensions of a narcissist who lived comfortably within a society that cannot fully comprehend the enormous amount of suffering these monsters cause innocent people. Many abusers lead a double-life. They appear as salvation to some while causing a great deal of pain to others.

After several years, I found the courage to sell my childhood home. Taking one last look inside, I felt Janice guiding the way to her bedroom. My sister had a large walk-in closet and when I looked inside, I saw something I had never seen before. At the height of a small child, wistfully scribbled on the wall, was the name *Janice* written in black crayon. I touched it and felt my sister's hope that someday, someone would remember her name.

The Lonely Nest has come to an end. If you found your way here, it was for a reason. I leave you Dad, and I leave you in peace.

ABSENCE

They left us here to fend alone
Our hands left grasping at the air
Just statues made of flesh and bone
No one left to lead us there

Our hands left grasping at thin air
As our feet still move along
No one left to lead us there
Now we sing a solo song

As our feet still move along
The absence does not cease or stop
Still we sing a solo song
Our shoes move on; clip and clop

By Garrett Fitzgibbons ©2009
Woodstock, Ct.

Changing the Silence of Abuse

The last photograph of Janice Lynn Falcone, March 1989.

Secrets are alive. They live and breathe inside of us. I believe secrets never die; with every passing day they can only become a stronger tornado of destruction, leaving disease and death in their wake. Audre Lorde is known for her passionate writing on social justice. She understood the harmful effects of silence when she said, *"My silences had not protected me. Your silence will not protect you."*

This story matters. It is a valuable tool in understanding why silence is the number one survival strategy used by children and adults living in abuse. *The Lonely Nest* joins the ranks of such movements as **#MeToo and #TimesUp** that awakened the public as to how difficult it was to break the code of silence. It should be noted when survivors do speak out, there is a systematic problem in our society of not believing them, such as in the 2018 landmark case of Dr. Christine Blasey Ford which prompted the hashtag: **#WhyIDidntReport**.

Janice Falcone experienced many forms of abuse, including incest. The word *"incest"* has a way of generating fear and terror in the mind. The idea of a father or mother hurting a child is beyond the comprehension of many. According to statistics, one in three-to-four girls, and one in five-to-seven boys is sexually abused before the age of eighteen, with overwhelming evidence that a family member is more than likely involved. Incest is one of the most underreported crimes in the world and the reason is linked to silence. It is estimated that survivors report only thirty percent of incest cases. The most significant reason Janice Falcone stayed silent was to protect the family structure which was supported by her abuser.

Incest is associated with secrecy, betrayal, powerlessness, guilt, fear of reprisal and shame. Incest has life-long damaging effects on future relationships. The longer the incest continues, the greater implications there are for disease and dysfunction. Janice's incest began at an early age and continued for decades resulting in severe psychological damage and physical difficulties that created a lifelong cycle of self-hatred and mutilating behaviors. Abuse, silence and shame go hand-in-hand. The cycle is an ouroboros eating its own tail to survive.

Hiding one's head in the sand will not change the circumstances for the survivors of incest. We must be able to say the word "incest" and acknowledge that it exists. It should be noted there are circumstances when silence is necessary for the victim to survive and what they share could mean the difference between life and death. We must also hold an understanding for the victims who cannot or choose not to name their abuse.

It is never too late to speak. I hope my mother and sister's story gives others courage. I believe when one female finds her voice, every generation of women from the beginning of time applauds.

If you are unable to help yourself, there are people who can. *The National Domestic Violence* Hotline has highly trained advocates available to talk confidentially with anyone in the United States who is experiencing domestic violence, seeking resources or information, or questioning unhealthy aspects of a relationship. Resources are found by calling 1-800-799-SAFE (7233).

Seven strategies to remember when leaving an abuser:

1. Lay the groundwork. You need to start planning your exit. This means planning all the logistical and legal details so you and your children can get out safely. The National Domestic Violence Hotline can connect you with a trained advocate to create your own plan.
A note about animals: Never leave pets behind with an abuser. Find pet-friendly shelters with the Safe Havens Mapping Project.

2. Do not mention your plans.
You cannot tell the abuser your intentions. There should be no threats about leaving or getting a restraining order. This will take an enormous amount of self-control on your part.

3. Beware of technology. Abusive people typically monitor their partner's email, computer, and cell phone. Technology could jeopardize your safety. Beware of shared computers and cell phones. The abuser could be monitoring you in secret.

4. Pack. Collect your important information: bank cards, birth and marriage certificates and leave them with a trusted friend.

5. Enlist the help of professionals. Consider getting a therapist and/or lawyer ahead of time for documentation, especially for the difficult days ahead.

6. Plan where you will go. Once you leave, you need somewhere to go. You can call Safe Horizon at 1-800-621-HOPE to find a domestic shelter near you. Begin by saving as much money as you can.

7. Once you decide to leave—get out fast.

There is no right time to leave. Remember Rose Falcone who stayed until she died. Leave as soon as you can, your life may depend upon it. Keep your whereabouts secret until you can get a restraining order. And even then, there is no guarantee the abuser will abide by this order. Be prepared for the unpredictable.

Janice and cousin Michael Falcone 1956, courtesy of
Michael and Phylis Falcone

Dear sister, I will remember...
How you looked in this photograph, the joy radiating from an inner beauty that no one can ever take from you.

Dear sister,
I will remember your laugh, your smile, and all the love in your heart for every living creature.

Dear sister,
I will remember...

Acknowledgements

To my heavenly family: Mary, Jesus and Joseph, there but for the grace of God I go! This book would not have been possible without the help and support of many people, including my husband Robert Chester Codding and daughters, Concetta Rose Codding and Cathleen Codding Frederick. Concetta Rose created the original book cover design and illustrated the Mama Robin for each chapter. Cathleen offered her technical support during the early years of this project that helped contribute to the book's success. A special thank you goes to Christine Kenney LaBrie, Steven Lerro, Lynda Schnurr and Kerry Butler for having the courage to provide the evidence to confirm this story. Special acknowledgement goes to Calanna Matriarch Barbara Joan Daniels Bevilacqua for providing the complete history of the Calanna family. I also wish to acknowledge Raymond Hackett, retired Editorial Editor of The Norwich (CT) Bulletin, who gave me my first job as a writer and the confidence to write this novel. Special mention goes to Mike Kowis at mikekowis.com whose books helped me and many others reach their goals. To graphic designer Mr. Robert Williams at ILoveMyCover.com. I extend my gratitude for perfecting the original cover design and to Polgarus Studio for excellence with print formatting and eBook conversion. To Phylis and Michael Falcone, who graciously forwarded several photographs that became an essential part of this story, thank you.

Within the ten years it took to complete this novel, I had several editors I wish to acknowledge, including Claire Galvin, who was with me from the early beginnings of this work. To my childhood friend Kathy Grabowy Bosworth, you were the first to believe my rough draft could become a novel, and is still with me, looking down from Heaven. Clara Zornado used her expertise and unique magic to hone my words to a higher level and from the beginning was dedicated to this story. Susan Cataldo Cooper edited with proficiency and determination; she honored my mother and sister as if they were her own family and was committed to making *The Lonely Nest* a shining star. Finally, I wish to thank everyone who traveled this life journey with me. Your company was invaluable. May this book expose the darkness and reveal the light.

About the Author

Concetta Falcone-Codding was born in Norwich, Connecticut where she attended the *Norwich Free Academy*. She holds a Master of Arts in Special Education and a Sixth-Year Diploma as a Reading and Language Arts Consultant from the University of Connecticut. She has been teaching reading and writing to teenagers with disabilities for over 30 years. She is a writer and humanitarian dedicated to leaving the world a better place than she found it. For over ten years she was a columnist for the Norwich Bulletin and developed a following bringing discrimination and injustice into the light. Since 2011, she has been an Associate for *The Daughters of The Holy Spirit* and serves on *The Justice Committee* advocating for human rights.

Concetta lives amidst the pines of New England with her husband and animals, including the American Robins that come back every spring. She wrote *The Lonely Nest* in the hope that she could change the way the world sees domestic violence and know that domestic violence could never survive without silence from its victims and those who indifferently watch. Her words to live by: When we resort to hate and violence, we become like our abusers. Use your voice to help others and follow the light from above.

Thank you for reading this book. I would appreciate it if you could leave an honest review on the website you purchased. Follow me:

https://www.facebook.com/TheLonelyNestSeries/

Made in United States
North Haven, CT
31 December 2022

30385700R00228